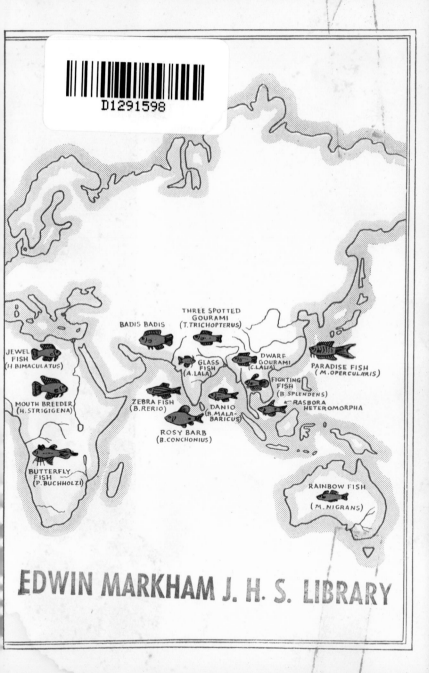

THREE SPOTTED
GOURAMI
(T. TRICHOPTERUS)

BADIS BADIS

JEWEL
FISH
(H. BIMACULATUS)

GLASS
FISH
(A. LALA)

DWARF
GOURAMI
(C. LALIA)

PARADISE FISH
(M. OPERCULARIS)

MOUTH BREEDER
(H. STRIGIGENA)

FIGHTING
FISH
(B. SPLENDENS)

ZEBRA FISH
(B. RERIO)

DANIO
(B. MALA-
BARICUS)

RASBORA
HETEROMORPHA

ROSY BARB
(B. CONCHONIUS)

BUTTERFLY
FISH
(P. BUCHHOLZI)

RAINBOW FISH

(M. NIGRANS)

TROPICAL AQUARIUMS, PLANTS AND FISHES

By the same Author

GARDEN PONDS, FISH AND FOUNTAINS

THE OBSERVER'S BOOK OF
FRESHWATER FISHES OF THE
BRITISH ISLES

THE OBSERVER'S BOOK OF SEA FISHES

AQUARIUMS AND FISHPONDS

THE MICROSCOPE MADE EASY

PLATE I.   *Frontispiece*

1 & 2. *Hyphessobrycon innesi*, Neon Tetra, Humming Bird Fish, Coronation Fish.
3. *H. heterorhabdus*, Flag or Striped Tetra.   4. *Hemmigrammus ocellifer*, Beacon or
Head-and-tail-light Fish, female.   5. *Hyphessobrycon rosaceus*, Black Flag Fish, male.
6. *H. flammeus,* Flame Fish, Red Tetra from Rio.

(Natural size)

TROPICAL AQUARIUMS, PLANTS AND FISHES

By

A. LAURENCE WELLS

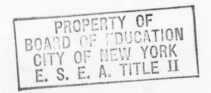
FREDERICK WARNE & CO., LTD.
LONDON AND NEW YORK

639.34
W

123,18

CONTENTS

5

CONTENTS

LIST OF PLATES

7

LIST OF PLATES

8

CHAPTER I

To keep tropical fishes with any measure of success it is necessary, in the first place, to appreciate their habits and the nature of their native environment. This advice, obvious though it may appear, applies also to the keeping of cold water fishes in captivity; there is this difference, however, nearly all cold water fishes suited for aquarium purposes belong to one great family, the Carps. These fishes have, in nearly all cases, very similar breeding habits, their taste in food is similar, and water that suits one particular species will suit all. Moreover, with the exception of the fancy varieties, they are found in a wild state within the temperate European zone, comparatively a small area. The aquarist, if he wishes, can observe them in their natural surroundings and consequently is more familiar with their normal mode of living.

Tropical fishes, on the other hand, do not all conform to the same methods or treatment. Some prefer slightly alkaline water, others prefer slightly acid water; some are at their best in an abundance of light, others seek the dark corners. Some are of placid temperament and will live harmoniously, more or less, one with the other, others are aggressive and require separate quarters.

In the matter of environment, too, there is considerable variation. The enthusiast draws upon nearly all the fresh-water streams contained within the tropic belt and on a great many within the torrid zone. The swamps of Florida, the streams of Carolina and other southern states of the U.S.A. provide a number of species. The rivers of Central and Southern America contribute, perhaps, the greatest variety of species, followed by those of India, Assam, Borneo, the Malay Peninsula, Siam, etc. From China comes the delightful Paradise Fish and from Old Calabar comes the Butterfly Fish. But the fact of a fish coming, say, from India does not mean necessarily that it will be at home with other Indian fishes. Maybe it came from one of the Himalayan streams where, at certain times of the year, great freshets of icy water descend from the mountains; maybe its native river was one that dried up completely during the hot season, leaving the fishes to make their own arrangements, or it came, possibly, from one of the larger deltas where the water would be brackish on occasion. Then again its original home may have been just an ordinary well-behaved river.

The same variety of environment is experienced by the fishes of the Amazon which, with its tributaries, waters an area of land nearly as large as the whole of Europe.

In the ordinary way tropical fishes are easier to keep in aquaria than their cold water brethren; there are, literally, hundreds of species with identical tastes that can be accommodated in one large community tank. The enthusiast whose aim is to amass a collection of diverse types of exotic fishes may find that some of his more choice specimens are not thriving as they should. In this case he should ascertain not only the country of their origin but also the precise locality or type of locality. One is reminded of an incident in the career of the great Linnaeus, when, as a youth, he was assistant gardener on a large estate. His master had been given a rare Himalayan plant which was placed straightaway in a hot house; the plant wilted and so the temperature was increased. Eventually the plant was assumed to be dead and the young Linnaeus, taking the matter in hand, transferred the plant to a cool greenhouse where it revived and later flourished.

Linnaeus coupled geography with his other learning, and by the same token the aquarist should keep an atlas on the shelf with his fish books.

At the other end of the scale are fishes from the sultry forest creeks where the overhanging vegetation renders the atmosphere 'airless', where the water is choked with aquatic plants and the average temperature is about 90 degrees Fahr. Also, as nearly all the 'pet' tropicals are tiny, they are the legitimate prey of large fishes and to escape these they fly to the shallows; here, under the pitiless rays of the tropic sun, the water may reach a temperature of over 110 degrees. Fishes from China and the southern states of the U.S.A. will live in water with a temperature of only 65 degrees or so. Thus it will be seen that the aquarist has a latitude of about 40 degrees of heat within which one species or other will exist. The happy mean, of course, is 74 degrees, at which temperature he can keep almost any tropical fish. At breeding time the water must be made warmer, the exact increase varying according to the species.

This brings us by easy stages to the question of breeding and its many problems, all of which, however, are not necessarily biological. Breeding habits of representative species are given in the chapter on 'Fishes' and the various appliances used in isolating the pairs, etc., are dealt with in the chapter 'Heating and other apparatus', but there are several other sides to the question, and not the least of these relates to the disposal of the progeny. This may give rise to a smile on the part of experienced aquarists who know just how difficult it is to rear the offspring of their fishes. The parents may not be particularly disposed to mate, and if they do they will eat many of the resultant eggs and, later, the fry. Nevertheless, it is possible, by patience and the correct system, to raise fair-sized broods, and it is well to be prepared for this eventuality.

Two courses are open to the aquarist who has managed to rear, say, forty or fifty fry. He can set up extra tanks for them or he can sell them to a dealer. The price obtained, except for the more expensive species, is, naturally, relatively small. Still, as the Ancients used to say, "it is better than a poke in the eye with a burnt stick," and in any case is cheaper than buying extra tanks. One may give them to larger fishes to supplement their diet, a hard-hearted procedure that very few aquarists care about, but a sound one nevertheless.

At mating time, too, the fishes look at their best, especially the males, when all manner of unsuspected colours are revealed, particularly in the fins. The Siamese Fighting Fish, for example, is a glorious sight as he woos his mate, showing off the flaming tints of his fins as he circles around the aquarium.

The beauty of the fishes is apt to make one lose sight of the fact that there are other equally beautiful organisms, in the shape of plants, available for the delectation of the aquarist. In the ordinary way the oxygenating plants used in cold water aquaria will acclimatize themselves to the warmer water. It is a pity, though, for the aquarist to let it stop at that when there are a number of tropical plants available, many of which are both interesting and beautiful. In America, where the cult of the tropical fish has reached tremendous proportions, as much money will be paid for an unusual plant, such as the Madagascar Lace Plant, as for a pair of good fishes.

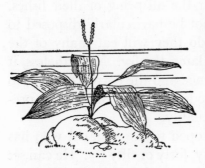

MADAGASCAR LACE PLANT

Tropical flowers, generally, are more than a

PLATE II.   *A-14*
1. *Nannostomus trifasciatus.*   2. *Pristella riddlei,* X-ray Fish.   3. *Aphyocharax rubripinnis,* Bloodfin.   4. *Poecilobrycon unifasciatus.*   5. *Hemmigrammus unilineatus,* Feather Fin.

(Natural size)

little attractive, and the aquatic varieties are not an exception. When they do flower in the aquarium the effect adds greatly to the general scheme of things. The hot-house pool, whether it be a tub or a properly constructed water garden, has a great range of wonderful flowering plants from which to choose. Tropical lilies, for example, as one would imagine, are as exquisite as it is possible for flowers to be. Not only are all the colours usual among water lilies obtainable, but bright blues as well. Then there are the Sacred Lotus lilies of Egypt, rushes from China and Japan, Water Hawthorns from South America and Africa and a host of other plants to delight the heart of the water gardener. Among the roots of these plants the tiny fishes find much to occupy their minds in the form of minute organisms; moreover, the fry stand a better chance of survival in the tangled mass of roots. Such a pool is almost self supporting: the heat within the 'house' heats the water sufficiently and the isolation methods called for when breeding in tanks are unnecessary. If a large community of fishes is kept, then, of course, extra feeding is necessary.

Generally, however, the actual principles of setting up either an indoor aquarium or a greenhouse pool differ in only a few respects from those employed for cold water fishes. The hygiene of

the aquarium and its balance are the same fundamentally, rules of maintenance for the one apply,
with just one or two exceptions, equally well for
the other. Yet, why is it that one person will be
a confirmed cold water enthusiast and refer to
tropicals as 'insipid little beasts' and another will
aver, in all good faith, that keeping cold water
fishes may be all right for small boys, but give
him the bewitching tropicals?

It is, I suppose, just a matter of individual
taste, but there is no doubt that the delightful
tropical fish is insinuating itself into homes hitherto innocent of aquariums and is fast coming into
its own as a form of indoor decoration. For the
past twenty years or so the cult has been tremendously popular in the United States of America,
and in Florida there are vast farms where exotic
fishes of all descriptions are bred in the open.
These are conveyed in a few hours by air or rail
to all parts of America. In Germany and France,
countries well advanced in the study of fishes, the
hobby was established some time before we tried
our 'prentice hand at it; in fact, most of the supply
to-day is imported from the Continent, although
during the past few years several very successful
breeders in this country have assisted the
supply.

The enthusiasm of the aquarist has created an

industry entirely its own—that of the collector. Men, who for years have supplied museums, zoos and colleges with tropical animals, have now equipped themselves with special thermos flasks and similar containers and set out for the out-of-the-way streams and, often at considerable danger, sought to appease the insistent demands for 'new' fishes. A successful journey may yield a great reward; in the summer of 1936 on the airliner *Hindenburg* were some 20,000 specimens of a tiny fish hitherto unknown to science. This little fish, barely an inch in length, was a vivid red on the underside and tail and along its back ran a flashing blue-green line, so flashing, indeed, that it was at once dubbed the 'Neon Light Fish'. Shortly before the 'Neon' (now known as *Hyphessobrycon innesi*) appeared, another fish, known by the delightful title of White Cloud Mountain Minnow, held sway. This in turn had stolen the thunder of a previous high-priced favourite, the Pompadour Fish, otherwise *Symphysodon discus*. In a year or so these three fishes, although still admired for their undoubted beauty, may be among the ordinary rank and file as regards price, etc. Other stars will have arisen in the piscine firmament, for the collector is tireless in his efforts to find new specimens for the now somewhat blasé fancier. The fact that a fish is rare, however, is not necessarily a sign that it will be popular. Some of the rarest fishes are quite unattractive in colour and some of the very commonest kinds are exquisitely beautiful. In any case, if new fishes are discovered that are more colourful than the three mentioned, then almost any price could be obtained for them.

CHAPTER II

SETTING UP THE AQUARIUM

WELL begun, they say, is half done, and this old adage is especially applicable to the gentle art of fish keeping. The aquarist, in setting forth to purchase an aquarium, or, to be more exact, 'tank', is faced with a great array of glassware of all shapes and sizes, and the novice, in particular, is often at a loss as to which to choose. By a process of elimination, however, the matter can be resolved fairly easily. In the first place, reject all globes, bell-jars and other fancy shapes, no matter how ornately they may be designed. This leaves us with the rectangular tank, and the next matter for consideration is financial rather than aesthetic; if we can afford but little money for our hobby, then the choice is already made, viz., an all-glass rectangular tank. Those made of quarter-inch plate glass range in size from 7 in. × 6 in. × 6 in. to 24 in. × 12 in. × 12 in. —the intervening sizes are legion.

For the well-lined purse the choice is not so easily made, in fact, the really difficult part lies ahead. The scheme of decoration of the room in which the aquarium is to be housed must be considered, and the actual position also. Maybe the aquarium is to be a mantelpiece ornament, in which case it may have to be made specially; it may be that a corner of a hall, or a window with an ugly outlook, requires beautifying, then, for this purpose there are a variety of designs from which to choose. These designs, nevertheless, are rectangular basically—they represent a cross section of a stream, even though that cross section contains a concentrated flora and fauna. Triangular tanks, tanks surmounted with clocks and other extraneous ornaments, concave tanks, tall tanks, shallow tanks—all can be obtained in stock sizes, and other sizes, at a price, can be made to measure.

These tanks are formed of an angle iron frame in which plate glass is inserted. The glass should be of good quality, without distortion and, if the tank is a large one, of at least quarter-inch plate glass. The finish of the metal fittings may be bronze, chromium or enamel; or stainless steel, the best of all, may be used and this requires no adornment. The prices of the metal framed tanks vary considerably, the cheap kinds cost little more than the all-glass variety, whilst the *de luxe* types may cost up to £20 for the larger sizes. Cheap metal-framed tanks should be avoided, the all-glass kind are safer because, sooner or later, the flimsy metal and inferior cement will result in catastrophe. One fine morning you will awake to find the dining room carpet flooded and, in the empty aquarium, your fishes endeavouring unsuccessfully to accommodate themselves to a dry existence.

The ideal tank should have a slate bed, strong electrically-welded frame, well cemented at the joints and good clear glass. Such a tank should cost approximately 65s. enamelled or £5 to £8 chromium plated for the 24 in. × 12 in. × 12 in. size. Some tanks are obtainable with the slate bed drilled with holes to receive the electric heater and thermostat. The extra appliances necessary for the tropical aquarium and the modifications demanded by the heating problem are discussed in the chapter on 'Heating and other apparatus'. Our purpose here is to describe the setting-up of the tank of our choice—that is, of the size just mentioned which is referred to usually by aquarists as 'the twelve gallon tank'.

The bottom of the tank must receive a layer of sand, and on the exact nature of this sand much of the aquarium's efficiency will depend. Very fine sand is apt to go black owing to its habit of packing down hard and so giving bacteria a chance to develop. With larger grained sand there is a certain water movement which keeps it clean. In any case, should the sand go black it will be restored to its original state if placed in the sun to dry. This disruptive procedure will be unnecessary if coarse sand is used and decayed matter, particularly rotting plant roots, is re-

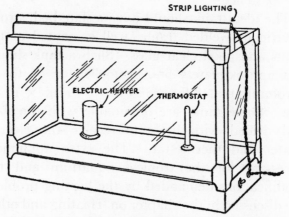

AQUARIUM WITH SLATE BED DRILLED TO RECEIVE HEATER AND THERMOSTAT

moved at once. A good sand is obtainable from dealers that does not require washing; still, it is a good plan to give it a slight wash as it is apt to make a certain amount of powder in transit. Naturally-black sand is used by some of the continental aquarists but, up to the present, this sand, which undoubtedly shows up the fishes to advantage, has not found favour in England.

Builder's and Silver Sand take far more washing than they are worth, in fact, it seems that the water never will be clear when they are washed. So, from more than one consideration, the coarse sand specially sold for the purpose is to be preferred. If rocks are to be employed it is better for them to be half buried in the sand, they increase the depth of the water without adding to the density. Fancy ornaments are in poor taste; moreover, from their sharp edges they are apt to injure the fishes either by rubbing scales off or, as tropicals are swift in movement, by cutting the flesh itself. The fishes and the plants should be sufficient ornament in themselves; if not, there is something radically wrong with the general layout.

The surface of the sand itself gives a more natural appearance if it is uneven and if it slopes slightly to the front of the aquarium; detritus, falling in that direction, is more easily removed. Cold water plants, as a rule, thrive better if their roots are in loam, and this is the case also with warm-water plants. A layer of loam, with its four edges and surface covered with sand, is to be recommended.

The number of plants required to stock an

aquarium 24 in. × 12 in. × 12 in. will vary according to individual tastes. Too many plants leave little room for the fishes and will absorb, during the night, more oxygen than the water will stand. A good plan is to plant fairly heavily with Vallisneria; the tape-like foliage, especially when forming a background, is very attractive. For our aquarium a dozen plants should be evenly spaced along the back, about three inches from the glass. At either side place a clump of one of the Myriophyllums, Cabombas, Sagittarias or other of the oxygenating plants suited to warm water. A visit to one or other of the dealers specializing in the requirements of the tropical aquarist will be well repaid in the matter of plants. Specimens not usually listed—many of them, perhaps, still to receive a name—will be seen. At the moment a plant resembling in foliage the Aspidistra is the current favourite. The name of this exceedingly attractive and hardy plant is *Anubia lanceolata* and it comes from west tropical Africa; its oxygenating value is great and there is no doubt about its decorative value. Cryptocoryne is another splendid all-round aquarium plant and one root at least should be planted.

The function of plants in the aquarium does not stop at oxygenation and decoration; they play an important part in the spawning process of many types of fish, and their foliage, especially if of the dense, feathery type as in Myriophyllum, forms sanctuary for the tiny fish fry.

Floating plants with roots that hang down in the water and do not require soil for their sustenance, add a pleasant touch to the 'ceiling' of the aquarium. *Riccia fluitans*, otherwise Crystal Wort, is the best of all the floating plants (if it can be called a plant, for it is really a kind of moss); growing as it does in a dense mass it forms an admirable shelter from their ghoulish parents for young fishes. Moreover, it is reputed to add considerably to the oxygen content of the water.

The planting and maintenance of the plants here mentioned, and others, are given in the chapter 'Plants'.

At certain times of the year the water becomes almost alive with a minute and lowly form of plant life loosely referred to as 'algal zoospores', or, in the usual way as just 'algae' or 'green water'. This, to the novice, is regarded as a kind of minor tragedy : his fishes are hardly visible and, as one particular type of algae prefers the glass sides of the tank, a general air of neglect overhangs everything. The mistress of the house may utter slighting remarks and refer at frequent and set intervals to smells and aesthetics. The novice will despair, but, strangely enough, the individuals most concerned, to wit, the fishes, will revel in such a murky atmosphere.

The point is, however, that an aquarium with a well-groomed look is the aim of every aquarist, and to this end the algae must be kept within reasonable limits. In the pond one may have recourse to Fresh-water Mussels, and in the cold water aquarium to the smaller and less destructive bivalves. The tropical aquarium is no place for this kind of mollusc. Their method of feeding consists of drawing water in through one siphon and exhaling it through another and this eventually clears the water. The fishes will imagine that these siphons are a new variety of worm, and the tropical fish is nothing if it is not speedy, and so the poor mussel may find himself badly mauled before he can withdraw into his shell. Mussels, too, perambulate through the sand, using their powerful 'foot' as a plough, and this, of course, greatly disturbs the plants. There is also the possibility of very young fry being drawn into the stomach of the mussel as it takes the water in.

So much for the mussels; but what of the snails, which, as everyone knows, feed largely on the algae that attaches itself to the glass and to the leaves of the plants? The snail, meaning the

26

'water snail', feeds by literally rasping its food from its anchorage with a flexible and retractable tongue. Thus, if the track made by a snail whilst feeding is closely observed it will be seen to be a thin, clear-cut line; a most negligible part of the aquarium's side. That is how it is with snails; they certainly feed on algae, but so slowly do they move and so minute is the result of their labours that, for a twelve gallon tank one would require at least three dozen snails. That is, if they alone are used to keep the green film down, and, having kept it down they will, in spite of protests to the contrary, devour plants as well. Furthermore, they consume a fair amount of oxygen, and eat the eggs of fish.

If snails are to form part of the ménage they should be regarded more in the light of ornaments and objects of interest, and the number limited, in our case, to six.

How, then, can one combat this intrusive greenness? In the first place, 'green water' is more prolific when the aquarium is situated near a window receiving much sunlight; the sun's rays, even after penetrating through the glass, will induce the algae to reproduce rapidly. The side of the aquarium nearest the window may be painted green on the outside, this helps somewhat. Again, as part of the cloudiness is caused by minute particles of floating detritus, systematic use of the siphon will help in keeping the water clear. Once a week, at least, the surface of the sand should receive a spring clean. Glass implements consisting of a length of glass tube with a reservoir near one end are obtainable for a few pence. The forefinger should be placed over the end farthest from the reservoir and the other end inserted in the water over the spot requiring treatment. The finger is slightly lifted and water and detritus will fill the tube. The water thus removed may be filtered; usually, however, it is only a small amount and tap water may be used to bring the water to its ordinary level.

The most efficient way of keeping the water clear is filtration, and several types of filter are outlined in the chapter on 'Heating and other apparatus.'

The green film on the glass presents but a very small problem. A safety razor blade is inserted in a piece of cane and moved up and down the glass until the film is removed.

Algae does not grow so profusely in water that is slightly acid as in alkaline or neutral water. Happily enough most of the tropical fishes prefer water that contains a little acid. Mention of acid brings us naturally to the profound question of hydrogen ion concentration, more commonly

known by the mystic symbol pH. Water with a
neutral pH value is indicated by the number 7;
below that figure it is said to be acid and above it
is alkaline. Equipment may be purchased quite
reasonably for testing the water, and with the
equipment there is usually a supply of chemicals;
by judicial use of these the water may be brought
to the desired condition. As full instructions are
supplied their method of use need not be described here. Suffice it to say that most tropical
fishes are at their best in water that indicates
between 6.6 and 7.

The water for the aquarium should be boiled
first and allowed to cool to the desired temperature, say 74 degrees Fahr., this is to kill any
lurking 'bugs' that may infect the fishes. Do not
pour the water straight into the aquarium, for if
you do the plants will be disturbed. Lay a sheet
of paper over the plants and sand and pour the
water on to that; in this way the force of the
water is more evenly distributed and there is less
risk of washing the soil from the roots. Allow the
aquarium to stand for a fortnight so that the
plants can establish themselves, or otherwise in
their exuberance the fishes will uproot any
plants that have not properly settled down.

CHAPTER III

PLANTS FOR THE TROPICAL AQUARIUM

THE functions of plants in the tropical aquarium are fourfold—they contribute to the oxygen content of the water, they form, especially those with dense foliage, ideal nurseries and sanctuaries for baby fishes; they provide, particularly the duckweeds, good green food for the vegetarians and, finally, add in no small measure to the beauty, interest and naturalness of the aquarium.

As one would expect, the warmer lands are drawn upon to supply the necessary plants; nevertheless, certain of the more common aquatic plants usually used in cold water aquaria will adapt themselves to tropical conditions. This is fortunate because two of the finest oxygenators, Elodea and Vallisneria, would not be available otherwise. The cold water plants should be acclimatized gradually, however, otherwise they may go soft and sickly-looking and eventually fall to pieces. Best of all they should be purchased from the fish dealer himself, in which case the plants will be taken from warm water tanks.

There are few points upon which all aquarists are in complete agreement, but on one point they are unanimous and that is that a fine, healthy plant is an adornment to any aquarium —even if a planted aquarium is anathema to them. The majority of fish keepers are plant enthusiasts, and the well-being of the plants is a matter for real concern. A certain amount of care and forethought is necessary if the greenery in the aquarium is to be up to the desired standard; it is not sufficient just to ram the roots in anyhow and once thus rammed in to leave the plant to its own devices.

Nearly all rooted water plants, including those that can be propagated by slippings, require loam if their growth is to be luxuriant. From the water, it is true, they absorb nutriment, and the sand provides an anchorage for the roots; with loam both anchorage and nutriment are enhanced. The loam should be introduced at the time the aquarium is being set up and should be covered with coarse sand—this to prevent clouding of the water. If the aquarium is already established and it is deemed unwise to disturb it, the plants can be placed in small pots of loam and the surface lightly covered with sand. Failing this, if a small quantity of soil, sufficient just for one plant, is wrapped in thin paper and the parcel gently lowered to the bottom of the aquarium at the required spot, when the paper is allowed to float away a small heap of soil will result. This, with the aid of a thin stick, can be incorporated with the sand, forming a good foundation for a plant. If a small depression is made first in the sand at the bottom and the parcel of soil lowered therein and then covered with sand, an even better result may be obtained.

Next in the list of aids to plant culture is the light factor. With only one or two exceptions water plants thrive better if subjected to electric light, especially during the winter months. In spring and summer the plants are naturally active, throwing out new shoots and adding to their foliage. Apart from that there is more light. In the cold season they are inclined to retire within themselves, quite unmindful of what is expected of them. Stimulation, then, is necessary, and the stimulus provided by an electric lamp placed directly over the aquarium often transforms weedy and dejected-looking plants into lusty ones. If strip lighting is used to display the fishes, extra light may not be necessary. Still, it should be remembered that a 60 watt lamp burning for eight hours provides far more stimulus than one of half that power burning for twenty-four hours. Again, it is possible to defeat one's ends by giving too much light; as with everything else in this most delightful of all possible pursuits the aquarist is called upon to use his own judgment. Each aquarium is an aquatic world unto itself—try as hard as you can you cannot evolve two exactly alike—and so each individual aquarium requires individual treatment. If the plants become lanky or do not progress as they should, cut down the number of hours; on the other hand extra light may be called for.

CRYPTOCORYNE

Dead and decaying leaves should be removed at once and if any particular plant looks as though it will never flourish, then it is well to remove it altogether and put a healthy one in its place. The humus or mulm formed by the excreta of the fishes and from the ordinary metabolism that takes place in this water community is invaluable as manure for the plants. Ordinarily this detritus is removed with the siphon, but if it is congregated around the roots of, say, Cryptocoryne or Sagittaria, the organic matter assists growth.

c

33

The actual planting methods differ slightly according to the type of plant, some are propagated by means of slippings and usually are sold in bunches. The individual sprays should be separated, the end of the stem weighted with a thin strip of lead or other suitable material, and the plant lowered into the water. Sometimes a slipping will 'strike' if the stem is merely pushed into the sand but, more often than not, the stem will rot and the plant die. The former method is by far the better and, in the course of time, the stem will send out rootlets which will seek the sand of their own accord.

ELODEA CANADENSIS
OR WATER THYME

The Elodeas are grown from slippings and these plants, of which four species are obtainable, are fine oxygenators. *Elodea canadensis*, otherwise Anacharis, is very useful for providing dense vegetation at breeding time—a tangled clump, placed in the aquarium temporarily, solves the problem when the other plants are not sufficiently profuse for this operation. Anacharis, however, compared with its near relations *E. densa*, *E.*

34

callitrichoides and *E. crispa*, has a weedy, un-
kempt look. The others are cobby; their leaves
are curled inwards slightly and, although there
is slight difference in their respective shades of
greenness, they are of a brighter green.

Incidentally, *E. densa* is pollinated by insects
—usually bees—as its three-petalled flowers
appear above the surface; *callitrichoides* and
canadensis are pollinated under water. *Densa* is
now, therefore, placed in a different genus and is
called *Egeria densa* whilst *crispa* has had its
name changed to *Lagarosiphon major*.

Cabomba is another plant that is propagated

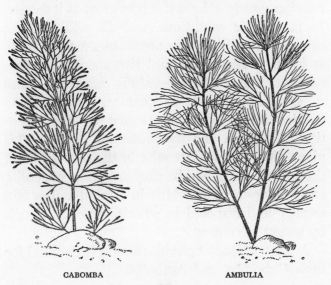

CABOMBA   AMBULIA

from slippings; indeed, nearly all aquatic plants are grown from slippings, and all the plants mentioned in the following pages, unless otherwise stated, are so grown. Four species of Cabomba are obtainable, in all of which the leaves grow fan-like around the stem. *C. rosaefolia* has reddish foliage, *C. aquatica* is sage green, *C. viridifolia* is conspicuous for its bright green leaves and, finally the most popular species— *C. caroliniana* which grows freely and is a good oxygenator.

Similar in habits and appearance to the Cabombas is Ambulia, a tough-leaved plant that requires plenty of light if it is to grow as it should. In favourable conditions Ambulia will send out side shoots until the plant resembles a small bush. It is an Indian plant and two species are now cultivated in aquaria—*Ambulia heterophylla* and *A. sessiliflora*—good oxygenators, with finely divided leaves admirably suited for the reception of fish ova and the protection of fry. This plant differs from Cabomba in the disposition of the leaves—in Cabomba they are placed opposite each other in pairs whilst in Ambulia they are smaller and disposed in whorls. Propagation is by means of runners.

A layer of loam beneath the soil is essential for both Cabomba and Ambulia.

Fontinalis, especially the fine-leaved species (*Fontinalis gracilis*) has a two-fold function in the aquarium—it covers stones with a delicate green carpet into which non-adhesive fish eggs may fall to their advantage, also the mossy carpet which ultimately develops appears to trap much of the detritus. Consequently, if the moss-covered stone is removed and washed it can be returned to the aquarium all the better for its spring clean. This, of course, is one of the non-flowering types and is propagated by tying a small clump to a stone with thread and lowering it into position in the aquarium.

Closely related to Salvinia, the Quilworts and the Pillworts is an intriguing fern, *Marsilea quadrifolia* otherwise known as Water Clover or Australian Four-leaved Clover. The resemblance of this plant which, incidentally, is also found in parts of Asia, Europe and North America, to the clover of our fields is quite striking. The stipes, at the end of which the clover-like lobes are carried, vary in length from an inch upwards: the greater the depth of water the greater the length of the stipes. The 'leaves' seem to have a liking for the surface when they have long enough stems, but in any case they do not unfurl until the stem has reached its allotted length. In favourable conditions, i.e., with plenty of light and a rich soil in which to root, new stipes are formed every other day.

Marsilea is really a marsh plant but, like most marsh plants, it will flourish even when completely submerged. Propagation, from the aquarist's point of view, is by dividing the root and replanting the pieces; in nature it is by spores formed at the base of the stipes.

Myriophyllum, or Water Milfoil, from its way of growing in dense bushes is ideal for the breeding tank. A number of species are available for the aquarist, their principal differences being in the tints of the leaves. The best all-round species, however, is *M. hippuroides*.

MYRIOPHYLLUM OR
WATER MILFOIL

Like most aquatic plants it thrives best when rooted in loam, although it will grow (and root) in sand.

The Utricularias or Bladder-worts form a tangled mass of twig-like stems and are favoured by many enthusiasts. One should take care, though, that only *U. minor* is planted, for the larger species is dangerous to baby fish. The plant is carnivorous and is provided with a number of bladders that serve to keep the plant afloat and as food catchers. The bladder opens and, its unwary prey entering therein, closes, to the intense surprise of small daphnia and fish fry. The smaller species of Bladderwort can manage nothing larger than infusoria and the smaller rotifers.

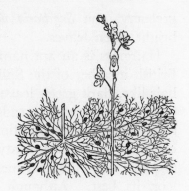

UTRICULARIA OR
BLADDER-WORT

There is also a dwarf Bladder-wort from Africa —*U. prehensilis*—that has finer foliage and smaller bladders than have either of the foregoing. The leaves consist of fine threads of a pale green colour amongst which are innumerable tiny bladders. Apart from its undoubted value as an oxygenator this plant, which will grow readily either from a small clump anchored to the bottom or just floating loose in the water, will form a dense mass near the surface and so be an ideal refuge for the tiny fish fry.

For the shallow aquarium there are two suitable plants, Hairgrass (*Eleocharis acicularis*) which carpets the bottom with a mass of hair-like greenery, and *Sagittaria natans* with its waving bright green leaves.

Hairgrass is an apt name for this dainty little British member of the Spike-rush family. It has hair-like, dark green leaves growing to a height of four inches and spreads rapidly by means of runners when the conditions are ideal. Being a bog plant it requires plenty of light and good soil and not more than six inches of water if it is to look its best. Although the species generally available for tropical aquaria is *E. acicularis* there are two tropical species—*E. acuta* from New Holland and *E. geniculata* from the West Indies— that grow to a greater height, seven inches. Both have been grown in this country and are the more suitable for tanks kept above 75 degrees Fahr.

The tall aquarium, on the other hand, and especially one designed for the breeding of Angel-fish, calls for *Sagittaria sinensis*, a plant with long, stout stems on which the fishes deposit their eggs. This type of aquarium, unsuited as it is to the needs of cold-water fishes, will accommodate quite a number of the less fussy tropicals. With *S. natans* or Hairgrass carpeting the bottom, a few clumps of Myriophyllum and a few Water Ferns, these deep tanks can be made to look really beautiful; they demand considerable care, otherwise they soon run to seed.

Hairgrass and the Sagittarias are already rooted when bought from the dealer.

There are several species of Sagittaria from the tropics that are obtainable at times, and one of the most colourful and prolific, as regards foliage, is that known formerly as *Sagittaria guayanensis* and now as *Echinodorus radicans*. It has an abundance of broad green leaves that turn reddish with age and is of rapid growth. Propagation is by the large seeds

SAGITTARIA

which develop from the white flowers and also from new plants which arise from between the seed pods. Just as botanists in recent years have separated some of the Elodea species on their floral characteristics so this one-time Sagittaria has been removed to another genus of the Alisma family, Echinodorus—the members of which are known popularly as Bur-heads. In the true Sagittarias the male and female flowers are borne on separate plants, whereas in the Echinodorus species both stamens and pistils are produced in the same flower thus making self-fertilization possible.

The Water Ferns (*Ceratoptera*) are very intriguing plants indeed; two species are obtainable, one of which is definitely a floating plant. The Floating Fern (*Ceratopteris pteryoides*) grows in thick, spongy clusters, bright green in colour, which send out new shoots every few days. The roots hang down in the water and afford protection to fish fry.

The protection thus given is not just a 'token' protection; the rootlets are stout and the underwater leaves form small nooks and crannies into which the little ones can creep to avoid fishes with evil intentions. In its native South America, where it has plenty of elbow room, the Floating Fern may develop rosettes—consisting of tongue-like fronds with indented edges—with a diameter of nearly a foot. As with many another floating plant—Frogbit, for example—better foliage will result if the water is sufficiently shallow (in this case about nine inches. for the roots to reach the mulm on the bottom) In the aquarium with not too bright a light the rosettes will consist of floating fronds, fronds in the process of growing and projecting out of the water and fronds just below the surface. The young plants are produced from the edges of the floating fronds from which, if necessary, they can be nipped off when about an inch in diameter. Usually the old plants look bedraggled in the winter through the curtailed sunlight, consequently, as the young plants are not so inconvenienced and as there usually are plenty of them by the latter end of the year, it is best to remove the old plants and retain the young ones. The other species, the Indian Water Fern (*C. thalictroides*), roots in the soil and has large, deeply-indented leaves. It can be grown from the many shoots that form on the leaves and send out rootlets, these in time floating away from the parent plant; if they are allowed to float around in the water for a while they will grow sufficiently sturdy to be planted.

The roots gradually lengthen—as do the roots of *pteryoides* in shallow water—until they reach the soil. In ideal conditions and when completely submerged the plant will grow to a height of just over a foot with a span of ten inches. If the leaves project above the surface they change somewhat, becoming narrower and darker.

For the shady corners of the aquarium there is in my opinion no plant to equal Cryptocoryne, of which some half a dozen species are sold. It is a good oxygenator and its strap-like leaves with their red undersides add to the aquarium's charm; also, it is indispensable if the various *Rasbora* species are to be bred. The roots are like those of Sagittaria, and it is necessary when

INDIAN WATER FERN

planting to see that every part of the root-stock and the filamentous roots is covered by the sand. When planting Sagittaria and Vallisneria it is customary to cut the filaments down to about half an inch of the root stock and to have the crown of the root just resting on the sand. Do not cut Cryptocoryne's roots down, and make sure, as previously advised, that the whole of the root is covered.

The most popular species are *C. griffithii* and *C. willisii*; the former will thrive in a deep aquarium and, as its native haunts are overhung forest streams in Malay and other densely wooded parts of tropical Asia, it will thrive best in the shade. The broad, oval leaves are glossy and smooth and on their underside is a suggestion of pink. Occasionally it will favour its owner by producing a dark red flower. *C. willisii* will thrive in water as shallow as six inches. It has pale green, strap-like leaves with attractive wavy edges and well defined ribs.

A more recent importation, something like

Cryptocoryne in shape and habits, is *Anubia lance-olata* (Water Aspidistra) a native of west tropical Africa. The leaves are wider, however, and rather thick

CRYPTOCORYNE

and tough and are a glossy, dark green in colour. Like Cryptocoryne it will thrive in the more dim corners and they both propagate in the same manner, that is, by small rootlets sprouting from the main root. These may be nipped off and planted. The humus that forms on the bottom of the tank, if placed around the roots, will stimulate growth.

WATER ASPIDISTRA

The Water Aspidistra is a marsh plant and does not attain its full height of nearly two feet unless planted in shallow water; in deeper water it rarely grows to a greater height than eight inches. It has useful qualities as an oxygenator, and as an adjunct to the beauty and interest of the aquarium it is most valuable. As background in shallow open tanks in the hothouse it is perhaps seen at its best.

Perhaps the most popular of the rooted plants is Vallisneria, also known as Italian Tape Grass. When planted along the back of the aquarium its long, light green leaves form an ideal background to the vivid pageant of the fishes. The roots send out runners which, in turn, produce at intervals small filamentous clusters which take root in the sand. In ideal situations, especially if there is a fair amount of top light, Vallisneria will thrive exceedingly and there are few things more beautiful than an aquarium in which there is a good showing of this fine, hardy plant. It is also a fine oxygenator.

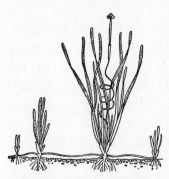

VALLISNERIA OR TAPE GRASS

A most charming plant, though of practically no oxygenating value at all, is Ludwigia, otherwise known as the Swamp Loose-strife. The true habitat of this plant, as the common name suggests, is boggy ground, but it will accommodate itself to an aquatic environment. Three species are

46

available, viz., *L. micro-carpa* with smallish bronze leaves, *L. mulertii* with fairly large green leaves, bronze on the underside, and *L. ramosus*, a more branched species than the foregoing, with reddish leaves.

LUDWIGIA OR SWAMP LOOSE STRIFE

Ludwigia is usually grown from slippings, and thrives best in a sunny situation. If the lower leaves are stripped off before planting (they will probably fall off of their own accord in any case) and just the last half-dozen fronds planted, the plant will grow quicker.

Pickerel Weed (*Heteranthea dubia*) is one of the mud-plantains and is found commonly over practically the whole of the United States and Mexico; consequently it has a wide range of temperature. The leaves are long and grow in an untidy sort of fashion alternately on a bent and weak stem from nodules about two inches apart. They are pale green in colour and whereas the leaves of most aquatic plants endeavour to reach the surface, those of the Water Star-grass (as it is often called) tend to grow downwards.

47

Propagation is from weighted cuttings lowered to the bottom of the tank.

Very similar in shape to Ludwigia is the delightful *Hydrophila polysperma* newly introduced to the aquarist but first grown in England in 1820. Like Ludwigia it also is a marsh plant that will grow and thrive when completely submerged; but, unlike Ludwigia, both sides of its elliptical leaves are green. In a good light and when planted in a rich soil the leaves will be larger and will break through the surface of shallow water. If the protruding shoots are nipped off a strong bushy plant will develop. When there is not overmuch light the plant may still thrive but it will bear smaller leaves. The stem is stout with numerous branches each bearing nodes from which root threads develop— consequently propagation is effected by pegging or weighting down stems which should take root in about a fortnight. Like most marsh plants it is not a particularly good oxygenator—on the other hand it makes a most attractive adjunct to the aquarium.

Another swamp plant is Bacopa of the genus *Herpestis*, a number of species of which inhabit the southern part of the U.S.A. From Carolina comes the species *H. amplexicaulis*. This plant likes shallow water and, as its native swamps are

48

PLATE III.
1. *Brachydanio nigrofasciatus*, Spotted Danio. 2. *B.rerio*, Zebra Fish. 3 & 4. *Rasbora heteromorpha*, Harlequin Fish. 5. *B. albolineatus*, Pearl Danio.
(*Natural size*)

usually exposed to the full glare of the sun, it flourishes best in a well lighted aquarium—also a good, rich soil is preferred. It grows slowly and the fleshy round leaves are neatly produced in pairs along the stem which they appear to clasp.

Limnanthemum lacunosum, the Banana Plant, is a semi-floating plant which grows in shallow water. It has heart-shaped leaves, green on the upper surface and purple beneath, about two inches in diameter and set singly at the end of long stems. The 'banana' part of the name arises from the tubers which form at the stem base of certain of the surface leaves and these tubers certainly have the familiar banana shape. From the ends of the tubers roots form and these grow downwards until they reach the bottom, the original stems die off and new leaves are formed some of which, in their turn, develop tubers. Good light is necessary to produce healthy plants and it seems to be at its best in shallow tanks in the hot-house, where it will grow to a height of eight inches.

An English relative of this American plant is *L. nymphoides* which is sometimes encountered in sluggish streams in the South. *Nymphoides* has five-petalled bright yellow flowers and this is the colour, it is said, of the flowers of *lacunosum.* Both belong to the Gentian family.

FLOATING PLANTS

RICCIA OR CRYSTAL WORT

As regards floating plants, there is no doubt that *Riccia fluitans* or Crystal Wort is indispensable, particularly if fishes are to be raised; apart from the decided oxygenating value the tangled mass of short, crinkly bracts provides a fine refuge for the fry.

The thread-like roots of Azolla, Salvinia and the various species of Duckweed hang down in the water like an inverted miniature forest and give, apart from the beauty of the floating leaves, an interesting touch to the aquarium.

AZOLLA

Vegetarian fishes are partial to duckweed as food. *Limnobium spongia* (also known as American Frog-bit) is the most suitable tropical duckweed; this plant hails from Brazil. *Limnobium sinclarii* is also a South American plant with oval leaves about one inch in length. There is a tiny flower which is very difficult to dis-

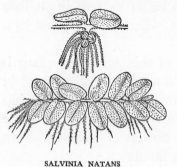

SALVINIA NATANS

50

cern. The roots hang down in clusters thus forming protection for fish fry.

Salvinia braziliensis, as the specific name denotes, comes from Brazil; it is a delightful floating plant with oval leaves of an attractive pea-green colour covered with silky down; short, hairy rootlets hang down in the water and in them some species of fish build their nests. *S. natans* is from India and has sea-green leaves also covered with down. The function of the downy covering in both species seems to be that of preventing the plant from becoming water-logged in rainy weather, the velvety nap throwing the water off almost as soon as it lands.

Phyllanthus fluitans also had its origin in Brazil and is a beautiful little floating plant with delicate green leaves tinted here and there with crimson and growing in massy patches; it is a pity that it is not so easy to come by, for it is an asset to any aquarium. The roots are crimson and look very pretty hanging down in the water.

EICHORNIA OR WATER HYACINTH

Few of the submerged plants have attractive

flowers, the blooms, when they do condescend to appear, are usually small and of insipid colouring. Some of the floating plants, however, present large and colourful flowers, and of the various species obtainable the Water Hyacinth (*Eichornia crassipes*) takes pride of place both for interest and beauty. The leaves are spongy, thus enabling the rather bulky plant to float. The flowers are large and of a delightful lavender shade and are borne on spikes standing well out of the water; it is a South American plant.

CHAPTER IV

HEATING AND OTHER APPARATUS

THE most difficult and at the same time the most vital of all the problems that face the tropical aquarist is that of heating the water efficiently and cheaply. It is not sufficient merely to state that one may purchase electric heaters, and thermostats to control the temperature automatically, because such apparatus is not always satisfactory—even where electricity is cheap. Unfortunately there are heaters and heaters, although I must admit that at the present there are several efficient and fairly cheap models on the market; but until quite recently a good heater was a *rara avis* and it seemed that the more one paid the worse was the equipment.

The ideal heater should be capable of keeping the water at a constant temperature, at least, within a degree either way. Some types are fitted with three-way switches and so one has the choice of, approximately, 65 degrees, 70 degrees and 80 degrees of heat according to the particular need.

Other types can be set to the necessary temperature and this will be maintained by a thermostatic control.

Another important point is that of insulation.

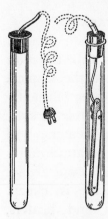

A 'leaky' heater will not only add considerably to the electricity bill, it may electrocute the fishes.

A really efficient electric heater is the cleanest and best of all types of heater, and, where electricity is cheap, about the most economical to run, and it requires very little attention. The aquarist who intends to invest in this type, however, should see one actually at work first or, failing that, insist on approval.

ORDINARY IMMERSION HEATER AND THERMOSTAT

However, if it is thought that electrical apparatus is out of the question, gas may be used. Immersion gas heaters, thermostatically controlled, are stocked by the leading dealers. A bunsen burner placed beneath the aquarium is a good method also, especially if the more expensive equipment is out of the question. If a naked flame, such as this, is used, do not allow it to play directly on the glass or slate bed of the tank—

even if it does not crack it the soil will become too hot for the peace of mind of the plant roots. A stand should be made so that the burner can be slipped easily under the tank, and the tank should rest on a shallow tray of sand; in this way the bottom will be protected.

Perhaps the most satisfactory and cheapest

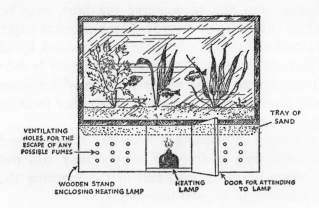

TRAY OF SAND

VENTILATING HOLES, FOR THE ESCAPE OF ANY POSSIBLE FUMES

WOODEN STAND ENCLOSING HEATING LAMP

HEATING LAMP

DOOR FOR ATTENDING TO LAMP

LAYOUT OF AQUARIUM HEATED WITH A NAKED FLAME

way of heating with gas is to enclose the tank in a cabinet. There is less loss of heat and, with the one burner, two tanks can be heated at slightly more than the cost of heating one.

The cabinet should be so constructed that the entire front of the tank is exposed and flush with the front, and one end of each tank is also exposed. Otherwise the remaining parts of the tank are enclosed within the cabinet. The tanks stand on a wooden platform, which is pierced with a hole to receive the burner. A small door at the back will enable one to attend to the burner when necessary, and through a hole in this door will go the metal flex connecting the burner with the gas point. The interior of the cabinet, as a safeguard against fire and to conserve the heat, may be lined with asbestos board. Thick asbestos paper is stocked by most wholesale chemists and I find this easier to manipulate than the thicker board; it can be cut to the required shape with scissors and fixed to the wood work with either tacks or heat-proof glue.

A word of warning is necessary if gas is used from a coin meter—the supply may run out during the night, say, and in the morning the fishes may be beyond recovery.

The cabinet just described may be constructed to receive three tanks—a large one in the middle and a smaller one at each end—and is, without doubt, the cheapest way of heating that number. Apart from gas, one may use, in such a cabinet, paraffin burners and these are one of the cheapest heating mediums, but they demand considerable attention.

A glass cover is essential over the tank if

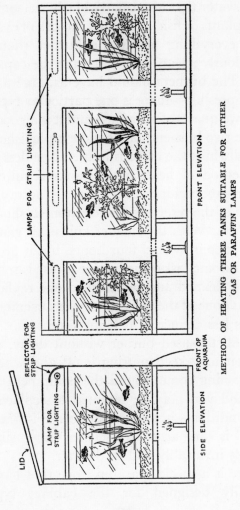

REFLECTOR FOR STRIP LIGHTING

LAMPS FOR STRIP LIGHTING

FRONT ELEVATION

LAMP FOR STRIP LIGHTING

FRONT OF AQUARIUM

LID

SIDE ELEVATION

METHOD OF HEATING THREE TANKS SUITABLE FOR EITHER GAS OR PARAFFIN LAMPS paraffin is used, as the fumes leave an oily film on the water that is not particularly welcomed by either plants or fish. To lessen the risk of excessive fumes everything about the burner should be scrupulously clean and only the best paraffin used. The burners should have as large a reservoir as possible—there is one particular type that holds two quarts of paraffin—and it is a good plan to have two burners; one can be replenished and cleaned whilst the other is in use. Needless to say this method of heating the tanks requires systematic supervision; at set intervals, according to the size of the reservoir, the equipment should be examined. With the smaller kinds this generally means once in twenty-four hours, but it need not be an irksome task—the burner in use is removed and the cleaned and replenished one replaces it. If this is done at the same hour every evening, say, there is less chance of it being forgotten. Clean and refill the used burner without delay, otherwise you may keep putting it off and when the next evening comes round the equipment is still dirty and you may be tempted to replace it in that condition—just for this once. Fish keeping to-day is an accurate science and slipshod methods invariably end in disaster.

There is a special paraffin stove that has been especially designed for the cabinet type of aquarium that requires attention only once a month and is also fume-proof.

If the aquarium is placed over a radiator there will be less heating required, obviously; but if it is situated in a north or east window where one side is cold, then extra heating is necessary.

Many experiments have been tried in the

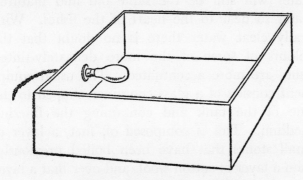

BASE OF AQUARIUM HEATED WITH AN ELECTRIC LAMP.
(NOTE ABSENCE OF AIR-HOLES)

matter of aquarium heating; electric light bulbs, for instance, if fixed in the base of the aquarium as shown in the illustration will heat the water efficiently. In this case the aquarist has plenty of latitude for experiment and by trying lamps of different wattage will eventually achieve the correct temperature. If immersed in the water bulbs are quite effective if painted black so that the fishes are not kept in perpetual light; candles too have been tried in the cabinet types but these, strange to relate, form the most expensive of all heating methods.

Another adjunct to the well-being of the aquarium is a water filter. A good filter will maintain that delightful crystal-clear look so dear to the aquarist's heart, and at the same time the water will still be the same old and matured water so dear to the heart of the fishes. With really clear water there is no doubt that the colours of some of the more delicately-tinted fishes are more accentuated. The usual equipment consists of a glass container clipped to the side of the tank and containing the filtering medium. This is composed of, first, a layer of small stones that have been boiled previously, then a layer of cotton wool, and over that a layer an inch thick of animal charcoal. If your chemist is out of stock of that particular kind of charcoal (vegetable charcoal is no good at all for this purpose) he can order it from his wholesaler. Even with this kind there may be certain impurities, and I advise that it should be well washed in running water before being incorporated in the filter. Over the charcoal—its function is to absorb gases—place another layer of cotton wool, and over that a layer, two inches thick, of well-washed sand. Then, on top of all, another layer of cotton wool—glass-wool is even better if you can obtain it. A length of glass tubing, bent to the necessary shape, has one end among the stones at the bottom of the filter and the other just above the water in the tank. This tube returns the filtered water. Another glass tube, also suitably bent, has one end well immersed in the tank and the other just above the top layer of cotton wool.

Unfortunately, it requires the services of an air pump to assist in returning the filtered water. A rather laborious method, if air pumps are beyond one's means, is to have two large containers, one placed well above the aquarium and the other below it. Water is allowed to enter the aquarium from the top tank and this replaces the water siphoned through the filter. From the filter runs a tube of glass that siphons into the lower tank. When the top tank is empty the lower one, obviously, will be full, and so they are reversed, that is, unless one has a small hand pump to return the water, via another tube, to the top tank.

In a properly constructed fish house the installing of tanks of sufficient capacity to run for twenty-four hours is quite a simple matter, but in the house it is not likely to meet with the approval of the powers that be. Consequently the best plan is to filter the water occasionally, a jugful at a time; if two jugs are used the filtered water from the full one can be gently returned whilst the other is receiving its rations.

The great point about filters is that minute floating matter is removed and noxious gases are absorbed by the charcoal, yet, all the time, the actual nature of the water is not changed.

Aeration, by means of a special motor-driven apparatus which forces a constant stream of minute air bubbles into the water, is serviceable in cases of overcrowding or in the cichlid tank, those fishes being intolerant of plant life. Efficient aeration, however, is by no means as satisfactory as filtration, for the latter system not only filters the water, it aerates it as well.

Artificial lighting adds greatly to the beauty of the tank and also assists the growth of most of the plants. At one time it was considered 'the thing' to have low-powered electric lamps behind the tanks themselves; this method certainly gave the tanks a fairyland appearance and was quite satisfactory in the cold-water aquarium with its coarser-built fishes. The tropical fish generally is a more delicately planned creature, and this back light turned most of them into ghost or glass fishes and revealed their interior anatomy disgracefully.

Now the vogue is for top lighting and the effect is far better. By the old method much of the delicate colouring in the fishes was lost, by the present method these colours, especially the prismatic ones, are enhanced. The most usual and at the same time the most charming way is by strip-lighting. Units can be obtained of any required length and these should be fitted, for preference, along the top front edge of the tank. They radiate a certain amount of heat also, thus two purposes are served.

SUCTION
DISC

SMALL
SHOT

THERMOMETER

Another instrument of great value, and of no great price, is a thermometer. Special types are procurable fitted with a clip like that on a fountain pen, so that they can be attached to the side of the aquarium; others are fixed to a rubber disc and rely on suction to keep them in place. The thermometer can be so placed among the plants that it is almost invisible, although there are some aquarists who like to see a number of instruments in the tank, and what with electric heaters, thermostats, the inlet and outlet tubes of filters and so forth the aquarium looks like an instrument-maker's shop window. Some thermometers are not calibrated correctly and, although a few degrees either way will not unduly affect the community tank, they will affect breeding fishes. It is a good plan to check it up with a thermometer that is known to be exact.

For inserting plants after the tank has been filled, nothing is better that two slender pieces of wood, notched at one end; with one of the pieces a hole is made in the sand, and whilst it is still in position the plant, fixed in the notch of the other, is insinuated alongside. Then, by gentle manipulation of the two sticks, the plant is comfortably anchored without the rest of the aquarium being disturbed. Another handy gadget is a pair of scissors to the handles of which thin strips of wood have been lashed firmly, decayed leaves at the base of the plants can then be snipped off with ease and without alarming the fishes.

In the course of time the bottom will be covered with a layer of 'mulm' or humus formed by precipitated particles of organic matter and from the heavier dust that settles on the water: this gives rise to water-fouling bacteria. Nevertheless, it forms a good manure for the plants and some of it should be placed around the roots, the remainder being removed. The quickest way of doing this is to siphon it off, moving the end of the siphon over the bottom until no detritus re-

PLATE IV

1. *Barbus conchonius*, Rosy Barb, male (breeding season). 2. *B. nigrofasciatus*, Nigger or Black Ruby, Purple-headed Barb, male (breeding season). 3. *B. ticto*, Two-spot Barb, male. 4. *B. everetti*, Clown Barb.

(⅔ *natural size*)

mains. The drawback to this method is that unless one is very skilful a fair quantity of water will be removed in the operation, although if this water is passed through a sieve it can be returned to the tank. A 'dip-tube' with a large reservoir, although taking longer over the operation, is really more satisfactory. Place a finger over the end of the tube and the reservoir over the part to be cleaned, then gently release the finger and the detritus will be drawn into the tube. Little water will be removed by this method and it can be strained and replaced, or the deficiency can be made up with cold boiled tap water.

For removing the green algal growth that forms on the glass sides of the tank nothing is better than an old safety razor

DIP TUBE

blade fitted into a cleft in a piece of cane or into one of the metal arrangements especially made for this purpose. This implement, when worked up and down against the glass will easily scrape off the green film. The fishes as a rule will gobble up the scrapings, otherwise they can be drawn off with the dip-tube.

Another piece of apparatus of value to the breeder of 'live-bearers' is a breeding cage made

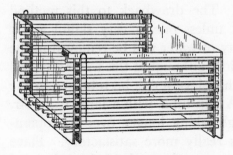

GLASS TUBE BREEDING CAGE

of glass rods. The pair of breeding fishes are placed in this cage, which is lowered into the water; when the young are born they are able to escape through the spaces between the rods and so avoid being eaten. The breeding cage has much to recommend it, particularly as it does away with having to remove the parents after the young are born.

Feeding rings are another essential to the well-being of the aquarium. Dried foods, from the surface tension of the water, will spread over the

FEEDING RING

whole of the surface of the water within a few seconds; uneaten food, in this way, falls among the inaccessible crevices of the plants and so decays. A feeding ring (usually one made of hollow glass) should be allowed to float at one particular corner of the tank and over a spot that is devoid of vegetation. The food, as a result, is restricted in its wanderings, and any that falls to the bottom can be removed easily with the dip-tube.

Finally, in this list of appliances, we come to the

GLASS INSPECTION PIPE

'dip-net'. This is a small muslin net, round, triangular or square at the mouth, and is used for removing dead fishes, fishes that are to be segregated for breeding or fishes that, having laid and fertilized their eggs, are likely to devour them. Some aquarists are adept at using the dip-net, they can capture the most lively of fishes with very little trouble; others merely succeed in chasing the frightened creatures round and round the tank, a proceeding that not only distresses them but that might prove fatal to a gravid female or to one exhausted by spawning. In this case it is far better to use a glass inspection pipe. This is shaped like an old-fashioned clay pipe and since it is transparent the fish can be captured quite easily in it; moreover they are not actually taken out of the water as they remain in the small quantity of water contained within the bowl. Fishes captured in this way can be examined with greater care and are less likely to receive injuries. In any case do not attempt to catch them by hand, for even if you are successful they will be really frightened and in their efforts to escape may leap right out of your hand to the unsympathetic floor below. Also the acid emanations of the human skin may cause inconvenience to the fish. If more than one aquarium is kept, dip-tubes, scrapers, inspection pipes, etc., should be washed in salt water after use to prevent transferring any possible infection from one tank to another.

CHAPTER V

FEEDING THE FISHES

WHEN the fish first leaves the egg it is provided with an egg sac, usually attached to the 'throat,' and from this it derives sufficient nourishment to tide it over the first few days of its independent existence. After this sac has been used up the baby fish has to fend for itself and seek its own food. Many of the tropicals are very small even when in the adult state, think then how small the fry are. As a matter of fact, even after they have consumed the egg sac, some fry are only just visible as tiny threads; consequently their mouths are minute and only capable of managing the smallest of food-stuffs. In their wild state they live on the tiny infusoria present in the water and it is the aim of the aquarist to supply this same food for his 'babies'. Fry of the larger species will take the very finest grade of dried food, but for the smallest species, if it is absolutely impossible to raise infusoria, other types of food must be sought. The yolk of a very hard-boiled egg if tied up in a piece of muslin and squeezed in the water will form minute particles acceptable to the fry. Boiled oatmeal if treated in the same manner will be taken also. In feeding these babies it should be remembered that they require frequent feeding, not too much at a time or the water will be fouled. Little and often should be the slogan.

Infusoria, however, is without doubt the ideal food for baby fishes and the question at once arises—"How can I obtain a sufficient supply of this all-important food?"

In the first place the word 'infusoria' is loosely used to describe the minute organisms, usually visible only with the aid of a microscope, that have their being in the water. They reproduce themselves, when the conditions are suitable, at a great rate; each individual divides into two halves which soon develop sufficiently to divide into two on their own account. These in turn go and do likewise and so the process goes on so long as there is enough food to go round.

The most popular way of obtaining a culture of infusoria is by boiling hay, lettuce, spinach or other vegetable matter and allowing the resultant infusion to stand in the air for a while in the hope that stray infusorians will alight therein and so breed rapidly. In about one case in twenty does a culture result from that method, which, to say the best, is but a hit or miss one. The best way is to make the infusion already referred to, and if possible to introduce a pure culture of Paramoecium (procurable in glass tubes from firms that supply schools with natural history materials). The uncorked tube should be placed in the infusion and before long a pale, ever changing cloud of tiny motes will be seen when the jar containing the infusion is held to the light. Once you have started a good culture of your own it is a simple matter to prepare a series of cultures from the original stock. The other method requires some knowledge of infusorians as a whole and a microscope or powerful hand lens.

The most common and at the same time the best all round infusorian for feeding either baby fishes or daphnia is Para-

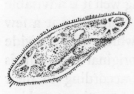

PARAMOECIUM OR
SLIPPER ANIMALCULE

moecium, otherwise the Slipper Animalcule. It is an oval, flat creature, and bears a number of fine vibrating hairs that serve to propel it through the water and to attract the minute food particles to the opening that serves as its mouth. You can recognize it easily by its unhurried undulating mode of progression. The best thing to do is to take a jar of water from a pond and place a drop on a glass slide and examine it with a lens. If only

Paramoecium is present then you can place the slide and its contents directly in the infusion; but if other organisms are present—they may be the larvae of pests—further drops should be sampled. After several attempts, if it is impossible to get a drop containing only Paramoecium, place a small piece of well teased out cotton wool on the slide and put a drop of water on it. The strands will restrict the movements of the organisms and so such as are required may be picked out with a bristle or a fine pipette. This sounds a rather difficult proposition; nevertheless, with practice it is possible to pick out by this means even the very tiniest of organisms, and Paramoecium is about the largest of the infusoria.

When the infusion is thriving well it is advisable to place on top of the water containing it a few pieces of chopped lettuce, which will provide organic matter when the original infusion is exhausted. Give the fishes, according to their number, a few tablespoonfuls at a time, making up the deficiency in the culture jars with water from the aquarium. When the fishes are able to feed on their own account they are very ravenous and unless fed frequently they will take it upon themselves to die, so it is advisable to feed them every two hours during the day if at all possible.

A drop of milk placed in the water will help to feed the infusoria already in the aquarium. As I have already indicated, the infusion will fall off considerably in its infusoria content if the nutrient salts are completely used up. These can be replaced by adding concentrated vegetable infusions or by preparing one or other of the solutions devised expressly for feeding infusoria, and of these one of the best is that known as Knop's nutritive solution. It is prepared as follows—take four parts of calcium nitrate and one part each of magnesium sulphate, potassium nitrate and potassium sulphate. The last three ingredients should be mixed together and dissolved in distilled water. Then dissolve the calcium nitrate in distilled water and mix the two solutions. So far the quantity of water has not been stated, but the omission will now be made up—the completed prescription should contain between 0.2 and 0.5 solids and so further distilled water must be added until that dilution is reached. By far the best way of setting about the job is to ask your local chemist to make it up for you. The amount required will depend on the amount of infusoria needed—a quart should suffice to provide enough infusoria to see quite a large family through the 'bottle' stage. The same amount will keep a tank of daphnia flourishing for several weeks—remove half a pint of water each week and replace with the same quantity of Knop's solution. The amount added will depend on the extent of the daphnia farm and on the demands made upon it.

The heterogeneous section of the Nature Kingdom known as Infusoria comprises both plant and animal organisms.

There are three principal animal forms of use to the aquarist—Ciliates, Flagellates and Rotifers.

CILIATES. We have already been introduced to the most useful species—*Paramoecium aurelia*—and this feeds on dissolved nutriment in the water. It reproduces by two methods: by dividing itself into two halves and by two individuals uniting and eventually breaking up into a number of separate organisms.

FLAGELLATES. The most common of these is *Euglena viridis*, considered by some to be a lowly plant-form, which breeds so rapidly in the summer that it is the chief of the 'green water' brigade and will cloud the outdoor pond in no time. It has a shapeless oval body with a whip at its stern which drives it through the water. It is considerably smaller than the ciliates and so is useful for fry with mouths of microscopic size. Reproduction is similar to that of Paramoecium.

ROTIFERS. To obtain a good brew of rotifers a good infusion containing ciliates and flagellates is necessary. The rotifers quite definitely are animals and most species are readily visible to the unaided eye, consequently they constitute a useful stopgap between the ordinary infusoria culture and the mikro or screened daphnia stage in the diet of fish fry. Rotifers may be divided into four groups—those that crawl over plants and stones and browse as they go, those that jerk about in the water or over stones and plants and frequently come to rest, those that swim freely and those that are permanently anchored. For our purpose the free swimming kind are the only useful ones, and they may be purchased from dealers in aquatic life, or collected from the pond with a fine mesh net. They are peculiar in the different kinds of eggs they lay. In the summer a large and a small kind will be produced, the large ones becoming females and the small ones males. In the autumn there is a form of mating from which results a statoblast—that is, a static egg which does not develop until the following spring. Daphnia also produces a similar type of egg: in both cases it is capable of being dried and will come to life when moistened again.

PLANT FORMS

ALGAL ZOOSPORES. These are the spores given off by algae such as 'blanket weed' and its kind, and known to the aquarist generally as *Confervae*. To the purist *Confervae* refers to just one of the many families of filamentous algae, but for all practical purposes they are fundamentally alike. That is to say, they have long silky strands, one small piece of which will suffice to start a thriving growth—to the dismay of those who like to see their tanks neat and tidy looking. Nevertheless, the extremely minute zoospores produced by those silky strands are ideal food for the very tiny fry and for rotifers and daphnae. They are as fat as butter and are produced in thousands by the parent plants; if one of the strands is examined under the microscope it will be seen to consist of long cells each of which is capable of orming a long strand on its own and in some of them the spores are formed. The spores after about two days of swimming about settle down to grow into filaments on their own. Consequently, such spores as escape the attentions of the fry will most certainly set up a colony which will be very difficult to eradicate. Most breeders prepare special breed-

ing tanks containing the dense vegetation necessary for spawning: if *Confervae* is introduced into
these tanks some days prior to spawning, there
will be already on hand an abundance of food
for the fry when the yolk-sac has been absorbed.
Conversely a separate *Confervae* tank—it need
only be of small dimensions—can be set up and
placed in a good light, not direct sunlight, and a
spoonful of the resultant green water added to the
breeding tank when necessary. In any case such
a tank is a boon in raising daphnae.

Not all algae are filamentous: many lead an
independent life and they are of somewhat larger
size than the zoospores, also they are useful food
for fry and daphnia. Of these the most famous
is the beautiful *Volvox globator* which rolls about
in the water like a tiny green bubble. Then there
is the bright green *Pandorina* which never seems
to know what shape it would like to be. *Pedias-
trum* is crudely star-shaped, it too is bright
green in colour and is quite common in the
pond.

DESMIDS AND DIATOMS. These unusual plants are
of very small size and are noted for their beauty
of design and for their place in the aquatic order
of things.

The Desmids do not move rapidly, they glide

77

gently over the plants or through the water in a very leisurely fashion. They are a rich source of food for many organisms, insect larvae, daphnia, rotifers, baby fishes, etc., also they oxygenate the water. They are mostly found in very clear water unless they themselves have decided to reproduce abundantly and so turn the water green. When this happens it is not unusual to see a mass of them rise in the morning sunlight with the multitude of bubbles of oxygen that they have liberated. These bubbles are formed throughout the day, then in the evening the mass sinks to the bottom again. Reproduction is by division and by two organisms uniting and producing sporangia which develop into the adult form. A type of fungus attacks desmids and, whilst the possibility of this fungus harming the fishes is extremely remote, it is only right that the fact should be noted.

The diatom is very similar in general appearance to the desmid except that the desmid has a tough leathery 'skin' around it whilst the diatom is encased in a hard silaceous envelope of divers beautiful shapes and sculpturings. Wherever there is water the ubiquitous diatom will be found: it is the ultimate food of all life in the sea, and it plays its part too in feeding the freshwater creatures. It is rich in oil, but, unfortunately, it does not form part of the ordinary infusoria culture. Specimens netted from the pond will, however, multiply in Knop's Solution.

In about ten days, more or less according to the size of the species, the fry should be sufficiently developed to be able to take screened daphnia or crushed enchytrae.

Daphnia are small crustaceans and are one of the finest foods for all carnivorous fishes. They may be gathered from ponds, where they can be seen easily as they roll and jerk their ungainly bodies through the water. At certain seasons they take on a ruddy complexion, when a jar full looks like tomato chutney. The drawback to

daphnia gathered from a pond is that undesirables, in the form of hydra and the larvae of aquatic insects, may be introduced into respectable society. To prevent this the aquarist should aim at making a pure

DAPHNIA

culture of daphnia by raising them at home in jars. The procedure is as follows: place the contents of the jar containing the pond daphnia in a shallow dish—a pie-dish will do—and with a dip-tube pick out several specimens and place them in a jar or, better still, another old pie-dish containing a vegetable infusion containing infusoria.

79

You need not worry about having a male and female together, for one thing males are very rare and for another, once a female has been fertilized she is fertilized for 'keeps'; not only that, the next generation or so is also fertilized. To obtain the strained daphnia for the young fishes pour the contents of the dish—after the daphnia have had a chance to breed, of course—through a piece of coarse muslin. This will retain the large individuals and allow the small ones to pass through, the resultant water can either be strained through fine silk and the silk rinsed in the water in the aquarium or poured straight into the aquarium. Perhaps the best way is to pour the water from the dish through a piece of fine muslin and bring its corners together to form a bag, and then suspend the bag in the aquarium for half an hour or so. The small daphnia will escape through the muslin into the water and the large specimens will still be alive when returned to their dish. If four or five dishes of daphnia are maintained they can be used in turn. When feeding the adult fishes with fully-grown daphnia they should be strained through coarse muslin, the water that passes through will contain the small individuals that will form the next crop, and the muslin rinsed in the water.

Cyclops is also a crustacean, though it is some-

PLATE V.
1 & 2. *Tanichthys albonubes*, White Cloud Mountain Minnow.   3 & 4.   *Barbus titteya*,
Rusty Barb.   5 & 7.   *Aphyocypris pooni*, female.   6.   *A. pooni*, male.
(*Natural size*)

what smaller than daphnia; it is more slender in shape and the female is particularly noticeable for the pale green egg-sacs that project from her sides like the wings of an insect. Cyclops, although

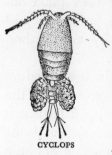

CYCLOPS

of indubitable food value, are not every fish's 'cup of tea'. The herring dotes on them but many tropical fishes leave them severely alone. Cyclops is extremely hardy and will 'make do' in conditions that would soon discourage daphnia. I have a specimen tube three inches long by one inch in diameter in which, four years ago, I took a dipping from a pond. The tube has been corked all that time yet the water is quite sweet and the cyclops are still jerking about merrily.

It is a much maligned little creature and is said by many to turn the tables and become parasitic on the fishes. The culprit is not cyclops but another member of the Copepod order, to which cyclops belongs, that is always parasitic on fishes. Indeed, there are many parasitic copepods one species of which, *Caligus rufimaculatus*, infests certain of the Killifishes. It is also true that they act as intermediary hosts to a type of parasitic worm which, when the infected cyclops is eaten by a perch, uses that fish as a secondary host and

F

finally, if the fish is insufficiently cooked, settles in man. In a pure culture the risk of this happening is negligible.

Many fishes, however, in the aquarium are partial to cyclops and for these they make an excellent intermediary between infusoria and daphnia. They can be raised by the method given for the culture of the latter.

Aquatic snails, when present in the breeding dishes, seem to encourage the growth of the daphnia culture, especially if chopped lettuce is placed in the water. An old kitchen sink with the outlet hole cemented over makes a fine daphnia farm. Frog-bit should be allowed to grow on the surface of the water, the snails will thrive on it, and the daphnia will thrive on the pieces of vegetation rasped off by the snails. If the sink has a layer of soil on the bottom the Frog-bit will send down its roots to it and the plant will grow much larger—at least, that is my experience.

Continuing with the crustaceans of value as fish food, we come to *Gammarus pulex*, otherwise known as the Water Flea, to which it is not in the least related. Gammarus grows to a length of half an inch and so is an admirable food for the larger carnivorous fishes such as the Cichlids. It may be found in slow-moving streams and ponds and it feeds on decaying vegetation. An old kitchen sink makes a good receptacle in which to breed it. Unfortunately, although a prolific breeder, this organism takes two years to reach its full size; nevertheless, it is quite a sizeable animal at a year old. Doubtless in its wild state it is omnivorous and will eat small insect larvae, tiny worms, cyclops and, probably, small daphnia. If one end of the sink or whatever receptacle is used for the Gammarus 'farm' is loosely packed with Elodea or some similar type of plant and a few cyclops and daphnia introduced, then it can be left to its own devices. At mating time the male and female embrace in a manner reminiscent of the bubble-nest fishes. The specimens themselves may be found around the roots of marginal plants or amongst the foliage of Elodea, Myriophyllum, Starwort, etc., in fact, one of my

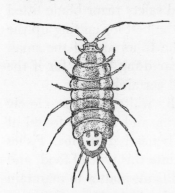

best colonies originated in some Water Cress that I had purchased for tea.

The so-called Freshwater Shrimp, *Asellus aquaticus* is slightly larger in size and it, too, makes a bonne bouche for the larger fishes. It may be

FRESH-WATER SHRIMP

found wild in the same situations as Gammarus and may be raised in a similar manner. Both Gammarus and Asellus cease breeding during the four winter months out of doors; they will, however, continue their activities if kept in a room with a temperature of 60 degrees or slightly over. There is one possible drawback to introducing a colony of either to the aquarium itself—they may develop a taste for baby fishes.

Common earthworms when chopped up into small pieces are not only good food, they also possess laxative qualities, and are unequalled, used alternatively with daphnia, in bringing fishes into breeding condition. The smaller worms are the best and, if possible, should be kept for a day or so in moss to clean themselves; in this way they are less likely to foul the water and are easier to cut up. An old safety razor blade fitted into a piece of wood is the best for cutting up the worms. Do not give the fishes any of the small yellow worms found near dung heaps, for if the fishes eat them they will certainly rue it.

Enchytrae are small white worms closely related to the earthworm, and may be found at times in the dank earth beneath dust-bins. Fishes as a rule greatly appreciate this type of food, and fortunately it is not a difficult matter to maintain a constant supply. In the first place procure a

84

wooden box (the kind that butter is packed in does very well) and half fill it with humus or leaf mould. Over the humus place the food, which consists of a variety of mashes—oatmeal, bread, potatoes, etc., boiled in sour milk. If the food is placed in small depressions in the humus, about 2 inches in diameter, the enchytrae will congregate there and the job of raking over the whole surface for them will be avoided. The enchytrae themselves may be purchased from any reputable dealer in aquarium needs. Sprinkle them lightly over the food pits, with another layer of humus over all. The humus should be slightly moistened, just enough to damp it, and a sheet of glass laid on the top—this to conserve the moisture. If the original stock is not used all at once there should be a continuous supply throughout the year, particularly if they are fed regularly. The correct generic name for these worms is not Enchytrae, but *Enchytraeus* (in full it is *Enchytraeus albidus*) but they will always be known, I fancy, to the aquarist as Enchytrae or by their popular name of 'White Worms'.

Tubifex is essentially an aquatic worm, living in the mud at the side of ponds in which there is an abundance of dead twigs, leaves and so forth. It is a bright pink in colour and makes a burrow for itself in the mud. If you remain quiet at the side of the pond for a while you may see the worm thrust its tail out of the burrow, waving it about in the water. At the slightest sound it will withdraw itself. The best way of collecting **Tubifex** is to scrape up about two inches of mud and place it in a box, then, if the mud is washed away the remaining worms can be placed in a jar of water. Those that are not grabbed by the fishes will establish themselves in the sand at the bottom of the aquarium, a proceeding that enrages many aquarists. It is galling, I admit, to see such valuable food waving its hinderpart about in the water to vanish as soon as a fish approaches. The Catfishes, however, more often than not, are too quick for them; in any case the slight current set up by the undulating worms helps to aerate the water at the bottom of the aquarium.

Another point in defence of the established colony is in respect of the feeding habits, which are typical of the Oligochaetes (to which group the earthworm also belongs); they live on the bacteria developed in earth and mud, and in so doing tend to cleanse the mulm that settles on the bottom of the aquarium and, in particular, the soil that has been placed there for the cultivation of soil-loving aquatic plants.

Another species of 'Sludge' or 'Mud' Worm, as

Tubifex rivulorum is commonly called, has within recent years come into the limelight. This is a species of tropical origin—*Aulophorus furcatus*—which was probably first introduced in its cocoon stage entangled in the roots of some imported plant. It is considerably smaller that Tubifex, being no more than five-sixteenths of an inch in length, and so is of ideal size for the young of the larger fishes that have outgrown Mikro. It has been reared in tanks set up for infusoria at a temperature of 80 degrees; the tanks in question, in order to encourage infusoria growth, were supplemented by lettuce leaves and Apple Snails —no doubt some of the raspings from the file-like tongue of the snail fell to the bottom and so provided food for both the infusoria and the worms.

The aquarist is ever on the look out for the ideal live food—a food that is easy to handle and that can be obtained in good quantities, but there is always some snag or other, especially in respect of food for baby fishes between the infusoria and the small daphnia and enchytrae stage. A few years after the war there came from Sweden what is thought to be the answer to the aquarist's prayer in the form of a tiny nematode worm known as Mikronematoder, or 'Mikro' for short. It is of the genus *Anguilula*, one of the best-known members of which is the Vinegar Eel (*Anguilula aceti*) which inhabits stale vinegar. The nematode in question is assumed to be either *A. aceti* or *A. silusiae*, but I am inclined to the view that it is none other than our old friend *A. glutinis* —the Paste Eel, which develops so rapidly in office paste that has gone sour. Be that as it may, experience has shown that Mikro, so far, is everything that has been claimed for it—an easily cultivated, nutritious and ideal-sized food for young fishes. There is also this about it—it does not readily drown, and so the uneaten specimens wriggle about in the water until they are eventually gobbled up.

For many years they have been noted in enchytrae cultures and taken as being young enchytrae, consequently the culture methods are basically the same.

The methods adopted in practice will be based on the quantity required: if there are many tanks of fry then there must be the necessary numbers of culture boxes. Also it is advisable to keep a succession of fresh cultures rather than continually draw on the main culture.

A wooden box about two inches deep or an old pie dish or other similar receptacle should be half filled with damp (not wet) mould and the entire container covered with a sheet of glass, this to prevent the intrusion of flies which are ever on the look-out for somewhere to deposit their eggs. A mixture of milk and fine oatmeal made into a creamy paste is placed on the mould in patches about two inches in diameter and on these patches a small clump of Mikro is dropped. In about six to nine days an amazingly prolific mass of Mikro will be swarming on the patch; if pieces of wood, slightly longer and stouter than match sticks are layed criss-cross over the culture the nematodes will crawl over and quickly cover them, then one of the pieces of wood can be removed and swished about in the aquarium or allowed to float for a while on the surface. The Mikro will soon swim away and be devoured. The length, incidentally, is about one-twelfth of an inch.

Do not use too much food when replenishing the culture patches, as there is always the risk of fungus forming.

Perhaps the greatest value of Mikro lies in its adaptability. If the fry are off your hands and it looks as though it will be some time before you will require this particular kind of food you can let the culture dry up. Special resting stages will result (like the statoblasts of daphnia and the rotifers) so that when a culture is again required the soil can be moistened and a new supply of milk and oatmeal added—then off we go again.

Bloodworms, really the larvae of a midge known as Chironomus, may be found in similar spots to where we found Tubifex. Gather them in the same manner, but instead of keeping them in water, place them in a box of slightly-damp moss, when they can be picked out with tweezers when required.

BLOODWORM

You will not find either Tubifex or Bloodworms in every pond; aquarists who have been fortunate enough to discover ponds inhabited by these valuable foods generally keep them a close secret, and set out for them at dead of night, using a devious route, and very often heavily disguised, in order to keep them to themselves.

Gnat larvae, very often the principal food of many tropicals in their wild state, are a splendid food for nearly all species of fish. The gnat

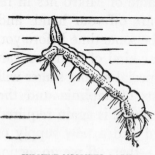

lays its eggs in the form of a raft on the surface of the water, when the eggs hatch the resultant larvae remain on the surface where they hang, head downwards, breathing air from a tube that

CULICINE MOSQUITO LARVA

90

projects slightly above the water. A muslin net drawn slowly but firmly through the water should capture a fair number. They are nearly half an inch in length and so they can be seen plainly as they wriggle at the surface.

Glass-worms, the larvae of another insect—Chaoborus—may be found swimming about in the water in the winter, which, to say the least of it, is very obliging on the part of the glass-worm, for the winter indeed brings its discontent to the aquarist who likes to give his fishes live food. A net drawn through the water may be found to contain small blobs of jelly; these are the glass-worms. You may keep them alive in a tank by feeding them on daphnia, that is, until they turn into midges.

Certain fishes, such as the Hatchet Fishes, are very partial to a fly now and again, some fishes, indeed are only really happy when there is a plentiful and continuous supply. Fortunately we have at hand a species of fly which can be cultivated with very little trouble, in a clean and easily controlled manner. In fact, the breeding of this fly, known as *Drosophila melanogaster*—the Fruit Fly—is quite a routine job in the biology laboratories of universities and most large schools.

It is as long as Mikro (about one twelfth of an

inch) with a wing span of one-quarter of an inch. The colour is a brownish yellow generally, and the abdomen is striped with black. The male has the posterior part of the abdomen entirely black, also he is slightly smaller than the female and has a rounded abdomen, while that of the female is pointed. The eyes of both sexes are red.

Although it is a native of the tropics every year numbers are brought over in consignments of fruit; in summer they fly around the country-side to die off at the approach of cold weather.

Their natural food is rotten fruit that has started to ferment: for breeding purposes a synthetic food has to be devised. The most usual method is as follows; procure an ordinary milk bottle, half-pint size and make a stopper for it consisting of a plug of cotton wool wrapped round with muslin—this allows the entry of air yet prevents the escape of the restless larvae.

The list of ingredients at first looks rather alarming, but they can be quite easily procured with a little thought; they are fine maize-meal (or mashed banana), molasses or treacle, agar, nippigin (to prevent the formation of mould) and water. Sufficient for 20 bottles will result from the following recipe; boil one ounce of agar in one and a quarter pints of water until the agar is dissolved. Soak six ounces of maize-meal in half a pint of water for ten minutes then add this to the agar solution. Dissolve four good table-spoons of treacle in the same quantity of water and add this to the mess already concocted and to the whole add a quarter of a teaspoonful of nip-pigin and boil the lot for three minutes. It should

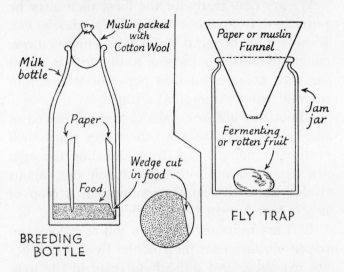

Muslin packed with Cotton Wool

Milk bottle

Paper or muslin Funnel

Paper

Food

Wedge cut in food

Jam jar

Fermenting or rotten fruit

FLY TRAP

BREEDING BOTTLE

be poured hot into the bottles to a depth of one inch and in the fulness of time should set solid—this is what the agar is for. Care must be taken not to crack the bottles with the hot solution.

When the food has set, in order to allow the gases set up by fermentation to escape, a small section is cut away next to the glass, thus making

93

a slot and into this slot push a sheet of paper and into the food opposite the slot push another piece. The best paper for this purpose is a pure sulphite toilet paper—its function is to absorb excess moisture. A drop of yeast is now added to the food—this sets up the fermentation.

We are now ready for the flies; these may be purchased from shops that supply schools, etc. with biology material or, if it is summer time, caught by putting a piece of rotting fruit in a jam jar with a funnel of thin paper or stiff muslin inserted into the mouth as a trap.

About half a dozen pairs of flies are placed in the bottles; they will lay their eggs which will eventually pupate and, from the time the eggs are deposited until the flies hatch out, about twelve days will elapse, resulting in a crop of nearly four hundred Fruit Flies.

It is not quite so difficult a job as it looks on paper—in any case most of the fly-eating fishes are expensive and difficult to rear; in the long run Fruit Flies are worth the trouble.

Finally among live foods, there is *Artemia salens*, commonly known as the Brine Shrimp. This shrimp-like creature lives in the salt lakes in the State of Utah and is, when fully grown, nearly half an inch in length. The water in the salt lakes is considerably saltier than the sea, and so a fairly strong brine solution is necessary in hatching the eggs out. The eggs may be obtained from dealers and are sold in packets. A small pinch of these eggs (there are something like a hundred eggs in a pinch) should be placed in a solution of four ounces of evaporated sea salt to a gallon of water. Failing sea salt, common cooking salt will do; table salt, because of added chemicals, should be used only as a last resort. Leave the solution to stand for twenty-four hours before adding the eggs. Hatching will be precipitated if the solution is kept at a temperature of 70 degrees Fahr., and should take place in about three days, the resultant fry being about the size of daphnia, but if they are fed with infusoria they will grow to the adult size, a size that brings joy to the hearts of the bigger fishes.

Owing to the hatching taking place in salt water, one must be very careful how the shrimps are given to the fishes; if too much brine is introduced the whole pH of the water will be affected. The best plan is to strain it through a piece of muslin and turn the muslin inside out in the water. Brine shrimps are a fairly recent innovation, but they are very welcome as they are a fine form of food and are available throughout the year.

As regards dried foods, there is really little to

95

say. The aquarist would be well advised, if he intends using such food, to obtain the grade required—fine, for the growing fry, medium for the general run of fishes, and coarse for the large ones—from a good dealer. There are several brands of fish food on the market that contain a variety of ingredients—dried flies, dried daphnia, dried mollusc larvae, egg powder, chopped spinach, oatmeal, meat meal and so forth, all making for a good, balanced diet. Still, if at all possible, an occasional treat in the way of live food will be of advantage to the fishes.

PLATE VI.   *F-96*
1. *Corydoras aeneus*, Bronze Catfish.   2.   *C. julii*, Leopard Catfish.   3.   *C. paleatus*.
Peppered Catfish.
                                    (*Natural size*)

CHAPTER VI

AILMENTS OF FISHES

OUR knowledge of the diseases of fishes is exceedingly limited: we can talk glibly enough about fungus, white-spot, congestion, tail-rot, furunculosis and so forth: we can trace the life histories of many of the parasites that infest the fish, but, as regards the clinical treatment of them we are almost in the dark.

'The fish', sagely remarks Shakespeare, 'lives in the sea', and that is the root of the whole difficulty. The diseases and disorders of dogs, cats, cattle, horses and other domesticated animals—and wild animals too, for that matter— are more understandable to us, they have their being in the familiar air; but we can only dimly appreciate an aquatic existence. Furthermore there is no pecuniary inducement to attract the student to this most difficult subject, and such research work as has been done has been more in the nature of biological recreation on the part of just a few scientists.

Consequently we must make the most of what we do know about the treatment of the sick fish, and it is fortunate, therefore, that the tropical fish is less liable to disease than its cold-water relations.

'Prevention is better than cure,' and this trite saw should be the slogan of every aquarist for, with the exception of congenital complaints, nearly every ailment to which his fishes may be prone is preventable.

A sudden drop in the temperature of the water, for instance, even if not of sufficient duration actually to kill the fishes, may give rise to a chill, with congestion of the branchial apparatus—very like broncho-pneumonia, in fact. Even if a chill does not result, the vitality of the fish is lowered and bacteria have a chance to assert themselves on the weakened fish. A fish suffering from a chill should be placed in a very shallow tank and the water raised to 90 degrees Fahr., then, after twenty-four hours, the water may be gradually lowered to the ordinary community tank temperature.

Foul water, caused by overcrowding, decaying plants or uneaten food, will weaken a fish; so also will constipation, a condition common to the greedier fishes. The symptoms of over-feeding and constipation are usually the same—the fish remains perfectly stationary in mid-water and gives an occasional shiver or 'shimmy', the scales may stand slightly away from the body and the fish will look 'off colour' generally.

It is obvious that one cannot remove a fish from the water and pour physic down its throat and, although Epsom Salts is perhaps the best medicine for this purpose, it is obvious that, if it is placed in the tank in sufficient quantity to cure the fish, the treatment will still be going on after the fish is better. The patient, then, should be removed to a shallow tank, containing water similar to that in the aquarium, to which has been added Epsom Salts in the proportion of a tablespoonful to the gallon of water. The fish may be left in this for twenty-four hours and then returned to its own quarters, the treatment may be repeated every other day, for a week if necessary. Once a month a small pinch of Epsom Salts and another of evaporated sea salt, the whole mixture being no greater than will cover a sixpence, may be placed in the aquarium; this amount being for the twelve gallon tank.

Judicious feeding—taking care that the greedy fellows do not exceed their rations—and a supply of green food such as Frogbit or an occasional feed of chopped spinach, should keep this distressing and serious complaint from the ménage. Daphnia and chopped earthworm are splendid laxatives for the fishes that will not touch green-stuff.

99

Healthy water, then, and judicious feeding should keep the aquarium free from the ordinary forms of piscine sickness. Disease, however, may be introduced with new plants or fishes. To prevent this the plants should be washed in a weak permanganate of potash solution before being planted, and the new fishes should be quarantined in a separate tank for a week. During that time, if they are harbouring any undesirable germs, such germs will manifest themselves.

Sometimes a fish may be suffering from a complaint that the aquarist cannot recognize— it may skulk in a corner or float helplessly on its side—and in this case the fish may be placed in a shallow dish of water containing two teaspoonfuls of sea salt to the gallon and the water raised to 90 degrees gradually. Keep the fish at this temperature for several days and then lower the temperature to normal again. This treatment is a good one for fungus, a most contagious complaint that gives the fish the appearance of being flecked with cotton wool. After the fish has reposed in the 'hospital' tank for three days it should be removed and, whilst being held in a damp cloth, the fungus should be removed with a soft brush dipped in weak iodine. Owing to the rapidity with which this parasite spreads, it is advisable to give all the inhabitants of the aquarium a weak salt bath; whilst they are being treated a few drops of mercurochrome should be added to the aquarium water. This will disinfect it and save the job of dismantling the whole tank; the plants may be tinged with yellow slightly, but this will wear off in time.

From the rapidity of their movements tropical fishes are liable to wound themselves on sharp rocks or other forms of ornament. If the wound does not appear to inconvenience the fish it is best to let well alone, but if it is severe there is a possibility of fungus forming over the lacerated tissues. The fish may be placed in a damp cloth and the wound painted with weak iodine or a 2 per cent solution of mercurochrome. Do not repeat this treatment at less than twenty-four hour intervals, as too-frequent applications may burn the flesh and a scar will form. The motto here is: 'Don't have sharp rocks or ornaments in the aquarium'.

One of the most troublesome and most difficult parasites to detect is Gill-worm, countless species of which exist, their whole aim in life being to settle on the gills of fishes, particularly baby ones. They are exceedingly small, usually about a millimetre in length, but they cause their host considerable inconvenience. When the fry are observed head on and the head region looks more swollen than need be, then the odds are there are Gill-worms about. The best treatment seems the mercurochrome tank treatment already referred to; this should rid the tank of the pest for, even if one could treat the fishes individually, the larval stages of the worm would still be lurking in the water.

Dropsy occurs in fishes that are not in the best of health to start with, at least, that is the general assumption. A bacterium, or to be more exact, a variety of a bacterium commonly found in water attacks the liver, kidneys and intestines generally and results in a quantity of fluid forming in the belly of the fish. There seems to be no cure for this complaint, the conditions which allowed the bacteria to flourish were already there and once the bacteria have taken a hold it is not possible to restore the patient to a sufficiently good state of health to resist its spread. The only thing to do is to try the mercurochrome treatment and to hope for the best. In any case the affected fish should be removed if it is with other fishes, for the fluid containing the bacteria is infectious.

One of the early symptoms of this disease is a 'staring' of the scales, which stand out from the body and not infrequently drop off. This symptom also occurs if a fish—usually a live-bearer or bubble-nest builder—has been damaged, thus allowing the responsible bacterium to establish itself. In its early stages the diseased fish is listless and does not swim with its usual vivacity, the breathing rate is considerably stepped up and later the tail seems unwilling to function and, later still, the fish looks obviously sick and droops from the surface of the water. In a day or so it dies, for there is no known cure. Healthy fishes without skin abrasions, even if they rub up against the diseased fish, are not likely to be infected—but it is better to remove the poor victim and to treat the aquarium as already described.

Finally, among the common ailments, is 'White Spot', also known as 'Ich' for short, or Ichthyophthirius if you have plenty of time to spare. This manifests itself in small white spots, more or less flush with the skin and not raised and fluffy as is fungus. An aquarium hitherto free from this infection may become infected when new fishes, plants or snails are introduced—hence the need for the quarantine tank.

Before discussing the treatment, let us make a brief excursion into the life history of the offender. The white spot itself is the outward and visible sign of a colony of microscopic parasites. As the individuals develop and grow, they drop off their host and, settling on the bottom of the aquarium, encyst themselves in a kind of cocoon about the size of a grain of sand, innocent enough in appearance. However, great things are going on within the cyst; it is breaking up into hundreds of minute spores which are liberated in about eighteen to twenty hours after the original encystment. These extremely minute spores, in order to live, must find a fish on which to feed. If they fail to find a host within three or four days they die; but if they do encounter a fish in their travels they settle under its skin and attack the red corpuscles in the blood. The spores develop rapidly, and when mature they divide into two separate units which continue to feed on the blood. In time, the colony, which has now been on the fish for some days, shows itself on the skin as a white spot, and this brings us to where we started at the beginning of this paragraph.

It is obvious that one infected fish is capable of setting up a thriving 'ich' colony, and so the whole tank must be disinfected, after the removal of the fish, in order to destroy any lurking cysts on the bottom. A few drops of mercurochrome added to the water in the tank will destroy the free-swimming spores. Although, in any case, if the fishes are removed for a week the colony will die off of its own accord.

As regards the infected fishes. Place them in the hospital tank and slowly raise the temperature to 90 degrees; this will hasten the parasite's development and in about three days they will leave their host. The next consideration is to destroy the cysts and any free-swimming spores by adding mercurochrome—six drops of 2 per cent solution to the pint—and allowing the fishes to remain in it for a quarter of an hour, repeating the performance every day for four days. Allow the fishes to remain in hospital for a week, gradually lowering the temperature during the last two days. Then, if all the spots have disappeared completely, the fishes can be returned to their own quarters.

I have assumed that the aquarist will give treatment to the fishes as soon as he sees the spots forming on the fins. If treatment is delayed the spots will spread to the body and finally to the gills, at which stage there is little hope of effecting a cure. The trouble is that, in attacking the red corpuscles, the parasite makes the fish anaemic, and if the infection spreads to any extent the fish may be weakened beyond recovery.

CHAPTER VII

AQUARIUM FISHES

THE fresh-water streams, rivers and lakes of the tropics provide the enthusiast with, literally, hundreds of different species of fish for his aquariums. Some of the fishes are vivid in colouring, others grotesque in build or habits; some are delicately coloured, many are fragile and nearly all are tiny. Fortunately for the aquarist who delights—and who does not?—in variety, these fishes, partly from their small size and partly from the small quantity of oxygen required, can be kept in considerable numbers in the one tank.

On the other hand, it is unfortunate that certain species are, to say the least, quarrelsome; owing to the carnivorous tastes of most tropicals the quarrels do not stop at arguing, as a rule the weaker specimen is eaten. The aquarist, then, must guard against introducing into an otherwise peaceful community large individuals of the vindictive types. Some of the worst offenders are often beautiful creatures and it seems a pity that one should be deprived of their society. If separate tanks are out of the question, then the only course open is to have specimens whose mouths are too small to tackle the smallest of the community.

The community tank should possess colour, movement and interest as well as uniformity of size among its denizens. Also, as the fishes may each have their own particular ideas regarding the ideal temperature, it is well to strike a good average and keep the water at that, with as little variation as possible—a fish may get used to a strange temperature in time, but it will never be really happy with variations. The most satisfactory average temperature is 74 degrees Fahr.

For a fifteen gallon tank the following fishes form a delightful community:—*Rasbora heteromorpha*, 4; *Brachydanio rerio*, 4; *Barbus oligolepis*, 2; *Aphysemion australe*, 2; *Ambassis lala*, 2; *Pterophyllum scalare*, 2 (small specimens); *Corydoras julii* or *C. aeneus*, 2.

One could fill a book almost with the various combinations of fishes for the community tank, and the enthusiast will find considerable pleasure in making ideal collections of his own choosing. Therefore I will give but one more suggested congregation for a tank of a similar size:— *Lebistes reticulatus*, 4; *Xiphophorus helleri*, 4; *Mollienisia sphenops*, 2; *Badis badis*, 2; *Barbus con-*

chonius, 2; Small *P. scalare*, 1; *Corydoras sp.*, 1; *Colisa lalia*, 2.

Breeding from his various fishes is usually a source of considerable interest to the fancier. Not only are most of the fishes more colourful and active at breeding time, but there is great satisfaction in actually raising baby fishes. Moreover, many species have yet to be bred in captivity and these, which perforce must be imported from their native haunts, are often expensive to buy. There must be a reason why such fishes do not breed in tanks, and in trying to find this reason (or reasons) the aquarist will learn more about his fishes than all the books in the world can tell him. Likewise, if successful, he will not only benefit himself but the biologist as well.

In the following list of fishes specimens of the various types are dealt with in detail, in all cases particularly in respect of breeding. The shorter descriptions deal only with fishes that are contained in the lists of dealers in this country. None of the marine or brackish-water species are included, beautiful as they are. Several species are obtainable, but as they demand a special treatment, beyond the scope of this book, I am leaving them out.

The fishes themselves are listed in ascending order of development; thus the lowly Characins open the programme and the lordly Cichlids conclude it. The line under the fishes illustrated by line drawings in all instances represents 1 inch, thereby giving a visual indication of the actual length of the fishes in question.

The peaceful fishes, such as are suitable for the community tank, are rewarded by the letter C after their name.

CHARACINIDAE (*The Characins*)

The Characins are small, active and hardy fishes and are distantly related to the carp kind. Where the carps have only one dorsal fin, however, the majority of Characins have two. The extra fin, when present, is small, fatty and without

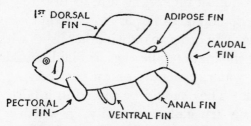

CHARACIN TYPE WITH ADIPOSE SECOND DORSAL

rays; it is known as the adipose fin and is situated between the main dorsal fin and the tail. Another feature of these fishes not found in the carps is the presence of teeth in the mouth—the true carps have teeth only in the throat.

Hardy as they are and, in their wild state, apparently most prolific, they are exceedingly difficult to breed in captivity.

Copeina guttata (STEINDACHNER). Brazil. 4 in. C. 72°–78°. Somewhat elongated body. In the male the body is blue merging into a reddish brown dorsally, on each scale is a red spot. The tail, ventral and anal fins are yellow fringed with red. The female is duller generally and without scale spots. There is a black mark in the middle of the dorsal fin in both sexes.

Copeina arnoldi (REGAN). Brazil. 3 in. C. 72°–78°. Slightly more elongated than *C. guttata*, and with slightly larger fins which are reddish at the edges. Otherwise coloration is very similar. This is a most interesting fish, its breeding habits being so remarkable as to warrant separate quarters. In order to outwit other fishes with egg-eating inclinations the eggs are laid actually out of the water, generally on an overhanging ledge of rock. They should be placed in a fairly large tank, say ten gallons capacity, in which a sheet of slate or roughened glass is placed. This should lean against one side of the tank at a gentle angle, and the water should be sufficiently shallow to permit the slate to project some two or three inches above it. Feed the pair on chopped earthworm and daphnia, and before long love-making should commence. After the preliminary skirmishings it will be seen that the pair embrace and literally leap out of the water, landing on the desired spot on the slate. Here they remain for some seconds during which time ten eggs are laid. The performance is repeated about nine or ten times and eventually the full complement of a hundred eggs are laid and fertilized. In the ordinary way the jelly-like mass of eggs would soon become dry, and to prevent this the male plays around in the water near the aerial raft, vigorously splashing with his tail. Thus the eggs are kept moist. In the space of three days the eggs hatch and the fry roll into the water. At first they rest in nooks and crannies, deriving nourishment from their yolk sacs. When this is exhausted the tiny fry set out in search of food and this, of course, must be supplied. (See Chapter V, 'Feeding the Fishes'.) Suitable partially submerged rocks may replace slate.

Pyrrhulina rachoviana MYERS. Argentine. 1¾ in. (rarely 2 in.) 65°–68°. This charming little member of the Characin family, although of a friendly nature, is not really at home in the community tank as it prefers a slightly lower temperature. It likes sunshine and light, but do not place it full in the sun. A small aquarium planted with such broad-leaved plants as Cryptocoryne,

Anubia and Sagittaria (as well as Myriophyllum) should keep it quite happy.

The colour is a warm brown becoming a whitish-silver on the under side with, overall, a greenish sheen; the lateral line is enhanced by a double zigzag stripe of a golden-brown colour over which is a bluish tint. In the male this stripe is supplemented by a row of red dots, also the male has a larger dorsal fin which, in both sexes, has black speckles. The anal and ventral fins are orange and these, in the male, are red tipped.

At breeding time the temperature should be raised to 73 degrees. The male prepares the way, at spawning time, by spring-cleaning a firm broad leaf to which he entices the female. Together they wriggle over the leaf when from six to ten eggs are deposited and fertilized; after the female has rested awhile the operation is repeated until, altogether, about forty eggs are liberated. In just over twenty-four hours the fry hatch out—during which time the male has been busily fanning the eggs—and a day later are ready to tackle larval crustaceans.

Pyrrhulina is a small yet omnivorous feeder and so it is best, if it is intended to raise many of the young, to remove them to another aquarium.

The females may be readily distinguished

when full of eggs, moreover the edge of the tail is markedly concave; the edge of the tail of the male is straight.

Sometimes the female will chase the males—always a good sign this—and then the tables will be turned and the males will take the initiative. If, after four or five days, nothing has happened in spite of the water being changed another female should be tried. The actual time taken to deposit the successive clutches of eggs is about two hours.

Hyphessobrycon bifasciatus ELLIS. Southern Brazil. 2¼ in. C. 75°–78°. 'The Yellow Tetra.'

The body is deep, though not so deep as that of the Flame Fish, and of a yellowish-olive colour; a slight iridescence gives a general brassy appearance. The bases of the fins are tinged with red and across the fore part of the body are two vertical black smudges. It spawns readily in ordinary aquarium conditions, merely requiring a dense patch of Myriophyllum or some other plant of a small-leaved nature with an open space for the preliminary skirmishes. Generally, breeding takes a similar course to that of the Flame Fish. A variety of the Yellow Tetra, known as the Golden Tetra, is occasionally encountered in the dealer's collections; it is noticeable for the deep gold colour of the body and the definite yellow of the fins. In its habits generally it resembles the Yellow kind but, unfortunately, for it is a really handsome fish, although it can be bred without undue trouble the progeny as a rule revert to the less colourful variety.

Hyphessobrycon flammeus (MYERS). Rio de Janeiro. 1½ in. C. 75°–80°. 'Red Tetra from Rio' and 'Flame Fish'. This glorious little fish is ideal for the community tank, it is brightly

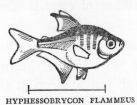

HYPHESSOBRYCON FLAMMEUS

coloured, active, peaceful and, with patience, can be bred. The body is silvery on the underside merging into an olive-green sheen on the back, the posterior half is bright red. The fins, too, are red and with the exception of the tail are bordered with black. Two distinct vertical black bars are situated just behind the gills. (Plate I, 1.)

In breeding the Flame Fish it is essential that the tank is densely planted with Myriophyllum or a similar type of plant. The water, two gallons of which should be allowed per fish, must be kept at a steady 77°–80° and the depth is best kept at no more than 8 in. Incidentally, if spawning is hanging fire matters may sometimes be speeded up if about one-fifth of the water is removed and then replaced by the same quantity of slightly cooler water, a drop in temperature of eight degrees being considered ideal.

To condition the breeding fishes they should, ideally, have quarters of their own and be well fed—daphnia, enchytrae, bloodworms and finely chopped earthworms varied with a reliable packet food should see them in good condition.

The eggs, which are small and transparent, are laid in the midst of the plants, whither the male has either coaxed or driven the female. In all about one hundred eggs are laid, necessitating several 'drives' into the plants. As the females often require persuasion, it is advisable to have two males to the one female. If they are well fed and if a few daphnia are allowed to remain in the tank during the three days during which the eggs are hatching, the parents may not eat the eggs. Otherwise they should be removed to separate quarters.

The adults are more inclined to eat the tiny, wriggling larvae when they emerge from the eggs. Also, it is well to remember that the yolk sac from which the fry derive their first nutriment will be used up in four days, thus a good infusoria culture must be already prepared. Otherwise, a prepared food of a flour-like consistency may suffice to tide them over until they are able to take young daphnia and brine shrimps.

Hyphessobrycon innesi (MYERS). Amazon. 1½ in. C. 70°–74°. 'Neon Tetra', 'Humming Bird Fish' and 'Coronation Fish'. This slender-bodied fish was one of the discoveries of 1936 and, superficially, does not resemble in either colouring or outline the two Characins just dealt with. The belly is cream-coloured and the back iridescent greens, purples and blues. From the middle of the body, just below the centre, to the tail root runs a vivid, almost luminous, red line. Above this, but starting from the head, is another vivid line, this time of brilliant blue-green. If the fish had nothing else to recommend it, its eyes alone would make it outstanding; they are flashing jewels, pure and simple. (Plate I, 1 and 2.)

It was some time before the enthusiast was able to do anything about the breeding of this fish, and when success did come it was of a very niggardly nature. The eggs were deposited all right (in numbers varying from fifty to one hundred and fifty) but somehow they were reluctant to develop even into larvae. True, the parents in nearly all of the recorded instances immediately set about devouring the eggs, but even when they were prevented the best efforts produced only a 50 per cent hatch.

The native haunts of this Tetra are shallow mountain streams almost hidden by overhanging vegetation. In such conditions the stream would be airless and dark and the water thick with dead leaves and twigs as well as shade-loving plants. The temperature, owing to the altitude and the shade, would not be exceptionally high considering the low latitude. All temperatures have been tried from 72 to 82 degrees with the better results seeming to come from the higher temperatures. A tank in a shady position seems to help and it is possible that bright light kills the eggs.

In brief, it would seem that a shallow, roomy tank (about 7 in. deep) with matured, slightly acid water, pH 6.8, well planted with Myriophyllum, Indian Fern or Ambulia, and kept well away from the light should produce results.

The fishes themselves are difficult to sex until shortly before breeding when the usual bright colour of the female becomes dull and the males develop a bright white border on the forepart of the anal fin. The eggs are tiny and transparent and, in the dim light, very difficult to discern. The young hatch out in from four to five days and, although only a tenth of an inch in length, can be seen readily for creatures of so small a size by virtue of their bright golden colour. Feed for the first fortnight on infusoria, then on rotifers and then, after another week, on young daphnia.

Hyphessobrycon rosaceus (DURBIN). British Guiana. 1¾ in. C. 72°–82°. 'Black Flag Fish.' Body shape typical. Flesh pink, first dorsal fin, high and erect, black with a white edge. The sexes can be distinguished by the larger dorsal fin of the male and the bright red tip at the top of that same fin in the female. Breeding habits are similar to those of *H. flammeus*, but few aquarists have met with any signal success in breeding this pretty fish. (Plate I, 5.)

Hyphessobrycon serpae (DURBIN). Brazil. 1½ in. C. 77°–80°. This fish is very similar in shape and colouring to the foregoing, except that the colours are more pronounced. The posterior half of the body and the crest region is a full red; the fins are white bordered and inclined to black.

There is a black edge to the anal fin and a black spot on the dorsal; the shoulder bears a long north to south black patch. Although of a friendly disposition itself and of a hardy, long-lived constitution, it is inclined to be starved out by the less retiring inhabitants of the community tank.

At breeding time the females, obligingly, exhibit a deep, rounded body; the adult male, on the other hand, is not so easy to distinguish. He is, however, livelier and brisker with a corres-

ponding gayer—or, rather, more sharply defined—coloration.

The tank should be light and well planted with
such plants as will retain the adhesive eggs. The
temperature should be raised gradually to 85 degrees. After chasing through the plant thickets
the pair will pause and as they rest side by side,
the tail of the male in close proximity to that of
the female, a clutch of eggs will be extruded and
fertilized. In the course of two hours or so about
100 eggs will be found adhering to the foliage.
After two days the tiny, transparent larvae will
emerge. They grow rapidly and, although minute
infusoria must be immediately on hand for the
newly hatched fry, they will take tiny crustaceans
in fourteen days. Nevertheless, the mouth never
attains any size and so, throughout their life, they
should be fed with the finer graded foods.

Hyphessobrycon heterorhabdus (ULREY). South
America. $1\frac{3}{4}$ in. C. 75°–78°. 'Flag' or 'Striped
Tetra'. This friendly, though by no means timid,
fish does not appear to have been bred in this
country, so we have had to rely on intermittent
supplies from South America. Nevertheless, the
sexes can be assumed with what one imagines to
be a fair degree of accuracy; there is a tiny hook
on the anal fin of the males of certain Characin

species and some specimens of *heterorhabdus* possess such a hook, moreover the deepness of body that we associate with females generally may be observed in some specimens.

As for the fish itself—bright scales, merging from gold on the dorsal surface to silver on the belly, cover a slender body, compressed laterally. A stripe, red on its upper part, silvery-gold on its middle and a deep blue below, runs from the gill covers to the tail. This stripe is wider at the gills than at the tail. A few black specks may be seen on the dorsal fin and some white specks on the anal and caudal fins. (Plate I, 3.)

Hemigrammus caudovittatus (AHL). Argentine. $3\frac{1}{2}$ in. 60°–85°. A silvery fish, this, somewhat like the Common Rudd in shape. The body is uniformly silver with a purple area at the base of the tail. The fins are rosy-pink in colour.

The ideal breeding temperature is 72°–74° and a fairly large aquarium is required—fifteen gallons at the least—with well established thickets of plants. The typical Characin breeding tactics are maintained with the exception that after the male has chased the female and she has deposited her eggs she, in her turn, chases the male. Both will devour the eggs and so the parents should be removed immediately after spawning.

Hemigrammus ocellifer (STEINDACHNER). Amazon. 1¾ in. C. 65°–85°. 'Beacon' or 'Head-and-tail-Light Fish'. A compact silver body with pale greenish-yellow fins does not sound very attractive, but, when one adds to this glowing red and blue eyes with black centres and a vivid spot of similar colours at the base of the tail, one can understand its popularity. A distinct yellow line along the centre of the body adds to the effect. The male has a white spot on the forepart of the anal fin. Breeding as for *Hyphessobrycon flammeus* but, usually, with more successful results. (Plate I, 4.)

Hemigrammus unilineatus (GILL). Orinoco. 2 in. C. 68°–85°. 'Feather Fin.' A hardy and amiable little fish, easily bred and easily kept; in fact it will eat almost anything. For these reasons, in spite of its lack of colour, it is a popular member of the community tank. The body is deepish in shape and of a silvery colour becoming pale olive towards the back. The fins are reddish-brown. The 'one line' of the specific name refers to the straight black

HEMIGRAMMUS UNILINEATUS

and white line which runs down the front edge of the anal-fin. Breeding habits similar to those of *Hyphessobrycon flammeus*. (Plate II, 5.)

Creagrutus beni (EIGENMANN). Upper Amazon.

2 in. 73°–76°. This fish, introduced to aquarists in the mid 'thirties, is notable for the over-shot snout. Otherwise it is not particularly remarkable. The body, slenderish and silvery, takes on a yellow tint towards the tail. The fins are reddish.

Breeding is best accomplished at 74 degrees when it will be noticed that the male does not come in close proximity with the female, and such chasing as takes place seems to be for the express purpose of helping the female to eject the forty or so eggs which constitute the average spawning. It is thought that, in some manner still inexplicable, the female is fertilized prior to the ordinary chasing operations. The male should be removed immediately the eggs have been deposited—he has the nasty habit of eating every egg in sight. The fry hatch out in 24–36 hours.

Pristella riddlei (MEEK). Guiana. 1¾ in. C. 75°–78°. Sometimes known as the 'X-ray Fish', *Pristella* is a most attractive creature, and typical of the Characins, both in shape and general behaviour. The colouring itself is not particularly

PRISTELLA RIDDLEI

striking, being silver on the underside and olive on the back. A dark-brown line extends from snout to tail, and the fins are reddish. Neverthe-

122

less, the whole fish has a soft, very pale rosy glow suffusing it, giving a most pleasing effect. The high dorsal and long anal fins bear large dark spots. In the male the spot on the anal fin does not completely cross it, as is the case with the female. (Plate II, 2.)

Thayeria obliqua (EIGENMANN). Amazon Basin. 2 in. C. 75°–85°. 'Oblique Tetra', 'Penguin Fish'. This attractive little Characin was first introduced into this country from abroad in about 1936 or 1937 and has since become very popular, principally because of its peculiar swimming habits and attractive shape. The body colour is a silvery olive but this is relieved by a firm black line running from the gill covers to the tail root and then obliquely downwards to the tip of the lower lobe of the tail which is somewhat longer than the upper lobe. The fish swims in the straight manner adopted by most fishes but when it comes to rest it does so at an angle of 45 degrees to the horizontal.

The eyes are black with a golden ring.

It breeds at 80 degrees and after a wild skirmishing through the plants side by side the small, dull brown coloured eggs are deposited. They hatch out in 24 hours and the fry retain the yolk-sac for about four days. At first the diet should consist of the usual infusoria or fine grade dried food and then of the nauplii of Artemia or Daphnia. After three weeks or so they will take mikro and a fortnight later enchytrae, which seems to be a favourite food of the adults.

Moenkhausia pittieri (EIGENMANN). Venezuela. 2½ in. C. 70°–82°. The body is fairly deep, and a uniform silver in colour, speckled with green and blue metallic dots. The fins form perhaps the most distinctive feature, the first dorsal being high and pointed, and the anal correspondingly long and deep. The eye is a bright red. The breeding habits are like those of *Hyphessobrycon flammeus*. The male may be identified by the larger and more pointed dorsal and anal fins.

Ctenobrycon spilurus (CUVIER and VALENCIENNES). Brazil and Guiana. 3 in. 65°–80°. The 'Silver Tetra'. A deep, thin body with small iridescent silvery scales and the suggestion of a yellowish band along the lateral line are the most distinctive features of the Silver Tetra. At the base of the tail there is a black spot, and the fins, especially the tail of the female, bear a suspicion of red. Sometimes known as the 'Knife Fish'. It will eat practically anything and is not averse to the fresh shoots of the growing plants which it nibbles with evident enjoyment. The breeding habits are similar to those of *Hemigrammus caudovittatus*.

Aphyocharax rubripinnis (PAPPENHEIM). Argentine. 1¾ in. C. 60° (and below if necessary) to 70°. 'The Bloodfin.' This small fish, especially when present in fair numbers, is certainly an asset to any aquarium. The slender silvery-blue bodies set off by the blood-red fins give a bold effect in the centre of the tank, where they prefer to swim about in a shoal. (Plate II, 3.)

The method used in sexing this hardy old favourite is a peculiar one. Visually the two sexes are much alike, the male, perhaps, somewhat brighter in colour and the female a shade fatter, but neither distinction being of a definite degree. The aquarist, therefore, resorts to the unusual tactics of netting the shoal and those that adhere to the net when he returns them to the water are males. The rays at the posterior end of the anal fin are curved forward, so forming the little hook that sticks to the net.

Prior to spawning the sexes should be separated and, in the meantime, a special tank, say, 24 in. × 12 in. × 12 in., should be prepared. The temperature should be 72°–74° and the depth 7 in. of clear, old water. There should be a central open space surrounded by dense masses of Myriophyllum, Nitella, etc., otherwise all other living organisms—such as snails, tubifex and daphnia—are best removed. At the same time a culture of infusoria must be prepared as the fry hatch out in two days and, as the brood may be up to 300 strong, it should be a rich culture.

As spawning time approaches, there is no doubt as to which are the females—they swell visibly—and they should be introduced, with the males, to the spawning tank in the evening. All being well, in the morning, spawning will commence, slowly at first and then speeding up so that in about half-an-hour a cascade of transparent eggs will be ejected. These will settle to the bottom or become entangled in the fine-leaved foliage.

Both parents will eat the eggs and so they must be removed. After three days of infusoria diet finely graded dried foods as well as crushed enchytrae will be required. In a month the fry will be sufficiently grown to be able to tackle daphnia and the like.

The Hatchet or Freshwater Flying Fishes

These fishes are not commonly found in the lists of the dealers principally because, as yet, no one has managed to breed them successfully. All our supplies have to be imported from South America where all the species have their home.

They are shy at first and unless treated intelligently in the matter of food may die from starvation. In their native haunts they feed largely on flies and frequently leap clear out of the water in their quest for those delicacies, and not infrequently will skim along the surface with the forepart completely out of the water.

The body is compressed laterally and the pectoral fins are large, both features being aids to leaping and skimming. When they have settled down they are quite at home in the community tank but, obviously, the tank should be covered.

Daphnia is an acceptable food, also, in time, floating dried foods; an occasional 'feed' of small flies such as green-fly and *Drosophila* (the Fruit Fly) will be appreciated.

Carnegiella strigata (Guenther). Guiana. $1\frac{3}{4}$ in. C. 75°–80°. 'Striped Hatchet Fish'. The Hatchet Fishes are among the most delightful of the tropical aquarium fishes. They are bizarre, petite and daintily coloured and spend most of their time at the surface of the water where, in their natural state, they are wont to seek insect food. The deep-chested and narrow body of this particular species is iridescent olive-green with alternate brown and gold oblique bands. The female is less narrow than the male.

Carnegiella marthae (MYERS). Orinoco. $1\frac{1}{4}$ in. C.

75°–80°. 'Black-winged Hatchet Fish.' The body colour of this dainty little fish is silver with liberal sprinklings of black. The dorsal fin, as in the foregoing species, is set far back, almost as though it were an adipose fin, and the pectoral fin is large with black markings— hence the popular name of 'black-winged'.

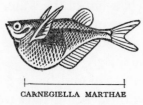

CARNEGIELLA MARTHAE

The Metinnids

Metynnis roosevelti (EIGENMANN). Amazons 4 in. C. 72°–80°. The body of this fish resemble. that of the fresh-water Sun-fishes, that is, it is compressed and deep. The fins are set towards the tail, and this is wide-spreading and powerful. The general colour is greyish-brown, and the fins are orange with black edging, a colour scheme that does not appear at all striking. Nevertheless, the shape of the fish is very fine, and it is one of the few fairly large fishes suited to the community tank. It is largely vegetarian and welcomes an occasional feed of lettuce or duckweed. In fact one of the bad habits of *Metynnis*, even before it is fully grown, is its ruthlessness with the growing plants. It will charge through, and at

PLATE VII.
1. *Aphyosemion australe*, Lyre-tail, Cap Lopez Blue, male.   2.   *Rivulus urophthalmus*, male.   3 & 4.   *Cynolebias bellottii*, Argentine Pearl Fish, female and male.
(*Natural size*)

them, and unless well rooted they will soon be floating about in the water without visible means of support. Young shoots, also, will be nibbled with relish. With age the appearance of the fish improves, its colouring deepens and the dorsal fin assumes greater proportions.

It is named after President Theodore Roosevelt.

The Nannostomids or Line Fishes

Nannostomus anomalus (STEINDACHNER). Rio Negro. 1½ in. C. 73°–80°. This tiny, darting fish would be quite commonplace were it not for the jet-black line that divides the whitish belly from the olive-green back. Along the top of the black line, running right from the snout to the base of the tail, is a bright golden line. The ventral fins of the male are tipped with light blue. Prefers small daphnia and cyclops as food.

Although quite hardy it takes some little time before it really settles down in the community tank and until it does settle its colours do not show off to best advantage. It is better, if possible, to keep say half a dozen in a separate small tank—the standard 14 in. × 8 in. × 8 in. tank being admirable for the purpose. The water should be old and soft—filtered rainwater, for example—with an abundance of Cabomba, Ceratoptera, and Myriophyllum growing in thickets.

At spawning time it is not necessary to separate the breeding pairs, they will pair off quite naturally; the female, of course, will be recognized by her greater depth and width caused by the accumulated eggs; the colours of the male are intensified and the darker parts glow with a violet and red blush. The eggs, after the usual Characin preliminaries, are deposited among the leaves in ones or twos. If the plants are sufficiently dense I do not think it necessary to remove the parents —in fact, provided the sexes are balanced numerically, it seems best to let them conduct the whole proceeding unmolested.

After two days the fry hatch out and after a further four days will leave the foliage from which they hang (like mosquito larvae hanging from the surface film) to bury themselves in the mulm of the bottom where they remain on and off for over a month.

All the Nannostomids have small mouths and equally small yet insistent appetites. Infusoria should be fed to them for the first two months when they will be just over half-an-inch in length, rotifers in the later weeks replacing the usual infusion of minutiae. Later, besides the daphnia and cyclops, tubifex, mikro and enchytrae will be welcomed.

Nannostomus marginatus (EIGENMANN). Orinoco. 1½ in. 75°–80°. This is a slightly more showy fish than *N. anomalus*, having reddish fins, and bands of that colour added to the gold and black bands of its relative. The body is also more compact. It is a very timid fish. For breeding habits see *N. anomalus*.

Nannostomus trifasciatus (STEINDACHNER). Amazon. 1¾ in. C. 70°–80°. The body shape of this fish is very similar to that of the last species but the fins, as regards coloration, are different; they are a transparent blue with large red spots at the bases. Along the middle of the body are black and gold stripes and, in the male, the centre gold band is dotted with red. (Plate II, 1.)

Poecilobrycon auratus (EIGENMANN). Guiana. 1¾ in. C. 75°–80°. 'Pencil Fish'. As the popular name suggests, this is a long slender fish, although there are quite a number of other fishes to which 'pencil' is more applicable. The black band from nose to tail, noted in the three previous species of Characin, persists here, but in this fish it is diffused over the greater

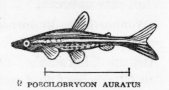

♀ POECILOBRYCON AURATUS

part of the tail. The usual body colour is a warm golden brown, with several deeper brown stripes and one golden one just above the black band.

Poecilobrycon unifasciatus (STEINDACHNER). Amazon. 1¾ in. C. 68°–80°. This is a very slim fish, graceful and attractive and, like the foregoing, languid of movement. It meanders gently through the water, not on an even keel but with its head about half-an-inch higher than the tail and in this position will remain stationary for minutes at a time. The general colour is silvery, inclining to grey, with a black line running through the eye to the lower part of the caudal fin where it is distinguished by two red splashes, one above the black line and the other below it. Above the black stripe runs a golden one. (Plate II, 4.)

A well-planted aquarium, it need not be large, with a diet similar to that given for the other 'Line fishes' will suit this species very nicely. Although spawning is conducted along lines similar to those of *Nannostomus anomalus* this species is not easy to breed.

Nannaethiops unitaeniatus (GUENTHER). Congo. 3 in. C. 75°–80°. 'The Golden Line' or 'African Characin'. This is one of the very few Characins found outside South America; its shape is neat and sturdy and its colouring interesting, though somewhat subdued. There is a dark line along the centre of the body, above which is a gold line. Above and below these lines the general colour is various shades of coppery-red which, in the fins, tends to a more reddish tint.

The Golden Line prefers a large, shallow and well-planted aquarium at breeding time. The male, now gaudy in its breeding dress, chases the female at high speed—hence the need for a roomy aquarium—until, eventually, she pauses over a mass of vegetation and ejects her pale yellow eggs. These are fertilized by the attendant male before they settle amongst the foliage. The further development and feeding requirements are similar to those of *Nannostomus anomalus*.

PANTODONTIDAE (*the Butterfly Flying Fishes*)

Pantodon buchholzi (PETERS). West Africa. $3\frac{1}{2}$ in. One species only is represented in this family, P. buchholzi. It is often referred to as 'The Chisel Jaw', probably because the sides of the head are bony. The sexes may readily be differentiated by the composition of the anal fin which in the male consists of four long rays behind which are five short rays; between these two sets of rays is a duct leading to the sexual

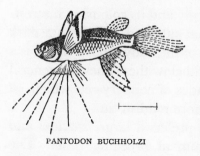

PANTODON BUCHHOLZI

organs. The anal fin of the female consists of fourteen rays. One of the first exotic fishes, apart from the gold-fish, to be introduced into the British Isles: there is no other fish quite like it. The ventral fins are produced into long spines and the pectoral fins, like those of the true flying fishes, are greatly enlarged. It spends most of its time in the aquarium near the surface; in its natural surroundings, where insects are only too plentiful, this 'surface complex' arises, no doubt, from the quest for food. So enthusiastic, indeed, is this fish in the matter of insects that it will fly along the surface of the water for several feet in quest of them. The first specimens that were ever captured by scientists were caught by an ento-mologist, who mistook them for some kind of butterfly, with a butterfly net. In the aquarium it does not attempt any great leaps, possibly from lack of surface space, although it is at night that it is most active, so maybe it waits until the household has retired before starting the per-formance. Consequently it is necessary that the aquarium should have a cover, otherwise the fishes may be 'on the carpet' in the morning.

One would imagine that vivid colouring would be a feature of this fish, unfortunately it is about as dull looking as any fish could be. The belly is silvery, and this merges into blacks and greys on the back and the fins. Another point about this queer animal is that, as its mouth is large and as its inclinations are carnivorous, it requires separate quarters. Furthermore, it will not feed off the bottom, and as it is inevitable that even with live foods some will sink to the sand, a scavenging fish is necessary—and one that is large enough to resist being eaten. The Armoured Catfish *Callichthys callichthys*, growing as it does to a length of four inches and more, seems to be the most suitable companion for this Butterfly Fish.

The Chisel Jaw has, on occasion, been bred in the aquarium but more, one imagines, by accident than by design. The fry seem to hatch out in two days and the food in the early days consists of infusoria followed by small daphnia. Like the adults the larvae feed on the surface. In the point of food generally it should be remembered that in the wild state this fish feeds on flies for the capture of which nature has endowed it with a large up-pointing mouth and wing-like pectoral fins. Consequently, an occasional treat in the way of a blue-bottle will be appreciated—in time the fish will learn to take the fly from one's fingers.

Temperature range 70°–80°.

CYPRINIDAE (*The Carps*)

The carps can be distinguished from all other fishes by the fact that they have only one dorsal fin, no teeth in the mouth, and that all the fin rays are soft—that is to say, none are spiny like certain parts of the fins of a Cichlid, for example. With very few exceptions they are peaceful fishes and make good citizens in the community tank.

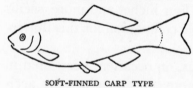

SOFT-FINNED CARP TYPE

Some of the most beautiful and attractive aquarium fishes are members of this family, of which the Common Goldfish is the classic example. Many of the smaller and more slender species, minnows in fact, are exquisite to a degree, and breeding, generally, is less problematical than with other groups.

Danio malabaricus (JERDON). Malabar Coast. 4 in. C. 68°–80°. 'Giant Danio'. Typical carp body, pale olive in colour and covered with a light-violet sheen. The fins are red, turning to deep violet-brown at the edges. Along the body run purple bands separated by bright gold. Behind the gill covers are three broken vertical stripes. The eggs of this particular fish are adhesive, and so bushy plants such as Myrio-

DANIO MALABARICUS

phyllum should be planted to receive them.

A really large, well-planted aquarium (say 30 in. × 12 in. × 12 in.) produces the best breeding results, also if two males are allocated to one female a greater proportion of the eggs will be fertilized. The male is the more intensely coloured whilst the female is slightly deeper-bodied. The three specimens should be removed to the spawning tank in the evening so that by the morning they will have become acclimatized to their fresh environment. As with many other species the actual spawning takes place at about dawn. The tropical dawn, like its sunset, is a sudden affair, consequently one may assume that the fairly sudden brightening of the sky induces spawning. The eggs are adhesive and up to 300 may be deposited, the male fertilizing them as they fall. As a safeguard the parents should be removed. In thirty to thirty-six hours the eggs hatch out and forty-eight hours later the fry will have absorbed the yolk-sac. The diet will consist for the first ten days of infusoria and then young daphnia until the youngsters are large enough to take enchytrae, brine shrimps and fully grown daphnia.

Brachydanio rerio (HAMILTON-BUCHANAN). Bengal. 1¾ in. 60°–110°. 'Zebra Fish'. Since its first importation into Europe in 1905 the Zebra Fish has been deservedly popular. With many of us it was our first love, still holding a corner of our affection in spite of the rare and exotic importations of later years. The fish itself is rather slender bodied, and this is accentuated by the dark-blue bands running from the gill covers to the tip of the tail. These bands, with the light-olive body colour showing between, extend from

BRACHYDANIO RERIO

the back to the belly, in fact, the appellation of 'Zebra Fish' is most apt. There is a barb at each side of the mouth. The female is deeper in the body than the male.

A tank 18 in. × 12 in. × 9 in. will accommodate two dozen specimens, indeed, this fish, which delights in swimming in shoals, looks at its best when in the company of a number of its kind. The temperature should be a constant 70 degrees

Fahr., except for breeding, when it should be raised to 80 degrees. It is mature at from three to four months, and for breeding it has been found that two males to one female produce the best results. The two sexes should be separated for a few days and then placed together in a small tank, say 10 in × 5 in. × 5 in., the bottom being covered with small stones or white marbles. The eggs are not adhesive and will sink to the bottom out of the way of the unnatural parents; even so, so swiftly do they flick about from one end of the tank to the other, their fins so disturb the water that the eggs often are dislodged from between the stones. The female releases from five to ten eggs at a time, until nearly two hundred are laid, when the chasing and skirmishing ceases; at this point the parents should be removed. Incubation varies considerably as regards time, maybe twenty-four hours, maybe three days. The young require an abundance of food if they are to develop into good fishes. In a fortnight or so the weedy and puny specimens will manifest themselves and so, for the benefit of the others, they should be removed. The axiom applies here, as it does in the raising of all fishes —a few fine specimens are worth a hundred indifferent ones, and to this end the aquarist must be ruthless in weeding out the undesirables. At two years of age *B. rerio* is old and decrepit, it is obvious then, unless one is to be buying fresh stock frequently, that breeding should be tried; in any case, before attempting to breed the more difficult species, it is well to try one's 'prentice hand on the amiable Zebra Fish—even though its stripes do not run the same way as its equine namesake! (Plate III, 2.)

Brachydanio nigrofasciatus (DAY). Burma. 1½ in. C. 70°–80°. 'Spotted Danio'. The stripes in this smaller and slightly less active relation of the Zebra Fish are rendered less distinct owing to the lower ones, along the underside, being broken up into dots. The lines and dots are bluish in colour and extend into the tail fin. Also there is a hint of blue in the dorsal and anal fins. The females are deeper bodied than the males, the latter being the more conspicuously coloured.

Although the breeding tank should be prepared as for *B. rerio*, the actual spawning routine is vastly different. After an introductory flirting and skirmishing, instead of continuing the chasing and in the process depositing and fertilizing the eggs, the pair meet with abdomens touching, and a batch of eggs is ejected and fertilized. The eggs fall to the bottom and the pair separate for a short spell. The process is repeated several times until upwards of seventy eggs have settled amongst the stones on the bottom. The subsequent feeding and development is more or less the same as in other species.

Nevertheless it is a delightful fish and has a slight rosy blush over the head region that is quite attractive. (Plate III, 1.)

Brachydanio albolineatus (BLYTH). Lower Burma. 2½ in. C. 72°–78°. 'Pearl Danio'. The body is less slender than in the other Danios and the stripes are reduced to a red one, fringed on the lower side with blue, transversing the anal fin. The colour overall is mother o' pearl flushed with pink, which is consolidated into a short red stripe at the base of the tail. Above and below the red stripe and more accentuated in the male are purplish shadings. (Plate III, 5.)

The breeding tank should be of a large size and besides the stones on the bottom some large clumps of dense foliage should be weighted and placed in the tank. The 'Pearl' likes plenty of room for the preliminary chasings and the plants make a good sanctuary for the eggs and fry. About 200 eggs are deposited and although large the resultant fry are difficult to discern.

The Rasboras

These colourful fishes have medium to large-sized scales and a moderately wide mouth with a slightly protruding lower jaw. There are twenty-five known species of which ten have at one time or another been kept in aquaria. India, Ceylon, the East Indies and East Africa are their native habitats; there they live in forest streams, as a rule, where the water often carries a considerable quantity of humic acid. Consequently, a low pH is favoured—5.5 for preference.

Rasbora heteromorpha DUNCKER. Malacca and Sumatra. 1¾ in. C. 73°–80°. The 'Harlequin Fish'. One of the most popular of aquarium fishes this 'differently-shaped Rasbora' is in a class of its own as regards coloration. A background

of silver merging into red which deepens towards the tail and fins is the dominant note. Over all is a delicate bluish sheen. From the middle of the body to the tail root is a large dark

RASBORA HETEROMORPHA

wedge, tipped by a gold streak which is wider and more apparent in the female. (Plate III, 3 and 4.)

They prefer clear water and a fair amount of sunlight, and the tank should be well planted with Cryptocoryne and *Sagittaria sinensis*. Breeding these fishes is a difficult business, and failure is more frequent than success. When a pair with swollen abdomens are noticed, they should be placed in a small tank in which Cryptocoryne is growing, and should be well conditioned on a liberal diet of chopped earthworms. The female assumes an upside down position when spawning, in order to deposit the eggs on the underside of the Cryptocoryne leaves. When the male observes this, he dashes alongside and by twining his tail round the female's assists in the expulsion of the eggs, at the same time fertilizing them. Either the fishes or the egg-encrusted leaves should be removed to other quarters. The eggs hatch out in forty-eight hours, the fry being observable as small 'commas' on the sides of the aquarium. After a few days they are free swimming and then require feeding. In their wild state the adults ascend the streams to the shallows to spawn, and the water temperature may be anything up to 100 degrees Fahr. Needless to say, the change in temperature as the fish moves from the cooler waters of the deeper parts of the river to the shallows is not sudden. Therefore, instead of placing the breeding pair suddenly into warmer water, the temperature in the breeding tank should be raised gradually. The community tank, in which they have been living, is, say 74 degrees Fahr, and so the breeding tank should have a similar warmth, and this should be raised gradually to 82 degrees. This applies generally to the transference of breeding fishes—many a spawning has been spoiled by the sudden rise in temperature.

Rasbora maculata DUNCKER. Malay Peninsula. 1 in. C. 73°–80°. The 'Spotted Rasbora'. A slender, red-coloured body and upstanding dorsal fin is the general appearance of this dainty little fish. There is a largish dark-blue spot just behind the gills and a smaller one at the base of the tail. On the anal fin there is also a blue spot fringed with white as are the others. A golden line runs along the centre of the body from head to tail. This fish breeds in a similar manner to *R. heteromorpha*.

Rasbora elegans VOLZ. Sumatra. 5 in. C. 70°–80°. This, the largest of the Rasboras, has little to recommend it save that it is one of the largest fishes that will live at peace with its fellows. Its colour is a neutral grey and, except for a suspicion of brown on the dorsal fin and the yellow anal fin of the male, it is unrelieved other than by a dark spot at the tail base and another in the middle of the body. Perhaps by its very dullness it is useful to show up the smaller jewels in the aquarium. Breeding as for *R. heteromorpha*.

Rasbora leptosoma BLEEKER. Malay Peninsula. 2½ in. C. 72°–80°. Similar in shape to its

PLATE VIII.   1-144
1. *Panchax chaperi*, Barred Panchax. 2. *Jordanella fioridae*, Flag Fish. 3. *Mollienisia sphenops*, Liberty Fish. 4. *Aplocheilus lineatus*.
(*Natural size*)

tiny relation *R. maculata*, the main feature of this fish is the central band dividing the darker olive of the upper surface from the pale tints of the lower. This band is black, gold and red and is continued to the snout. The eye is golden red.

Rasbora vaterifloris DERANIYAGALA. Ceylon. 2 in. C. 73°–80°. This little fish from the jungle streams of Ceylon is spectacular neither in habit nor in colouring. It droops about the aquarium as though life had but little to interest it, yet its variable, delicate colouring 'grows' on one so much that ever since the late 'thirties it has remained a favourite with the aquarist. The general shape is that of *R. heteromorpha*; the eye is a shining orange-brown and although the basic body colour is a pale olive green there is a delicate sheen which varies in colour considerably according to the individual. Some have a sheen of varying shades of bronze, some are brassy, whilst others have a pastel blue tinge over all. They have been bred in captivity and the best results have been obtained in a large tank well planted with Myriophyllum or Cryptocoryne at a temperature of 78°. The eggs are ejected in batches of about twenty-five and hatch out in thirty-six to forty-eight hours, the fry being self-supporting after five days when infusoria or very fine dried food should be fed to them.

The Flying Barbs

In their native haunts the Flying Barbs inhabit shallow ponds, paddy fields and ditches where they feed largely on mosquito larvae. Most of their time is spent on the surface and there can be no doubt that their large pectoral fins enable them to leap out of the water after their prey. In the aquarium they are partial to fruit flies and, of course, mosquito larvae but they will take, from the surface, dry foods. There are two pairs of barbels depending from the upper lip, the front pair being relatively short whilst the rear pair are long and extend to half the length of the body. The breeding habits and requirements are the same for the three species here listed.

Esomus danricus (HAMILTON). India and Ceylon. 4 in. C. 75°–84°. The general body colour is olive-green relieved by a double line extending from the root of the tail to the eye and is coloured golden above and dark brown below. The male has these two lines more accentuated and there is a russet tint on the underside. The female's underside clearly indicates when she is full of eggs.

The breeding tank should be large and well planted with the usual thicket-forming vegetation, also there should be a layer of stones on the

146

bottom in the crevices of which the eggs will have some sanctuary from their egg-loving parents. Needless to say the adults must be removed immediately after spawning.

The male assists the depositing of the ova in an individualistic sort of way; after a few playful chasings the pair dash rapidly from one end of the aquarium to the other with occasional pauses to deposit small clutches of eggs, what time the male prods the female with his head. This doubtless assists in the ejection of the eggs. The female, in her turn, butts her partner and in consequence, one supposes, the release of the milt is facilitated.

The ideal breeding temperature is 82 degrees and additional aeration is recommended. Hatching takes thirty-six hours, and after the same length of time the yolk-sac will have been exhausted. The fry will need an abundance of infusoria for the first month and then graded daphnia.

Esomus metallicus (HAMILTON). Siam. 2 in. C. 75°–84°. The body of this second species of Flying Barb is silvery but otherwise is less colourful than the others of its kind. There is a single dark brown line along each side whilst the posterior pair of barbels are remarkably long. It is active, swift swimming and hardy and is not difficult to breed.

Esomus malayensis AHL. Malay Peninsula. 3 in. C. 75°–84°. A gold stripe divides the olive of the back and the silver of the belly in this large-finned individual. At the base of the tail is a 'peacock-eye' spot, around which is a golden ring. The general body coloration is pale silver with a yellowish tinge. The barbs depending from the lower jaw are nearly three-quarters of an inch in length.

The Barbs

These are the 'carp-minnows', members of that huge unwieldy family whose members include the Barbel, a fish well-known from our own Trent and Thames, and which range in size from the inch and a quarter long *B. phutonia* to the great Mahseer of the Indian rivers with scales as large as the palm of one's hand. Even the tiny species of *Barbus*, however, have relatively large scales. A separate genus has been formed for the 'carp-minnows,' namely, *Puntius*; but to the aquarist they will always be 'Barbs' and so here that title will be retained.

Barbus conchonius HAMILTON-BUCHANAN. India. 5 in. C. 70°–80°. The 'Rosy Barb'. The Barbs, ten species of which at least are stocked by one or other of our dealers, are the most 'carp-like' of the tropical cyprinoids, and for this reason, possibly, English amateurs are more successful in breeding them than many others of the tropical fishes. The species here under consideration has large glittering scales, greenish-silver in colour, radiating gold in certain lights. There is a black spot, faintly edged with gold, at the base of the tail. In the male the tip of the dorsal fin is black, and at breeding time the lower half of the body is flushed with bright red. (Plate IV, 1.)

It is a general and adaptable feeder, usually on the bottom of the tank. Dried foods, with an occasional treat in the way of daphnia or brine shrimps, will suffice; vegetable matter such as chopped lettuce is appreciated, although the algae that grows on the plants and the sides of the tank is usually sufficient. The temperature need not be high, in fact it suffers discomfort in the community tank if it is too warm.

For breeding, a ten gallon tank is large enough, and this should receive a layer of largish stones or marbles among which the eggs will drop. One end should be loosely packed with Myriophyllum or Anacharis, for the fish will 'drive' through them during the egg-laying process, and the eggs that fall among the entangled vegetation are more likely to escape being eaten. The temperature should be raised to 75 degrees Fahr. Spawning starts at dawn and the courtship proceeds at a high speed. They are a most prolific fish, laying anything from 500 to 1,000 eggs during the two or three days occupied by spawning. The eggs hatch out in 48 hours, and the fry cling to the stones for several days until, exhausting their egg sac, they set out for the infusoria that the aquarist has thoughtfully raised for them. They grow rapidly if well fed, and it will be seen that certain individuals outstrip their brethren, developing in the process cannibalistic tendencies. These advanced specimens should be removed, not only for the peace of mind of their less sturdy relations, but because they make the best breeding fishes. The Barbs that follow have similar breeding habits.

Barbus dunckeri AHL. Malay Peninsula. 4½ in. 72°–80°. This fish is a uniform olive colour with silvery scales. The fins are yellow, a colour that appears in light patches over the body, and at the base of the dorsal fin is a large spot.

Barbus everetti BOULENGER. Borneo. 5 in. 72°–80°. 'Clown Barb'. On account of its large size and resplendent colouring this fish deserves quarters of its own, well planted with strongly-rooted plants. Ordinarily they would resemble the Common Goldfish in shape and in the pale gold background colouring. The resemblance ends here, for the fins are definitely red, and on the body are four large blue spots and two smaller ones. Also, from the large spot in the middle of the side a blue line runs to the base of the tail, terminating in a darker blue spot. (Plate IV, 4.)

The barbels are very pronounced in this species and so, as with most fishes that possess those sensory organs, the Clown is fond of rooting about on the bottom for whatever it can find in the way of food. Its favourite food is earthworms which should be cut up finely for the small fellows and fed whole to the big ones. Daphnia and coarse dried foods will give variety to the diet.

Barbus lateristriga CUVIER and VALENCIENNES. Malay. 6 in. 72°–80°. The 'Spanner' or 'Plus Eleven Fish'. Very similar to the foregoing except that the large spots are resolved into two bands across the body and the blue band terminating at the tail is thicker and darker. This is a similar fish in many ways to *B. everetti* especially in the matter of food and its zest for life in general.

Barbus gelius (HAMIL-TON-BUCHANAN). India 1½ in. C. 65°–80°. A small and uncolourful edition of *B. everetti* is

BARBUS GELIUS

this tiny fish. The fins are pale yellow and the spots and lateral stripe are brown.

Barbus oligolepis (BLEEKER). Sumatra. 2 in. 72–80°. 'The Island Barb'. This is one of the most delightful of all the tropical carps. The scales are particularly large, and along the middle of the body they are black. The fins, especially in the male, are deep orange and the dorsal, anal and ventral fins are fringed with black.

The female generally is less strikingly marked, and the fins are more of a yellowish colour. Variety in the diet will help to maintain the coloration—small daphnia, dried food of medium grade and algae. This last named food is a particular favourite and this is probably why the Island Barb spends most of its time browsing leisurely amongst the vegetation.

Barbus pentazona FOWLER. Siam. 1¾ in. C. 75°–82°. The body of this fish is silvery and is crossed by six dark blue bands, two of which are confined to the root of the tail whilst the foremost of the bands crosses the head and is continued through the eye. The dorsal fin has a red streak which is more intense in the male— and with age generally. This, and the following four species, are known as the 'Tiger Barbs', doubtless on account of the bands. It is bred in similar manner to *B. conchonius*.

Barbus partipentazona (FOWLER). 2 in. C. 73°–78°. This differs from the foregoing by having the central band (from the front of the dorsal fin) cut short at the base of the dorsal, moreover there is only one band across the tail root. The general body colour is of a metallic nature—silvery for the most part but with, dorsally, a coppery effect. The bars are dark blue and there is a red area in the dorsal fin. It is a sprightly fish, always flitting along the length of the tank, pausing now and again to browse on any algae that may have developed on the plants. It will take readily small to medium grade dried foods as well as cooked spinach that has been rubbed through a kitchen sieve.

Barbus nigrofasciatus (HAMILTON). Ceylon. $2\frac{1}{4}$ in. C. 72°–80°. 'The Purple-headed Barb', sometimes called the 'Nigger' or 'Black Ruby'. This beautiful species is noted for the absence of barbs, the deep body and the purple coloured forepart of the male. There are four black bands, fairly wide and, in the female, the more distinct. Both male and female have an overall olive-green body colour which the large scales make metallic. The pectoral fins do not carry colour but the tail is yellow suffused with pink and the other fins are dark brown to black. The female lacks the purple head coloration. (Plate IV, 2.)

Feeding habits similar to those of *B. partipenta-zona*; the breeding is as that of the other barbs.

Barbus semifasciolatus GUENTHER. Southern China. 2½ in. C. 70°–80°. 'The Green or Half-Striped Barb'. This fish is a typical barb in shape, the colour is greenish-gold, and the fins are yellowish. The dark bands, about six in number, are black.

It is a gentle, 'goldfishy', creature and ambles about the aquarium in mid-water in a manner reminiscent of its cold water relation, and invariably is a favourite in any collection. Breeding, comparatively, is not difficult and is along the usual Barb lines, the female being recognizable by her deeper body and, as a rule, larger size, whilst at breeding time the male develops a reddish-brown coloration on the under-parts.

A good and diverse diet should be maintained, otherwise it will soon go out of condition: sieved boiled spinach, chopped earthworm and daphnia are among its favourites.

Barbus phutunio (HAMILTON-BUCHANAN). India. 1¼ in. C. 68°–78.° 'The Dwarf Barb'. This is a silvery fish with large scales edged with black which gives a diamanté effect with top light. There is a semi-transparent black spot behind the gills and there is a similar spot at the root of the tail. Four bands cross the body but they are only faintly marked and only the one across the tail extends as far as the lower edge. It is a colourful fish with its pale orange fins and the red from its gills showing through the transparent gill plates. They are difficult to sex—the females, of course, are fatter at breeding time and the male is more distinctly coloured. They are used in India to assist in the control of mosquitoes and there is little doubt that their fondness for the larvae of that insect must hinder the formation of swarms. Consequently, an occasional feed of mosquito larvae is a good thing, as are finely graded daphnia. They should not be fed on cyclops.

Barbus ticto (HAMILTON-BUCHANAN). India. $3\frac{1}{2}$ in. C. 72°–80°. 'The Two-spot Barb'. The colour of this well-shaped Barb is a silvery-red deepening in redness towards the middle of the fish. A large dark coloured spot towards the root of the tail bears a golden aura whilst the large eyes have gold rims. The scales glint in various metallic colours. On the shoulder is another spot but this is not so distinct as the rearward one. The fins are yellowish except in the male which has a distinctive broad red fringe to it. As it is a robust fish its food should be of a robust nature—daphnia, tubifex, chopped earthworm, etc.—but not of too large a size as the mouth is not particularly capacious.

Barbus titteya DERYANAGALA. Ceylon, in overgrown forest streams. 1½ in. C. 73°–80° (should be raised slightly higher at breeding time). This delightful and beautiful little fish was first discovered in 1935 in the rain forest some seventy miles from Colombo. 'The Rusty Barb', as it is sometimes called, has a light reddish-brown body with a pale silver belly along which is a bluish area. Overall is a pinkish 'blush'. From the snout, through the eye, to the base of the tail runs a brown-purple line above and below which are shining green lines. Add a pair of glowing orange-red eyes and you have one of the most discreetly coloured fishes possible. (Plate V, 3 and 4.)

At breeding time the pinkish blush deepens in the male to a rich purple. Breeding is along the usual Barb lines except it will be seen that the male is inclined to be impatient and will nip and push the female until the eggs start to be ejected.

As regards feeding, it must be remembered that this species has a very small mouth, nevertheless, it will take almost anything of an animal or vegetable nature that will not overtax its jaws. The aquarium should be well planted, especially with Vallisneria, which thrives in its native streams.

Tanichthys albonubes LIN. Southern China. Males 1 in., females 1¼ in. C. 68°–78° (but can withstand temperatures as low as 50°). 'The White Cloud Mountain Minnow'. This, one of the most startlingly beautiful of fishes, came to this country closely on the heels of that other little beauty—the Neon Tetra, in 1936. It was first discovered by a Chinese Boy Scout named Tan (the generic name means, literally 'Tan's fish'— a pretty compliment) in 1932 whilst netting fishes in one of the streams of the White Cloud Mountain in Canton. He took it to the Fisheries Experiment Station at Canton where Mr. Lin Shu-yen gave it its present name. In 1935 some specimens were sent to the U.S.A. and a year later a Mr. Sugars of the then Hong Kong Aquarium Society sent some specimens to a dealer in Chelsea, Mr. A. H. Boughton. That, then, is the background of a little fish that set the aquarium world agog shortly before the war, and commanded fantastic prices.

The body colour of the fish is not extraordinary, the fins are tipped with vivid red, and there is a large silvery area on the belly, but—from the eye to the root of the tail is a brilliant, flashing stripe of a blue-green colour. This stripe tends to become yellowish with age but as a compensation the red of the fins becomes more intense. It swims in a delicate, almost fastidious way, which helps to display its finery. (Plate V, 1 and 2.)

At a temperature of 70 to 75 degrees egg laying may be induced. The tank should be about 18 in. × 9 in. × 9 in., and the depth of water about 8 in. with a carpet of vegetation and a profusion of Sagittaria, Myriophyllum or other similar plants. There is the usual preliminary chasing, in this case with fins extended, and then the eggs are deposited. Being non-adhesive mostly they fall to the bottom or become entangled in the plants.

The parents are very elusive and by no means easy to catch, so really it is better, if the plants are sufficiently dense, to leave them in the aquarium. The actual spawning may be spread over two days and in a further two days the fry should hatch out. Infusoria then becomes the order of the day, but the fry will take finely powdered dried foods, especially dried egg. Larval brine shrimps will later be avidly eaten for, in spite of its diminutive size, the mouth opening is comparatively large.

The brilliant colouring becomes evident at an early age, a fortnight or less, when the blue tint of the body, the blue of the eye and the red in the fins appears. At about ten weeks old the fish is at its colourful best, at six months it will be mature. The older fishes will take enchytrae and tubifex if these are chopped up fairly small.

158

Aphyocypris pooni LIN. Fan Ling (Southern China, opposite Hong Kong). Males 1 in., females 1¼ in. C. 68°–78°. After Scout Tan's discovery of the White Cloud Mountain Minnow there was a rare impetus in tiddler hunting in the Canton area, and included in consignments of *Tanichthys albonubes* were a number of equally beautiful fishes that, to all but the scientific eye, were of the same species. Mr. Lin, however, discovered anatomical differences and at the same time differences in coloration were also noted. These differences are confined particularly to the fins. Whereas in *T. albonubes* the red of the fins is restricted to the tips of the fins, in *A. pooni* the bases of the fins are red, the dorsal bearing a white fringe tipped with blue. The anal fin also has a blue tipped white fringe. Otherwise the two fishes are alike in their breeding and general habits. (Plate V, 5, 6 and 7.)

COBITIDAE (*The Loaches*)

Acanthophthalmus semicinctus FRASER-BRUNNER, *Acanthophthalmus kuhlii* (CUVIER and VALENCIENNES). Malay. 2¾ in. C. 70°–80°. 'The Coolie'. A long, eel-like creature is this fish, salmon-pink in colour. The mouth is fringed with barbels and the body is well banded with

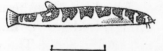

ACANTHOPHTHALMUS SEMICINCTUS

brown. The fringes on the mouth indicate a bottom-feeding fish, in this respect it is comparable with the loaches of the English streams.

A. Fraser-Brunner, the English ichthyologist, in 1947 showed that the species *A. kuhlii* which had hitherto been accepted as the species known to the aquarist was, in fact, a different fish altogether. Our old friend the Coolie had been living under an assumed name, but he made an honest fish of it and gave it the name which now heads this paragraph.

CALLICHTHYIDAE (*The Armoured Catfishes*)

Callichthys callichthys (LINN). Northern part of the South American continent. 5 in. C., (provided its small companions are lively.) 66°–86°. Known as the 'Hassar' or 'Cascadura'. If you particularly seek colour in a fish then the Hassar will not be your particular cup of tea for, truth to tell, the body is just grey—all over alike. It is, however, an interesting and a useful fish, even if it does stir up the mulm on the bottom in its efforts to 'scavenge' efficiently. Live foods or dead foods all come alike; if a small fish dies (or

PLATE IX.
1.& 2. *Lebistes reticulatus*, Guppy, Rainbow Fish, male.   3 & 4. *L. reticulatus*, female.
5. *Platypoecilus maculatus*, Platy, Moonfish, male.   6 & 7. *P. maculatus*, female.
(*Natural size*)

if it does not get out of the way in time) it also will be eaten. At times the Hassar will lumber up to the surface to gulp air which passes through the alimentary canal, the oxygen being absorbed by the blood vessels which line the gut.

This air gulping habit leads to a peculiarity that has been observed on the few occasions when they have bred in captivity—a floating bubble nest is made in which the eggs are encased, the male, the while, ostensibly guarding them. There always is, therefore, the chance—a slight one—that this rare event may occur in your aquarium.

The body is protected by two rows of overlapping bony plates or scutes each corresponding to the muscle segment beneath it. Also the skin covering the head is very thin and so the bones forming the skull can be readily seen.

SILURIDAE (*The Catfishes*)

Krypteropterus bicirrhus (CUVIER and VALEN-CIENNES). Java. $2\frac{1}{2}$ in. C. 72°–82°. 'Ghost Fish'. Even without a strong back-light the Ghost Fish displays its internal organs and back-

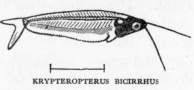

KRYPTEROPTERUS BICIRRHUS

bone to the public gaze, so transparent is its body. It is also known as the 'Glass Catfish', and there is no doubt about the glass-like appearance of the sides. The colour is silvery at the head and in some lights the sides take on many glinting colours.

Pimelodella gracilis (VALENCIENNES). South America. 3½ in. C. 70°–80°. A silvery fish this, with a distinct black line along the middle of each side. It is nocturnal in habits, as are most of the catfishes. An interesting feature is the length of the barbels, which are four in number. Both sexes seem identical to outward appearance.

Corydoras aeneus (GILL). Trinidad. 2½ in. C. 70°–80°. 'The Bronze Catfish.' The Corydoras, five species of which are obtainable in this country, are perhaps the most popular of the scavenging fishes. They are inexpensive, and are always interesting to watch, being active by day. *C. aeneus* is a dark bronze in colour, and, like the others of its kind, is happiest in a well-planted aquarium: especially valuable, particularly at breeding time, is the Amazon Sword Plant. The mating itself has not been noted particularly but the actual egg-laying covers several hours. The fry hatch out in four to five days and require feeding at an earlier stage than do most larval fishes. After a day they require something more robust than the minutiae that inhabit the mulm or the usual infusoria brew, and mikro seems to fill the bill. A week or so later the mikro diet may be supplemented by chopped tubifex. In four months the young fishes will be displaying the adult livery. (Plate VI, 1.)

Corydoras agassizi STEINDACHNER. Amazon. $3\frac{1}{2}$ in. C. 70°–80°. This species is the largest of its kind sold in England. It is similar in shape to the other species, but its colouring is extremely drab. The largish mottled tail, however, is a redeeming feature. This is a fish about which we know very little.

Corydoras julii STEINDACHNER, formerly *Corydoras leopardus* (MYERS). Brazil. $2\frac{1}{2}$ in. C. 70°–80°. 'The Leopard Catfish'. This is one of the most attractive of the Catfishes. The body is well marbled, and along the middle of the body are three black stripes starting from just behind the pectoral fins. The dorsal fin is high and semi-transparent and has a large black spot near the tip. (Plate VI, 2.)

Corydoras nattereri STEINDACHNER. Brazil. $2\frac{1}{2}$ in. C. 70°–80°. The ground colour of this species is yellow, the gill covers are green, and the darker parts of the body are brown. The fins are almost transparent. The eye is of a golden colour.

Somehow *C. nattereri* looks less like a garden slug than does its relations.

Corydoras paleatus (JENKYNS). Argentine. 2¾ in. C. The general colour of this, the most common of the Catfishes, is a dull marbling of dusky yellows, whites and blues; sometimes called the Peppered Catfish. None of the catfishes are particularly beautiful, still, they make a good foil for the more colourful specimens. Moreover, they are excellent scavengers, especially in the case of tubifex worms that have escaped the other fishes. These worms, if unmolested, burrow in the sand at the bottom of the tank and wave their bodies about in the most defiant manner possible, until a fish comes along, when they disappear into the sand. The catfishes rout them out with ease.

Otocynclus affinis STEINDACHNER. Rio de Janiero. 1¾ in. C. 68°–82°. This more or less neutral-coloured fish has a more slender body than the other catfishes. Its great value lies in the fact that it lives on the desmids, diatoms and other organisms that swarm on the leaves of plants. In seeking out these dainties, this fish gives the plants a good grooming.

CYPRINODONTIDAE

The true carps are remarkable for having no teeth in the mouth, but there is a great group of fishes with very similar characteristics, except that their mouths bear teeth. These are the Cyprinodonts, and they are divided, naturally, into two distinct groups, viz., those that lay eggs and those that bring forth their young alive. The two divisions produce some of the most popular of all tropical aquarium fishes.

The Killifishes or Egg-laying Toothed Carps, otherwise 'Top-minnows'

Cubanichthys cubensis (EIGENMANN). Cuba. 1¾ in. C. 70°–80°. The body colour of this fish is olive, fins included; the high-lights are supplied by six bright-blue stripes running from eye to tail root. Commencing from the snout a russet line runs the length of the body to the tail root. In the male the colours are the more distinctive, especially the blue ones and the reddish speckles on the fins. A thickly-planted tank is necessary at breeding time and as hatching may take up to a fortnight, it is advisable to remove organisms such as snails and other egg-eating creatures. Little seems to be known about the mating habits but the actual depositing of the eggs is quite interesting; five or six large eggs are ejected at a time and these are suspended at the end of a fine thread. As the female swims about they are drawn along, like so many toy balloons until at last they become entangled in the vegetation; this releases them and there they remain until they hatch. The fry, after the egg-sac has been absorbed will require, instead of the usual infusoria, baby Artemia, graded daphnia or chopped enchytrae—this, incidentally, is an occasion when mikro comes into its own.

Rivulus hartii (BOULENGER). Venezuela. $3\frac{1}{2}$ in. 70°–85°. This is a fairly large fish, as tropicals go, and is quite pleasing to the eye. On a greyish-blue background are about ten rows of red dots starting from behind the gill-covers and terminating at the base of the tail. The fins are yellowish. The female is distinguished by the usual dark spot on the tail and the male by a number of small, dull-red dots likewise on the tail.

In breeding members of the *Rivulus* genus, it is best to have an aquarium well planted with Hair Grass or a similar type of plant. The aquarium need not be large, but the water must be old and also clear. The best average temperature for the breeding tank is 75 degrees Fahr. Contrary to the usual procedure, there should be only one male to two or three females; all the breeding fishes should be brought into good condition by a liberal diet of live foods. After the 'drive', during which the male sends his mates scurrying through the fine plants, the eggs will be laid among the vegetation, where the male fertilizes them. If the eggs are to be removed to fresh quarters it is well to wait for a few days: they are more liable to suffer from the change when newly laid. However, if the tank is thickly planted, and if a certain amount of blanket-weed is present, it is not absolutely necessary to separate the parents from their offspring. The latter, incidentally, hatch out in about fourteen days. If blanket weed is used in the breeding tank, take good care that none is accidentally introduced into the regular aquariums. Blanket-weed is the greatest pest of either aquarium or pond; nevertheless it has its uses, sick fish often benefit from a sojourn in water thick with it and, from the refuge it makes and the oxygen it liberates, it is ideal in certain breeding instances. I have mentioned earlier that *Rivulus* is built for speed, it is also built for leaping, and unless the tank has a well-fitting glass cover there may be losses from the fish leaping to their doom.

Rivulus cylindraceus (POEY). Cuba. 2 in. C. 65°–80°. The species belonging to the *Rivulus* genus are all long in the body, eel-like almost, with fairly large well-rounded tails and with the dorsal smallish and set far back. The anal fin is fairly large and so it appears that the greater part of the finnage is in the rear. Needless to say, they are attractive swimmers. They frequently rest

RIVULUS CYLINDRACEUS

in mid-water in an ex-pectant attitude, like so many Mr. Micawbers 'waiting for something to turn up', of course noth-ing does really turn up, but they do not seem to be disappointed, nevertheless. The colour of the species in question is orange with dark-green spots. There are a few red spots here and there, especially on the anal fin. The female has a dark spot on the upper part of the tail, near the base.

Rivulus ocellatus HENSEL. Brazil. 2½ in. C. 70°–76°. The body colour of this friendly little fish is warm brown and bluey-grey. The tail is yellow, and the sex spot on the tail of the female is particularly well marked. It is not a difficult species to breed.

Rivulus urophthalmus GUENTHER. Amazon. 2½ in. C. 70°–80°. Two varieties of this fish are obtainable, in one the body is yellow with close lines of red dots, and in the other greenish scales are interspersed between the red dots. The general effect is blue-grey. In both varieties the fins are grey with red dots except the tail, and the

168

fins of the female. They
breed at 75° but should
be removed after spawn-
ing as they eat their
young. (Plate VII, 2.)

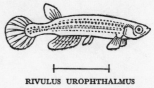

RIVULUS UROPHTHALMUS

Cynolebias bellottii STEINDACHNER. Argentine.
3 in. C. 68°–75°. This is a deeper-bodied fish
than its aforementioned relatives, with fins set
differently. The two sexes are most unlike, the
male being green-blue with white dots, and the
female olive-green with brown stripes across the
body and along the tail. One requires considerable patience in breeding the 'Argentine Pearl
Fish', as it is called: the eggs, so they say, take three
months to hatch out! Ordinarily they live in muddy
pools in the Pampas. (Plate VII, 3 and 4.)

Aphyosemion australe (RACHOW). Cape Lopez,
Africa. 2½ in. C. 73°–75°. 'Lyre-tail' or 'Cap Lopez
Blue'. The female of this species closely resembles
the related *Rivulus* species, being olive coloured
with red-edged scales and red-mottled fins. The
male is more spectacular, however, owing to the
peculiar 'lyre' formation of the tail, and the bright
blue tints and reddish-chocolate markings exhibited on the anal and dorsal fins, on the tail
and on the fore part of the body. (Plate VII, 1.)

They will breed in old water at a temperature
of 80 degrees and a pH of 6.8. The eggs are de-

169

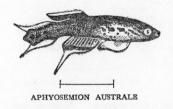

APHYOSEMION AUSTRALE

posited sparsely in the floating masses of Riccia, the process being a protracted one. In 24 to 36 hours the young hatch out and will seek the shelter of the floating vegetation.

Aphyosemion coeruleum (BOULENGER). Tropical West Africa. 4 in. 'The Blue Gularis.' 70°–80°. This beautiful fish is a strong jumper, therefore a cover to the aquarium is necessary. It is not an ideal community fish for, although it will not attack other fishes of its own size, it will readily devour small specimens. Indeed, it is essentially a 'live' food fish, yet it will in time make do with dried, prepared foods. The Blue Gularis does not perambulate the aquarium as do most other fishes, instead, it will remain stationary for quite long periods and then, as though it has suddenly remembered something, will dash away and remain stationary again with its fins just gently undulating. As regards the domicile—it likes plenty of plants and does not appreciate strong light, much preferring the shadows. The body colour is blue, as the specific name suggests, in various shades and mottled with deeper blue. The fins are olive-grey except the tail fin which has the lower half of the lower lobe dark blue and just abovethat, emanating from just before the tail root and extending to its tip is a reddish patch. The breeding habits are similar to those of A. australe.

Aphyosemion splendopleuris (MEINKEN). West Africa. 2 in. C. 70°-78°. Otherwise known as *Fundulopanchax splendopleuris*. This fish is very similar to the foregoing, except that the blue markings are lacking, and the fish generally is yellowish in colour with red markings in the male. The young hatch out in a fortnight, otherwise the breeding habits are similar to those of *A. australe*.

Panchax chaperi (SAUVAGE). Gaboon in tropical West Africa. 2 in. C. 65°-90°. Otherwise *Epiplatys chaperi* or *Haplochilus chaperi*. 'Barred Panchax'. The body colour of this well-known fish is olive, the fins are pale yellow, edged with black in the male. The mouth is also margined with black and, in the male, is red on the underside. (Plate VIII, I.) This was an early importation, having been introduced into this country in 1908. It is one of the few *Panchax* species that is really amicably disposed towards the other inhabitants of the community tank. In breeding this, and indeed most of this genus, a small tank well planted with dense vegetation or nearly half filled with Riccia is required. The breeding pair should be isolated for a few days and brought to condition with a plentiful diet of chopped earth-worm, brine shrimp or daphnia. The tank temperature should be raised slowly to 80 degrees Fahr., when the egg-laying process should start without delay. The male, in resplendent courting dress, chases the female into the mass of Riccia, where she lays three or four adhesive eggs. This process is repeated until eighty or so eggs are laid. The parents should be removed and separated for about a fortnight, and then replaced, when a further batch of eggs will result. Hatching out takes about ten days.

Pairs that are not yet at their full growth are the best from which to breed. When not in condition or if their surroundings are not to their liking their colouring tends to become insipid, especially if strong top light is used or the tank sparsely planted. *Chaperi* look their best in the shadow of broad-leaved plants.

Panchax playfairii (GUENTHER). Zanzibar. 3½ in. Otherwise *Pachypanchax playfairii*. The Panchax group are very like the Rivulus species in shape and position of the fins. The snout in all cases, however, is more pointed and the fishes themselves are inclined to be spiteful to smaller fry. The individuals of the species in question are yellowish in colour with red dots. The tail of the male bears several green dots.

Panchax fasciolatus (GUENTHER). Sierra Leone. 3 in. 70°–80°. The general colour of this fish, otherwise known as *Epiplatys* or *Haplochilus fasciolatus*, is a rich brown, on which are superimposed red and green spots. The fins are green and the tip of the tail is brownish yellow. The female is less colourful than the male.

Panchax sexfasciatus GILL, otherwise *Epiplatys sexfasciatus*. West Africa. 4 in. 75°–80°. An orange-green fish is this, with yellow semi-transparent fins. There are four or five dark bands across the posterior half terminating at the base of the tail. The eyes, in common with most of the egg-laying tooth-carps', are pale gold in colour. The Panchax kind are used throughout India for the destruction of mosquito larvae by the Malaria Bureau in their efforts to stamp out malaria. Supplies of Panchax are sent to those mosquito areas where it does not ordinarily live, and it is interesting to note that the containers used for their transport are the same as those used in the commercial transport of tropical aquarium fishes.

Aplocheilus blochii ARNOLD, formerly *Panchax blochii*. 1¾ in. 70°–84°. Metallic is the most apt epithet for this tiny, glinting creature. On a yellowish background are red and green dots and, in the male, the dots are carried into the

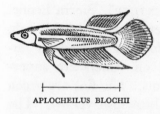

APLOCHEILUS BLOCHII

tail, where they are a light shade of brown. The back of the fish is also a light olive brown. The glinting scales show up especially well in the direct sunlight. The shape is typical of the group. (In fact, I do not think there is another group of tropical fishes in which the typical shape persists so uniformly as it does in the *Rivulus* and *Panchax* genera; irrespective of size the body is always slender and the fins arranged towards the tail.) Breed as for *Panchax chaperi*, but it should be noted that the young thrive best if given plenty of room.

Aplocheilus lineatus (CUVIER and VALENCIENNES), formerly *Panchax lineatus* and *Haplochilus rubrostigma*. India. 4 in. 70°–80°. A similar, glinting fish, though much larger than the aforementioned, and having a number of dark green bands across the body and the lower edge of the anal fin, while the top and bottom edges of the tail, are bright red. The eye is green. (Plate VIII, 4.)

It is easy to breed and the methods to be adopted should be along the lines given for *P. chaperi*. Broad-leaved plants are advisable, for the female deposits one egg at a time which is then fertilized by the male. As the eggs are

174

adhesive they stick to the leaf but it seems that those that fall to the bottom stand little chance of survival. The fry will require at first infusoria, later finely graded dried foods, then small daphnia. This seems to be one of the species that has a liking for tiny cyclops and these form a useful addition to the diet of the fry at a fortnight old. At a month they will be slightly over an inch in length with a nice taste in mosquito larvae and fully-grown daphnia. At a later age they will appreciate unwanted fish fry.

Incidentally, it is from fifteen to eighteen days before the fry hatch out.

Oryzias latipes (SCHLEGEL), formerly *Aplocheilus latipes*. China and Japan. $1\frac{3}{4}$ in. C. 40°–80°. 'Medaka' or 'Rice Fish'. There is nothing spectacular in either the shape or the colouring of this popular little fish. The back is olive-gold shading down to pale silver on the underside. Still, it is a peaceful, easily managed little chap, with a most delightful swimming movement. Moreover it is easy to breed—the eggs hang from a thread from the vent of the female, in which position the male fertilizes them. In a day or so they drop off, but neither the eggs nor the young are eaten by the parents.

By the same methods of selective breeding that resulted in the colourful goldfish being evolved from a dull-coloured native fish, a golden variety of the Medaka has been produced which sometimes comes into the dealers' tanks.

Jordanella floridae (GOODE and BEAN). Florida. 2 in. 70°–78°. 'The Flag Fish.' A stouter built fish is this, with larger scales and the fins set farther forward than in the Panchax groups. The background colour of the body is green, upon which numerous rows of red dots are superimposed.

Both the male and female have a small black spot just behind the gill covers. The male is more generally red with dotted red bands on the dorsal, caudal and anal fins, but both have a short, dark bar running vertically through the eye. The female has a dark green spot at the tail end of the dorsal fin, also she is of a duller green colour with the fins tinted pink.

A well-planted tank is necessary at breeding time as a protection for the female—the male is a vigorous wooer. Eventually, with fanning fins, a shallow pit is made in the sand of the bottom, and into this the female deposits singly about a hundred eggs spread over a period varying from an hour to a day. The father acts as 'nurse' and in that capacity will brook no interference from his mate, viciously driving her away, consequently, for her own safety she should be removed.

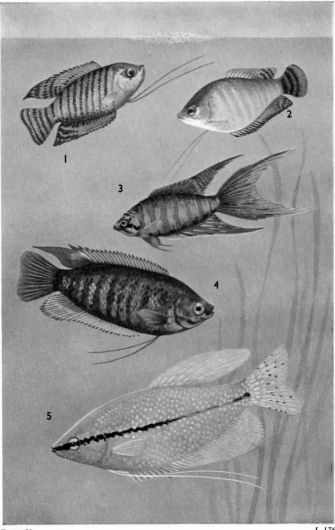

PLATE X.
1 & 2. *Colisa lalia*, Dwarf Gourami, male and female. 3. *Macropodus opercularis*, Paradise Fish, male (breeding season). 4. *C. labiosa*, Thick-lipped Gourami, male. 5. *Trichogaster leeri*, Pearl or Lace Gourami, male (breeding season).
(⅔ *natural size*)

The father continues his duties even after the fry have hatched out and delights to swim about the aquarium with them in tow. The young are individualists, however, and soon decide on their own ways of living. In water with a pH slightly above neutral and with plenty of green food the colouring is enhanced and they become really beautiful fish. They will nibble the living Cryptocoryne leaves and are partial to an occasional feed, say twice a week, of algae and/or chopped lettuce.

The Live-bearing Toothed Carps

Live-bearing among fishes is not unusual, nor is it confined to exotic fishes alone. Several fishes common to the British coast are viviparous, notably the Viviparous Blenny and certain of the sharks. In these, as with the group now under discussion, the male, by means of an intromittent organ—usually developed at maturity from the anal fin—fertilizes the female. The process is quite promiscuous, the male choosing such opportunities that may come his way. As one would imagine, when several species inhabit the same tank, hybrids are not uncommon, nevertheless, nature, by giving the different genera differently-formed gonopodia, checks this in great measure. Certain species, however, produce well-defined hybrids not only in the aquarium but also in the wild state. Many aquarists have made extensive experiments in hybridization, and to the biologist the results have been of interest. The amateur is not so much interested in Mendelian theories as in rearing fine fishes, and, to my way of thinking, the hybridizer does the hobby a better service by infusing, say, a rather colourless but well-finned species with the dominant colour of another, and so establishing a new and improved strain. This is known as 'cross-breeding', and refers to the crossing of different species of the same genus; it should not be confused with 'line-breeding', which deals with selective breeding among members of one species only.

The female is fertilized by the merest touch of the gonopodium on her vent, and the one fertilization will last for several broods. Consequently it is useless to attempt cross-breeding with other than virgin females. Usually there is a month's interval between broods, and as the time approaches the under part of the female will be noticeably darker and swollen, the dark area taking the shape of a crescent or triangle. She should be removed to a small well-planted tank and be well fed. Even additional food, however, does not prevent the parent from devouring her offspring, but with dense vegetation the minute fry are afforded a fair protection. The fry, in nearly all species, will eat screened daphnia from the first. There is little variation in the breeding habits of the live-bearers, the principal exception being *Mollienisia*.

Gambusia affinis (GIRARD). Florida and adjacent States. Male 1½ in. Female 2¼ in. 70°–80°. The general colour scheme of this fish is grey with a slight black edging on some of the scales. Aquarists are trying hard to line-breed an all-black Gambusia that will breed true to itself. In the wild state black males are occasionally found, very rarely black females. It is a strange thing that from all the gorgeous colours in which the tropicals may be obtained, your fancier prefers an all-black fish to all others. A fish that is only half black, whether it is a Gambusia, a Platy or a Molly, is, to my eyes, an abomination; it looks like an ordinary fish that has been dropped on a dirty floor. Yet . . . a fish that is completely black has a fascination entirely its own and often, especially with the 'Midnight Mollies', looks like a fish cut out of black velvet.

There are several 'wild' varieties or sub-species which exhibit particular colorations, one of the most interesting being the Golden

Gambusia (*Gambusia nobilis*) from West Texas which has a distinctive gold colouring.

An interesting fact about this little fish (*G. affinis*) is the part it played in making the construction of the Panama Canal possible. The disease-carrying mosquitoes that ruined de Lesseps' earlier attempt suffered a severe set-back when this Top-minnow was introduced to the swamps of the Isthmus from Florida. In India, where they were introduced in 1929, they have bred prolifically and are available free of charge for anti-malaria work. Breeding is along the usual lines for 'live-bearers'.

Belonesox belizanus KNER. Guatemala. Male 3½ in. Female 5½ in. 72°–85°. 'Dwarf Pike'. The popular name of this fish is indeed apt, for in shape and disposition it is very pike-like. Its colour on the upper surface is light brown,

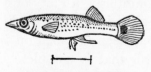

BELONESOX BELIZANUS

turning to olive and yellow until, on the lower surface, it is silvery-yellow. Along the sides are a few straggly rows of small black dots, and on the tail, near the base, is a large, distinct round spot. They require large separate quarters, well-planted with Vallisneria, Myriophyllum, etc., and the surface of the water should bear a profusion of floating plants. The temperature should be high, say 80 degrees Fahr. at breeding time. The young will take small daphnia immediately— no 'infusoria' slops for them. Very soon the little thugs will require young Guppies, and unless these or the young of some other fish are available the young *Belonesox* will cease to take an interest in life. Therefore, if one is line-breeding any of the 'fancy' fishes a tank of the 'Live-bearing Pikes' is a good proposition—the problem of what to do with the unwanted population is solved. It is a hungry fish and will only eat live animal foods, preferably small fishes.

Heterandria formosa AGASSIZ. Southern U.S.A. Male ¾ in. Female 1 in. 55°–85°. This is the smallest of aquarium fishes. It is an active little fish and popularly called 'Mosquito Fish' owing to its use as a great feeder on mosquito larvae. It is not an ideal fish for the community tank because, from its lack of inches, it is liable to be bullied by larger members.

The colour is olive with a definite dark line running from the snout to the tip of the tail with dark vertical bars. Underneath the dark line the belly is white. There are two spots on the

HETERANDRIA FORMOSA

dorsal fin, one black and the other red. The brood is not delivered in one operation as in most other species but is spread over a period of days— sometimes as many as ten, when two or three are ejected per day. The tank should be thickly planted and also have plenty of floating vegetation for the benefit of the helpless fry. Feeding as for the fry of other small fishes. The temperature of the aquarium at breeding time should be kept at 70 degrees.

Girardinus metallicus POEY. Cuba. Male 2 in. Female 3 in. 68°–84°. The most outstanding feature of this fish are the fifteen or so chevrons of pale silver along the sides. The body colour is gun-metal with a slight metallic sheen and the gills have a greenish appearance. The shape is typical of the live-bearers.

The gonopodium of the male is double pointed, the longer point being slightly hooked.

Limia caudofasciata REGAN. Jamaica. Male 1¾ in. Female 2½ in. C. 70°–80°. 'The Steel Blue Limia'. The general body colour is olive-green paling to silver on the underside; this drab raiment is relieved by the startling, flashing blue of the scales. At the base of the dorsal fin (paler in the female) is a yellow patch, in the centre of which the male has a black mark. The male is quite a 'gold' fish, having an orange coloured tail and a similarly tinted belly. In the female the fins are practically colourless. The eyes in both sexes are golden coloured. They breed in the accepted way of their kind but are notorious eaters of their young. At 75 degrees they breed best.

Limia nigrofasciata REGAN. Haiti. 2 in. C. 70°–78°. 'The Hump-backed Limia'. This is a hardy fish and is one of the oldest of aquarium fishes. The colour is not very striking, at least, not in the younger stages, being a general grey colour with ten darkish vertical bars. With age the colour intensifies and in the male the shape of the body changes somewhat—it becomes deeper and sturdier and on the back a definite hump develops. The most striking change is in the dorsal fin, also of the male, which becomes very much larger and develops a black coloration with an inner yellow band. When he swims the old gentleman certainly shows off his fins. Breeding—at 72 to 75 degrees—is along the usual lines with the subsequent routine of feeding the young also the same.

Mollienisia velifera REGAN. Yucatan. 5 in. 70°–80°. There are few fishes with a more spectacular dorsal fin than this one. It is almost as large as the rest of the fish, and is a mottled iridescent blue. The body colour is olive, and the large tail is mottled with blue and gold—altogether a most attractive fish. Frequently one encounters specimens with the chest area suffused with a golden colour. The female is much less spectacular, her colouring is subdued and the dorsal fin is of normal size. Breeding is along the same lines as for *M. latipinna* and it should be noted that for both species there is no particular temperature at which they breed best—anywhere between 60 and 90 degrees, but care should be taken to ensure that there is no great temperature variation and also that the female is not removed from one tank to another when she is in a gravid condition—it may cause an attack of the shimmies. Also, and this is most important, the tank should be so placed as to receive the maximum of sunlight, this being an essential in the growth of the algae which forms the staple diet.

Mollienisia latipinna LE SUEUR. Mexico 3¾ in. 70°–80°. 'Sailfin' or just 'Mollie'. This is perhaps the most popular of all aquarium fishes, it is colourful, well-shaped, active and not too

MOLLIENISIA LATIPINNA

difficult in the matter of food, being a vegetarian. Its colouring ranges from that of *M. velifera* to jet black. Some of the black varieties have a

184

bright orange fringe along the top of the dorsal
fin which, in a measure, accentuates the intense
black effect.

When a female in the community tank shows,
by the dark and swollen appearance of the underside, signs of being gravid, it is usual to remove it
to separate quarters. This is not because it might
consume its young, but because the other fish
will. The sooner a gravid fish is moved the better,
the commotion caused by netting or by the better
'glass pipe' appliance may result in fatal injury
to the fish or in misshapen or even dead offspring.
If one intends to breed with really good Mollies
it is best to have the parents in their own private
tank at the outset. The temperature can then be
raised to breeding heat (about 78 degrees)
without discommoding the other fishes. The tank
should be large, well lighted and thickly planted,
and in these conditions the young should thrive
and be a credit to their lord and master. I have
remarked that they are vegetarian, and not only
do they appreciate a slight greening of the water
and an occasional nibble at the plants, they also
welcome additional green food in the form of
chopped lettuce or spinach. The fine filamentous
algae that one removes so assiduously from the
sides of the tank are their favourite food, and with
plenty of light this algae, and also the fishes, will

do well. Dried packet foods containing vegetable matter should be used when the algae die down in the autumn; it should be given in small quantities at a time and about four times a day if possible. Live foods such as blood worm and enchytrae should be given sparingly.

Mollienisia sphenops (CUVIER and VALENCIENNES). Gulf Coast. 3 in. 'The Liberty Fish.' This has the typical wide-spreading tail of its relations but lacks size in the dorsal fin. To com-

MOLLIENISIA SPHENOPS

pensate the aquarist for that deficiency it dresses itself in a greater variety of colours, the most attractive being, I think, the blue kind, in which the body is various shades of blue and purple with a white belly, green pectoral and dorsal fins and a deep purplish-green tail fringed with orange. (Plate VIII, 3.) All the wild varieties came originally from the estuaries of the Gulf Coast and thereabouts; sometimes they would move seawards, and when the fancy took them they would seek the fresh-water streams; at other times the estuarine mud would attract them—algae are very prolific in such a place— and the name by which they were known generally before the days of aquarists gives

the lie to their muddy taste
—'Mud Pussers'.

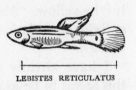

LEBISTES RETICULATUS

Lebistes reticulatus (PETERS).
Trinidad and Venezuela. C.
Male 1¼ in. Female 2 in.
'Guppy', 'Rainbow Fish' or 'Millions'. One day
someone will write a poem eulogizing this little
jewel beloved by every aquarist, and I suggest
that the opening lines should be:

> 'My Guppy, 'tis of thee,
> Fish of variety,
> Of thee I sing.'

For of all the infinite variety of colour arrangements to which the tropical fish lends itself, none
can surpass Master Guppy. It is said, indeed,
that no two male Guppies have identical markings. About the only constant factor is the pale
green of the fins in both sexes and the suspicion
of green on the back. The female is an insipid
creature, being a uniform pearly-white colour.
The male, on the other hand, wears the finery;
nearly every shade of the rainbow is utilized. By
intensive line-breeding certain colour characteristics have been stabilized in various strains.
One of the prettiest strains is the Lace-tail, in
which a number of colours combine to make well-
defined markings. The strongest colour is usually

bright yellow. Also, either on the body or tail, or both, are dark eye-spots. (Plate IX, 1, 2, 3 and 4.)

I have already mentioned line-breeding, and this seems to be as good a place as any to enlarge upon that most interesting subject. Line-breeding is responsible for the various breeds and strains of horses, cats, dogs, birds and other domestic animals; from practically wild stock the breeders have chosen specimens that exhibited features that appealed to them, and by systematic breeding back the offspring with the parents these individual characteristics, whether good or bad, have become exaggerated and stabilized. Moreover, the finished product will breed true to type although, by injudicious mating, the stock may revert to the wild type in a few generations. The goldfish as we know it to-day is the result of centuries, almost, of intensive line-breeding; from the dull-olive Asiatic carp the Chinese and Japanese have evolved the richly-coloured and elaborately-finned fish of the present. Tropical fishes, from their being so prolific and from maturing at an early age, lend themselves readily to this science; on the Continent the fish breeders have made considerable progress and there is no doubt that in time this country will be responsible for some fine strains.

HYBRID FINNAGE OF THE GUPPY

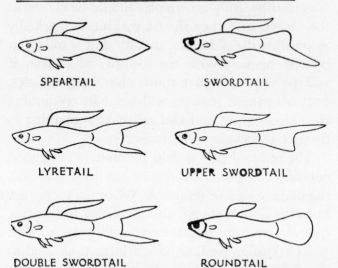

SPEARTAIL   SWORDTAIL

LYRETAIL   UPPER SWORDTAIL

DOUBLE SWORDTAIL   ROUNDTAIL

NORMAL FINNAGE

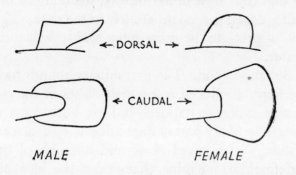

← DORSAL →

← CAUDAL →

MALE   FEMALE

For the varieties of tail recognized by breeders consult the illustrations on the previous page.

A healthy, fully-grown pair should be chosen at the outset, and they should exhibit as markedly as possible the particular quality that is to be improved upon. With the Guppy, of course, it will be the male that shows the characteristics, but subsequent females will assist in continuing the colour strain and also will have something to do with the shape and finnage.

The selected pair should be brought into good condition and, after the female has been fertilized, the male should be removed. When the young are born the female should also be placed in separate quarters and not into the community tank. The fry, to develop well, require a large tank, and as they grow the runts must be removed. This culling process should be ruthless and thorough so that, out of a brood of, say, a hundred, only half a dozen specimens are left in the tank. They will appreciate the extra room and so will thrive better.

So far so good. The preliminary rounds have, we hope, produced a few good fishes of the particular type we require, and we enter now on the really tricky part of the business. Patience and system are required now, and a touch of that indefinable something that makes the ideal fish breeder, a good 'eye' for colour and shape, is also essential. When mature the young are mated with the parents, and the resultant offspring with the grandparents and with their cousins. Exact records must be kept of the various matings, and this may be done by labelling each tank with the generation and relationship of the occupants. In time one's ideal fish may appear and, to continue the strain satisfactorily, it is essential to know whether it was produced from second cousins of the sixth generation, say, or from grand-parent and a grandchild and so forth, and no one save the breeder himself really knows, and if he has not kept accurate records he may never quite repeat the achievement. Because, having at last found the ideal fish, it must be stabilized by breeding back with the successful pair, and the two pairs responsible for them may have to be called upon again. It is an absorbingly interesting hobby but, as you have seen, it is not one to be entered on lightly.

There is a likelihood of the physique of the line suffering from too intensive inbreeding, and to avoid this it is a good plan to run two 'lines' from the original parent stock, then, by judicious crossing not only the physique but the colour may be improved.

In the feeding of Guppies generally, it should be

noted that they should be fed four times a day, a light meal each time, not one square meal a day.

Platypoecilus maculatus GUENTHER. South Mexico. Male 1½ in. Female 2 in. 70°–90°. 'Moon Fish' or 'Platy'. This is a slightly larger and more robust fish than the foregoing, very like the Mollie except for the smaller dorsal fin. In this fish, by selective line-breeding, we have six distinct colour varieties, viz., the Blue, the Variegated (this is a bold mixture of all the varieties), the Golden or Yellow, the Red—it is almost like a goldfish—the Black—this is really black and green—and the Berlin which is red with a heavy black smear along the sides. It is a really colourful fish, no matter

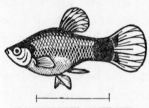

PLATYPOECILUS MACULATUS

which variety is kept, but requires fairly high temperatures, from 70 to 90 degrees Fahr. The breeding habits are the same as described for live-bearers generally. By mating with Swordtails the various colour types can be evolved. (Plate IX, 5, 6 and 7.)

The name 'Moon' arises from a moon-shaped marking at the base of the tail in the early imported specimens, in the female, usually, it consists of two large dots, one above the other.

PLATE XI.   *N-195*,
1. *Cichlasoma biocellatum*, Jack Dempsey.   2.   *Hemichromis bimaculatus*, Jewel Fish
Red Cichlid, male.   3.   *C. severum*, Striped Cichlid, male.
(½ *natural size*)

Platypoecilus variatus MEEK. E. Mexico. 2 in.
C. 70°–90°. The females are of a general bright
olive-green with a blue tint along the back and a
white belly colour, and it is unfortunate that
many of the males also are on the dull side as
regards colour. As a rule the males have a bright
yellow dorsal fin with black speckles. There are
two colour strains (the variations are carried only
by the male)—yellows and blues, and these, in
their turn, have many variations. Basically, the
'yellows' have a yellow body with a red tail and
the 'blues' are yellow speckled with black and
green and have blue at the base of the tail. In
both the tail is brown. Breeding is the same as for
live-bearers generally. They are most prolific.

Xiphophorus helleri (HECKEL). Eastern Mexico
and South thereof. Male (including sword) 6½ in.
Female 6 in. 'Swordtail'. Colourful and spectacular are these fishes, the males in particular
with their long pointed swords and largish dorsal
fins. As with the Platies there are a number of
evolved colour varieties in all of which, however,
the sword of the male is bordered with black. The
original colouring was a bluish metallic green on
the body with a red line running through the
eye to the tail. Now, of course, we have them
with green bodies and green spikes, green bodies
with orange spikes, a completely yellow variety,

N

one with a red sword and one completely red. The breeding of these fishes is typical of their kind, but it should be noted that segregation of the sexes of the fry should take place as soon as the sex characteristics are apparent, as too early mating will only produce runts and at the same time spoil the parents themselves.

NANDIDAE (*The Nandids*)

These are really a marine form of fish, although a few species inhabit streams. They have spiny-rayed fins like the perches, and share the same pugnacious traits of that group. All are egg-layers.

Badis badis (HAMILTON-BUCHANAN). All India excepting Madras. 2 in. 73°-82°. The dorsal fin of these fishes is exceptionally long and the first fifteen rays are spinous. They have a peculiar habit of standing rigidly still on their tails when the mood takes them. The general colour is deep

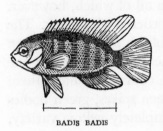
BADIS BADIS

blue with a suspicion of green, but all kinds of colours from chocolate to pearl may predominate. A line of black dots running across the gill cover and through the eye is a

194

remarkable feature. The male is usually of a more intense colour than the female.

As regards the breeding of these rather beautiful though temperamental fishes, a well-planted tank is necessary and in it should be placed a small flower pot—one with a diameter of three inches at the mouth will do. After the preliminary chasing the female will lay her eggs in the flower pot, some eighty in all. She should be removed when it seems certain that no more eggs are forthcoming. The male will enter the flower pot and, by violently agitating his fins, will keep the water circulating around the eggs. Until the eggs actually hatch out he will be an ideal parent, but he is not to be trusted with the fry. Consequently he must be removed when they hatch out in two to three days. The best breeding temperature is 80 degrees Fahr. In their wild state they feed exclusively on live foods, particularly mosquito larvae, consequently, to keep them at their colourful best a diet of tubifex, enchytrae, chopped earthworms and daphnia is indicated with, of course, an occasional treat in the way of larval mosquitoes.

Monocirrhus polycanthus (HECKEL). Amazon. $2\frac{1}{2}$ in. 70°–80°. 'Leaf Fish'. If your purse is sufficiently deep you may indulge yourself by possessing a pair of this really interesting fish, for they will never fail to evoke surprise if one has never seen one. They actually are leaf-like and, perhaps for that reason, have been a rarity for years. The colour is that of a dead leaf and so is the shape. The mouth is also interesting, for when the fish yawns, which it does very frequently, it expands enormously—and talking of the mouth suggests food which, with this fish means 'small live fishes'. A healthy pair will consume a couple of thousand Guppies in a year, consequently they are useful in disposing of the runts.

The eggs are deposited and fertilized in the same way as are those of the Cichlids, and are fanned in the same manner. The parents are inclined to cannibalism. Breeding temperature 78 to 80 degrees Fahr.

ATHERINIDAE (*The Silversides*)

These are the Atherines so common to the estuaries of England; but, where the English species are dull silver in colour, the tropical varieties are most colourful. One species only is sought after for aquarium purposes.

Melanotaenia nigrans (RICHARDSON). Australia. 4 in. C. 60°-90°. 'Australian Rainbow Fish'. The body of this fish resembles that of the Common Dace: along the sides are numerous red and yellow stripes, on the gill cover there is a large brilliant red spot. They breed readily in captivity and in similar fashion to the other egg-layers; they do not eat their young.

Melanotaenia McCullochi AHL. Australia (exact locality not known). 2¾ in. C. 60°–90°. This is a smaller edition of *M. nigrans* which it resembles in colouring and in breeding and other habits. The pectoral area, however, is red. Also like *M. nigrans*, it breeds so prolifically as to be embarrassing at times. Some aquarists turn the offspring into the outdoor garden pond in the summer and treat them in just the same way as they do ordinary pond fishes.

ANABANTIDAE (*The Anabantids*)

Nearly all the members of this family, known also as the Labyrinths, possess a small chamber within the gill cavity in which air can be stored, and the reason for this is that, on occasion, their native streams dry up and so the fishes are able to exist even when there is no water. They are commonly found in the rice fields in the Far East.

Macropodus opercularis (LINNAEUS). China. 3 in. 50°–80°. 'Paradise Fish'. This is a really beautiful fish, especially at breeding time when

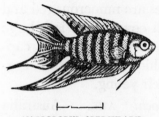

MACROPODUS OPERCULARIS

the male sets out to attract his mate. The back of the fish is a dull grey but the sides are marked with bright bands alternately blue, or greenish-blue and vermilion, the ventral fins are orange. (Plate X, 3.)

At breeding time the male will begin to make a nest of bubbles on the surface of the water. This he does by taking gulps of air into his mouth, and as he blows the air out again the saliva makes a thin skin around the bubble. The nest is circular in shape and, when completed, about two inches or more in diameter. As the work progresses the female is enticed under the nest. If she is not interested it is more than likely that the male will attack her, sometimes with fatal results. A fairly large and densely-planted tank gives the lady a chance to evade her savage mate, but if his attentions become too drastic she should be removed. In the meantime the male will probably start to build another nest, and after an interval of twenty-four hours the female may be replaced in the breeding tank. This reluctance on the part of the female to mate is by no means unusual, but if she is brought to condition with chopped earthworms and daphnia and if one is not too precipitate in removing her from the irate male, then she may oblige. When eventually she does consent to dally beneath the bubble-nest, the male wraps himself around her as though he is trying to squeeze the eggs out. As they are extruded the male fertilizes them and, catching them in his mouth, blows them into the nest. Ordinarily the eggs float into the nest without assistance. The egg-laying process takes about an hour, in which time 500 eggs may be laid.

When it seems that no more eggs are forthcoming, the female will proceed to eat those in the nest; that is, if the male will let her, for as soon as all the eggs are laid he chases her out of the way. If the female is not removed, her chance of surviving his savage onslaughts is slender.

The eggs hatch out in three days, and during that time the male never leaves the nest and, indeed, he finds plenty of work to occupy his time; burst bubbles must be replaced and eggs that escape must be returned. When the fry hatch out he has even more work to do, because for the first thirty-six hours they hang tail downwards from the nest; if they lose their hold the parent takes them in his mouth and puts them back. When the egg sac is exhausted, however, and they set out to find food, the queer parent will take them in his mouth—and that is the end of their story. Consequently the male should be returned to his usual quarters.

The breeding tank should have a well-fitting glass cover, because the slightest suspicion of film on the water may be enough to suffocate the baby fishes during their sojourn on the surface; do not forget that they are Labyrinths and have to breathe dry air occasionally.

Macropodus chinensis (BLOCH). Eastern China. $2\frac{1}{2}$ in. 60°–80°. 'The Round-tail Paradise Fish.' This is a smaller and less colourful edition of the foregoing, moreover, instead of the tail being forked, it is rounded. The male has a reddish tail. The breeding habits are similar to those of *M. opercularis*.

Betta splendens REGAN. Siam. $2\frac{1}{2}$ in. 70°–85°. 'Siamese Fighting Fish'. This beautiful fish may be kept in the community tank provided there is only one male; in fact, so antagonistic do the males become to each other at breeding time that fights are staged between selected fish in Siam. The fishes will fight until, with fins torn and tattered, the loser succumbs to his injuries. Not infrequent-

BETTA SPLENDENS

ly the victor also expires in the hour of his victory.

The female, the cause of all this to-do, is a rather insignificant fish; she has smallish fins and a slender body deeply coloured in rich green-, red- or blue-bronze. The male, on the other hand, is an undulating richly-coloured veil. His tail is vast, his dorsal fin high and the anal fin, which is deep, extends from just behind the pectoral fin to the tail. A deep bronze-green is the usual body colour and this gradually changes, deepening towards the edges, to various other colours on the fins. By selective line-breeding strains have been evolved in which the tails are blue, green, mauve, red or pink. Breeding is similar to that of *Macropodus opercularis*.

Colisa labiosa (DAY). Burma. 3 in. 70°–85°. 'Thick-lipped Gourami'. These are a deep-bodied fish and, like nearly all the Gour-amis, banded with al-ternate colours which, in this instance, are dull orange and sea green. The lips are

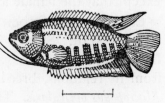

COLISA LABIOSA

thick and prominent and from the forepart of the underside two long 'thread fins' project. These are reddish in colour and so are the fins except the anal fin of the male which is blue posteriorly. The top of the female's head is domed, the male's is straight. This is also a nest breeder. (Plate X, 4.)

Colisa lalia (HAMILTON-BUCHANAN). Bengal. 2 in. C. 68°–84°. 'Dwarf Gourami'. The male of this delightful species is easily distinguished by

COLISA LALIA

his fine raiment. He is banded, from gill cover to the tip of his tail, with narrow blue and red bands. The female sports delicate pastel shades, also banded, of pale pinks and greens on a mother o' pearl background. (Plate X, 1 and 2.) Breeds in the usual nest-builder's manner, except that the female assists in making the nest.

Colisa fasciata (BLOCH and SCHNEIDER). Bengal. 4 in. 70°–80°. 'Striped Gourami'. Although this large Gourami makes a different kind of nest from its relations, breeding directions are as for *Macropodus opercularis*. The body colour is brown, slashed with ten or so blue bands. The shape is very similar to that of *C. labiosa*.

The aquarist very often—indeed, nearly always —sees in his fishes only their colouring, shape and

habits, and is inclined
to forget that in their
native haunts they are
thought of in a very dif-
ferent way. In Bengal
this fish is regarded in

COLISA FASCIATA

the same light as we regard plaice or trout—not
for their beauty, but for their value as food; in
fact the 'Striped Gourami' is one of the most
valuable of India's food dishes.

Trichogaster trichopterus (PALLAS). Malay and
Indo-China. 5 in. 68°–85°. 'Three-spot Gourami'. The colouring of this large though amiable fish is not vivid, being a silvery olive; never-

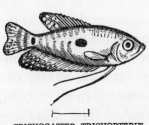

theless, from the variety
of markings and the fine
fins it has some claims
to beauty. On the sides
are two large dark
spots, the eye forming
the third. A typical nest-
builder.

TRICHOGASTER TRICHOPTERUS

Trichogaster leeri (BLEEKER). Sumatra and
Siam. 4 in. 68°–85°. 'Pearl' or 'Lace Gourami'.
Although not really brightly coloured, this fish is
decidedly attractive. The fins are yellow, and
the body, which is whitish, has a light purple
sheen. Both fins and body are covered with

many small light-coloured dots. The female has a dark line running from the eye nearly to the tail and along the centre of the sides. The male flushes on his underside a bright pink at breeding time. (Plate X, 5.) Breeding is typical of the bubble builders. The eggs float and the parents do not eat either them or the fry.

Helostoma temmincki (CUVIER and VALENCIENNES). Java. 10 in. 'Kissing Gourami'. This large silvery fish seems to spend the greater part of its time in kissing its mate. The lips curl right back during this osculatory process, the reason for which is quite a mystery and is not associated, apparently, with courtship. They breed when they are half-grown and deposit up to 2,000 pale yellow floating eggs after having embraced in the usual Cichlid manner. The parents do not eat the fry which should be fed for the first week on infusoria and then with tiny daphnia, mikro, etc.

Anabas testudineus (BLOCH). India. 6 in. 65°–90°. 'Climbing Perch'. The Climbing Perch is, perhaps, the least satisfactory of all the fishes sold for aquariums. It is yellow-brown in colour with reddish-brown fins, not at all beautiful; it requires immense quantities of live food or

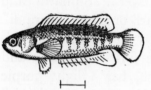

ANABAS TESTUDINEUS

raw meat; fortunately however, it is not averse
to canned dog food; it is quarrelsome and, finally,
very rarely does its climbing act for the benefit
of its owner. The tank should be very large and
shallow and a rock should project above the water
level. When the fish does condescend to walk, it
does so with a rolling sort of gait, using the ser-
rated undersides of the gills in the process.
Although it is a Labyrinth fish it does not make a
bubble nest. The eggs are deposited in the
ordinary way and then they float to the surface
where they hatch out in twenty-four hours. The
parents do not eat either the eggs or the fry.

CICHLIDAE (*The Cichlids*)

The Cichlids are a branch of the delightfully
entitled *Acanthopterygii pharyngognathi* which, being
interpreted, means 'the spiny-finned fishes with
teeth in their throats', as distinct from the carp
kind, which have the latter feature but have all
the rays of their fins soft. In spite of this rather
formidable title, the group contains some of the
most beautiful fishes known to man; the colourful Wrasses, the Coral Fishes, many of the gorgeous species from the West Indian and Japanese
seas, and, of course, the freshwater Cichlids of
the tropics are members of the order.

Very few Cichlids are sufficiently amiable for the community tank, and some are on the large side. Moreover, nearly all species are impatient of plants, pulling them up, tearing the leaves apart, uprooting them and generally playing havoc. They are happiest in a sanded aquarium of their own and, even at breeding time, with few exceptions which include the Angel Fish, plants are unnecessary.

UNITED IN THE CICHLIDS

DORSAL FIN

1ST

2ND

PERCH TYPE IN WHICH THE FIRST RAYS (SOMETIMES ALL) OF THE FIRST AND SECOND DORSAL, VENTAL AND ANAL FINS ARE SPINOUS

There are two forms of breeding in this group, viz., the nest-builders and the mouth-breeders. I will deal with the mouth-breeders first.

Haplochromis multicolor (HILGENDORF). Also known as *Haplochromis strigigena* and *Paratilapia multicolor*. Egypt. 2¼ in. 70°–80°. The 'Egyptian Mouth-breeder'. This is an interesting, colourful and inexpensive fish. The head is particularly large and well it need be, as the female carries forty to fifty eggs about in her mouth for a fortnight. The huge head gives the rest of the body a fore-shortened appearance. The dorsal fin is very long and, like the rest of the fins, is yellowish and bears broken stripes of blue and green. The body is light blue and is marbled with yellow, red, blue and green, an iridescent sheen covering the whole. The female is not so vivid as the male, and at breeding time the latter sometimes has a red spot on the anal fin.

A fairly-large tank is necessary, say twenty inches long, well-stocked with plants, for the male is inclined to treat his mate roughly and she needs that protect-

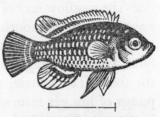

HAPLOCHROMIS MULTICOLOR

ion. A good temperature for the breeding tank is 76 degrees Fahr. There should be a fairly thick layer of sand, say three inches. Healthy fishes of a year old are the best for breeding, and they should be well fed beforehand. The courtship commences by the male circling round and round the female, and eventually the pair actually kiss. This circling movement usually takes place directly over a smooth stretch of sand overhung by a bushy plant, and the very slight current caused by these evolutions results in a small depression forming in the sand. The female lays her eggs in this small hollow and the male immediately fertilizes them, whereupon the lady returns and picks them up in her mouth. At this point the male should be removed; he is hungry and can see no reason why his spouse should have such a tempting mouthful all to herself. The female is made of sterner stuff, and during the fourteen days or so which the eggs take to hatch she does not feed at all, neither does she swallow any of the eggs that all this time have been in her mouth. When the fry hatch out, they leave their maternal shelter in search of food, but at the slightest hint of danger return to the fold. The female, after a few days, feels the pangs of hunger returning and so she too should be removed, otherwise her infants may return once too often to her mouth. Owing to the tremendous strain on the system, three broods at most should be expected from each individual female. *Tilapia macrocephala* (Bleeker) is another mouth-breeder and it also comes from Africa. I do not think it has been seen in England yet. It is a larger and less colourful fish than its Nile relation.

Hemichromis bimaculatus GILL. Africa. 4 in. 60°–90°. 'Jewel Fish' or 'Red Cichlid'. This and

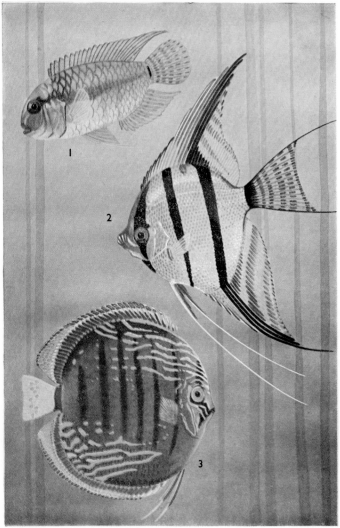

PLATE XII.   *N-208*
1. *Aequidens portalegrensis.* 2.   *Pterophyllum scalare*, Angel Fish.   3.   *Symphysodon discus*, Pompadour Fish.

($\frac{1}{3}$ *natural size*)

the succeeding Cichlids are nest-builders. The female is generally red and orange in colour and the male a brownish-green with brownish-orange on the underside. Both are 'jewelled' with small blue dots scattered over body and fins, and there are also two large, dark 'eye-spots', one at the base of the tail and the other on the middle of each side. At breeding time the colours are greatly intensified. (Plate XI, 2.)

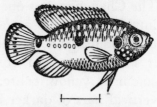

HEMICHROMIS BIMACULATUS

Their breeding habits are typical of the nest-building Cichlids as described under *Cichlasoma facetum*. They breed at 80 degrees, but care should be taken to see that the aquarium contains numerous nooks and crannies in the shape of arches, flower-pots, etc., in which one or the other can hide, as they fight like cats and dogs at breeding time.

Geophagus brasiliensis HECKEL. Brazil. 6 in. 70°–80°. The 'Mud-eater'. The tips of the fins of this fish are orange and all the rest is olive. Over this is superimposed, as though radiated from the scales, a bright bluey-green sheen. The shape is very like that of the Common Perch. Its habitat is sluggish streams and estuarine creeks, where it spends much of its time turning the mud over with its snout, seeking, possibly, for molluscs and worms. The eye is richly coloured with gold and black, and with age the other body colours improve considerably. Breeding is along ordinary lines but, in the aquarium, is infrequent.

Cichlasoma facetum (JENKYNS). Argentine. 6 in. 70°–80°. 'Chanchito' or 'Chameleon Fish'. The Chanchito was one of the first Cichlids to be introduced to the aquarist. It is fairly easy to breed and it is a typical nest-builder. The body is fairly deep and compact, and the general colour is yellow ochre. There are about nine vertical bars of darker hue and the suspicion of a dark bar along the sides. It will eat almost anything, and grows to quite a large size; in La Plata it is used to supplement the larder.

In breeding this fish a large tank is necessary, and the bottom should have a three-inch layer of coarse sand. One or two flower pots with the bottom sawn off or a piece of narrow drain pipe, the size depending on that of the fish, should be placed in the tank. It is a rather tricky fish to mate, and the sexes, too, are difficult to separate except at breeding time. Three-inch specimens should be chosen if possible, and if temperamentally suited they will soon go through the preliminary evolutions. These consist of scooping out two pits in the sand, about four inches in diameter and about two inches deep. The female will enter the flower pot and lay a string of eggs and the male will follow slowly, fertilizing them as he proceeds. The operation is repeated until there are several hundreds of eggs in the flower pot. Incidentally, if a flower pot is not available, a largish flat stone will suit the parents; failing that, the eggs may be laid on the side of the glass. It is safe to say that hardly any two pairs have quite the same ideas about breeding.

However, the eggs have been laid and the parents take turns in aerating them; this they do by mounting guard, either in the flower pot or wherever the eggs may be, and fanning the water with their fins. In about three days the young hatch out and are transferred by mouth to one of the pits. Now, cleanliness is a strong point with nearly all Cichlids, and for some intuitive reason they know that the presence of organic matter will cause an epidemic of fungus amongst their offspring. Therefore, when the pit shows signs of becoming foul the entire brood is removed, again by mouth, to a fresh pit. At this stage the young are mere specks attached to the much larger yolk-sac, and it is on this sac that they live. In about a fortnight the sac is absorbed, during which time the fry may have been in three or four pits and have received as many 'baths' in their parents' mouths. From then onwards the proud parents take their shoal of offspring for airings and it is indeed a thrilling sight to see the little family being kept together as they swim. Some parents eat their young and, on the other hand, some do not; whether they are to be removed to different quarters or not depends entirely on the judgment of the aquarist. The temperature for the breeding tank depends on the individual species, but a good average, which may be adjusted according to the locality from which the fish came, is 75 degrees Fahr.

Cichlasoma cutteri FOWLER. Honduras. 3 in. 70°–85°. This is a somewhat deeper-bodied fish than the foregoing. The ground colour is pale blue on which are eight well-defined vertical bars. The eye is green, an unusual colour for the eyes of a fish. This species comes the nearest of all the Cichlids to being a community fish, in the ordinary way it is docile and unassuming. It breeds in the typical Cichlid manner at 80 degrees.

Cichlasoma tetracanthus (CUVIER and VALEN-CIENNES). Cuba. 5½ in. 70°–85°. The most striking feature of this fish is the way in which it is marked; on a pale, dull-yellow background, from snout to tail, are sharply-defined markings of dark brown giving it a leopard-skin effect. The back is bluey-green. Breeds at 80 degrees in the usual Cichlid manner.

Cichlasoma severum (HECKEL). Amazon. 5 in. 70°–85°. At its best the 'Striped Cichlid' can hold its own with any fish for delightful colouring; unfortunately it is never quite sure whether it wants to show off or not, and in that case it is a greenish brown. When, however, it really tries, a vivid green appears on the body, the brown standing out as rows of dots. Across the fish, slightly in advance of the tail root, is, usually, a dark-brown bar. The fins are large and finely formed. The anal and caudal of the male are reddish-orange in colour. He also has the brown dots very definitely arranged in horizontal rows, the female has fewer dots and they are not so distinctly arranged. (Plate XI, 3.) It is very difficult to persuade to breed. The best temperature seems to be 80 degrees, and mating may be induced by a liberal diet of chopped earthworm.

Cichlasoma biocellatum REGAN. Brazil. 6 in. 65°–90°. 'Jack Dempsey'. Imagine a deep chocolate-brown fish, typically Cichlid in shape, and on it, splashed all over, deep-blue spangles, and you have a rough idea of what this popular fish looks like. The colouring improves with age and as it is a long-lived fish its owner certainly gets value for his money. (Plate XI, 1.) It is a good breeder

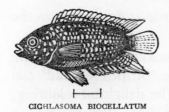

CICHLASOMA BIOCELLATUM

and adopts the usual Cichlid methods, likewise as a parent it is exemplary; indeed, one of the aquarist's greatest thrills is to see Papa Jack Dempsey taking his progeny for their morning perambulation.

Cichlasoma nigrofasciatum (GUENTHER). British Guiana. 4 in. 70°–80°. This is a similarly-shaped fish to 'Jack Dempsey', but it is not nearly so colourful. Its chief points of interest are the well-formed black bands, eight or nine in number, that cross the body. In some specimens these bands are dark green, but in all cases the background is some shade or other of creamy-grey. It differs but little in breeding habits from *C. facetum* excepting that nooks and crannies should be provided for one or the other to hide in—the female is apt to turn the tables on the male and give him a Roland for his Oliver. She is the more colourful, and she takes on herself the task of looking after the eggs.

Mesonauta insignis (HECKEL). Amazon. 4 in. 70°–85°. There are two features for which this rather timid fish is noted; one is the attenuated anal and dorsal fins, and the other is the dark line that runs upwards from the eye to the sharp

posterior part of the
dorsal fin. Otherwise it
has a well-banded body
similar to the other
cichlids, save that it is
generally deeper—a step
in the direction of the

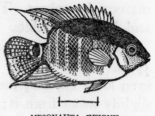

MESONAUTA INSIGNIS

Angel Fish, in fact. It is a brassy-green in
colour, the bands being a darker shade. The
best breeding temperature is 82 degrees, but
although the method is similar to that of the
others of its kind it is difficult to mate. I have
already mentioned that it is timid and probably
its reluctance to mate is aggravated by its fond
owner continually staring at it and upsetting its
nerves generally.

Aequidens latifrons (STEINDACHNER). Panama.
6 in. 70°–85°. 'Blue Acara'. A greenish body
with sparkling bluish facets to the scales seems to
hit this fish off fairly well. There is a suggestion
of brown at times, a colour that is quite usual to

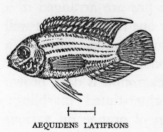

Cichlids, and the fins
are brownish-orange
with blue splashes.
Three rather indistinct
bars cross the body,
the centre bar, usually
the most distinct, is

AEQUIDENS LATIFRONS

maroon in colour. Typically Cichlid in shape and breeding habits.

Aequidens portalegrensis (HENSEL). Amazon. 4½ in. 68°–85°. The head of this fish is heavy, even for a Cichlid, the rest of the body tapering slightly away from it; the fins slightly resemble those of *Mesonauta insignis*. The colour is metallic green and the scales are edged with dark brown. The eye is large and chocolate coloured. (Plate XII, 1.)

A good breeding temperature is about 78 degrees. It is just as imperturbable at breeding time as *Mesonauta* is edgy, consequently it is fairly easy to breed—but it is difficult to sex. *Aequidens* is a friendly sort of fish and soon becomes 'finger tame'.

Astronotus ocellatus (AGASSIZ). Amazon. 6 in. 70°–80°. The 'Marbled Cichlid'. It may seem invidious to single out any one individual Cichlid for the title of 'marbled', so many, indeed, have that characteristic. The body is rounder than in most of its kind and the fins are arranged in a slightly different way, for one thing they are well rounded and also they are opaque. There is a very distinct 'eye-spot' on the tail near its root and, for the rest, the background is dark brown over which are the lighter-tinted marblings. There is also a suspicion of orange on various

parts of the body, particularly on the gill covers,
It is difficult to breed but a liberal and varied
diet of live foods and a temperature of 80 degrees
seems to help.

Pterophyllum scalare (CUVIER and VALEN-
CIENNES). Amazon. 5 in. 70°–80°. The 'Angel
Fish'. A body colour of pale silvery-brass with
four black vertical bands does not sound like the

description of one of the
most popular aquarium
fishes. Still, the Angel
Fish seems to give visitors
to the fish house far more
pleasure than some of
the expensive and vivid
species. The body being
so narrow and the anal
and dorsal fins so attenuated—to say nothing of
the long rays projecting
from the top and bot-
tom of the tail and the

PTEROPHYLLUM SCALARE

two long feelers depending from the chest—give
to this Cichlid an air entirely its own. Small
specimens up to 2 in. in length are suitable for
the community tank. (Plate XII, 2.)

For breeding, a large deep tank is necessary,
and this should be well planted, especially with

TROPICAL AQUARIUMS, PLANTS AND FISHES

the Giant Sagittaria, for on its smooth, green stems the eggs will (perhaps!) be laid. The fish dash about in a most energetic fashion just prior to spawning, and so the tank must be as large as possible, otherwise they may injure themselves on the sides. A good average temperature is 80 degrees Fahr. After the eggs are deposited the parents do one of two things; either they eat them or hang around, violently agitating their fins, to aerate them. Consequently, in order to save the infants, it is advisable to remove the parents and aerate the tank artificially, taking care that the air bubbles play over the eggs. In the absence of plant stems green glass rods have been tried, but with small success.

The natives who collect these fishes are said to do so at night, by the aid of a lantern the oblique rays of which cast a shadow of the fish on the sandy bottom of the stream.

There are two other known species of *Ptero-phyllum*, they are the smaller *P. eimekei* and the very rare *P. altum*.

Symphysodon discus (HECKEL). Amazon. 5 in. 70°–85°. 'Pompadour Fish'. This beautiful fish shares the peculiarity common to most Cichlids by its dull, uninteresting colours when first placed in the aquarium, or when not in the best of health. The ground colour is olive-brown with several dark vertical bands. From the head and well into the long dorsal fins run irregular blue streaks which are repeated on the opposite corner of the fish. The belly and fringes of both dorsal and anal fins bear reddish-orange tints. The

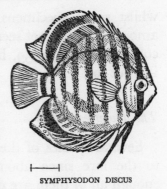

SYMPHYSODON DISCUS

tail is a peculiar shade of light green. There are other colours in the composition of this fish which appear at breeding time. In shape it resembles a brill stood on end, or a five-shilling piece with a short tail. (Plate XII, 3.) Live food is preferred, and some specimens are said to refuse everything save tubifex worms. It breeds in similar fashion to the Angel Fish, which, except for the elongated fins, it greatly resembles. The young hatch out in three days at 84 degrees, but are very difficult to raise—the parents eat the eggs and the resultant fry from the remainder do not seem to have any great ambition to survive. There must be some particular feature of their native waters that is lacking in the aquarium.

When they were first introduced into this country shortly before the war the prices were high, large specimens easily fetching £10 each whilst small specimens cost a quarter of that amount. I have not seen it in any of the dealers' collections since 1939, but it is well worth looking out for.

The Dwarf Cichlids

Several species of the Cichlid kind have come to the fore since about 1947 or 1948; oddly enough all of them are of diminutive size and all shew a determination to be as difficult as they can regarding their identities. Mostly they belong to the *Apistogramma* genus and one species has, so far, so successfully resisted being properly identified that it is known as *Apistogramma U.*2 (the 'U' stands for 'unidentified'). In shape, type of colouring and breeding habits they closely resemble their larger brethren.

Apistogramma ramirezi MYERS and HARRY. Venezuela. 2 in. 70°–80°. This is one of the more readily recognized of the Dwarf Cichlids; it is easily bred and is not unduly aggressive. The dorsal fin is large and is saddle-shaped; the body colour is blue-green and violet spangled with a broken dark line running from the eye to the base of the tail. The fins are a transparent green whilst the front of the 'face' is outlined in red. There is a prominent spine in front of the dorsal fin and this is darker in the male. The female at breeding time very conveniently develops pink spots on her sides. Like the other 'dwarfs' it is not difficult to breed, but it does prefer alkaline water. The eggs, as a rule, are deposited on a flat stone and are 'fanned' by both the male and the female, likewise both share in the after-care of their progeny. By nature they are carnivorous and imported wild specimens will not, if they can help it, look at any food of an artificial nature—for them worms, daphnia, brine shrimps and other meaty food—but those born in the aquarium will eventually take dried foods, the routine being—infusoria at first, then small daphnia or brine shrimp larvae, mikro or chopped enchytrae.

AMBASSIDAE (*The Ambassids*)

The Ambassids are the smallest of the perches. They are found principally in the seas of the Indo-Pacific region, but some of the smaller forms have ventured into the estuaries of the greater rivers and several species—*Ambassis ranga*, *A. nama* and *A. lala*—have become acclimatized to completely fresh water such as is found in the swamps and rice fields. The body is compressed from side to side. There are two dorsal fins, the

first of which is spiny, as also are the front rays
of the pectoral and anal fins. The scales are large
and thin and subject to being shed in due season.
They are interesting little fishes and, whilst not
being brightly coloured, have a beauty entirely
their own. In India they are landed by the hun-
dredweight and used on the land as fertilizer;
even so, their price in this country before 1939
was half-a-crown each—at the time of writing
they are listed at nine shillings each.

Ambassis lala (HAMILTON-BUCHANAN). India.
1½ in. C. 65°–85°. 'Glass Fish'. This tiny fish
with its transparent body and host of unexpected
flashing colours is worth a place in any community tank. It is as transparent as it is possible
for a fish to be, and along the edge of both dorsal
and anal fins forming almost a thin crescent
across the fish, is a thin blue fringe which is
deeper in the male. The general colour is
greenish yellow with a splash of quicksilver where
the internal organs are housed.

It is really a brackish-water fish, and such
fishes are difficult to breed in ordinary conditions. A little sea salt added to the water alters
the colours somewhat and may assist in spawning.
The eggs are ejected upwards and so the aquarium
should be well supplied with Riccia, moreover
the water should be from 4 in. to 5 in. in depth.

The Riccia retains the eggs which hatch in eight hours at 82 degrees, but they are very tiny and are likely to be eaten. Daphnia is the favourite food of the adult, and the fry are particularly partial to that crustacean in its larval stages. Enchytrae chopped up will be taken later as well as the larvae of mosquitoes.

GOBIIDAE (*The Gobies*)

The Gobies form one of the most interesting of all groups of fishes, and are found in inshore waters and estuaries the whole world over. In nearly every species the ventral fins meet on the under-side of the body near the throat, sometimes forming a suctorial disk which the fish uses for climbing, etc. Incidentally, it is a Goby from the seas near Japan that has the distinction of being the smallest-known fish—it is just under half an inch in length when fully grown.

Dormitator maculatus (BLOCH). Tropical America. 4 in. 68°–85°. This is one of the larger Gobies and it bears the typical Goby mottling of browns and greys. To make up for this rather dull ensemble there are occasional blue spots, and on the fins there are bright blue fringes. They seldom breed in captivity and on the rare occasions when they do the young invariably die.

223

Brachygobius xanthozonus (BLEEKER). Malay Peninsula. 1½ in. 72°–85°. 'The Bumble-bee Fish.' Like most small Gobies this fish, in its native state, prefers small, brackish pools such as one finds on saltings. In its wild state it lives in rice swamps, etc. It is not averse to freshwater, where it can be induced to breed. The fish itself is very attractive looking and never fails to steal the thunder from its more spectacular comrades. The body, from head to tail, bears bold transverse bands of black and gold.

For breeding, a large tank is advisable, but with a depth of water of only 4 in.; the temperature should be around 75 degrees. A flower pot of such a size that, when laid on its side, the water just covers it, should be placed in the tank. The female will enter the flower pot and deposit her eggs in a string on the upper side to which they will adhere. The male then enters and fertilizes the eggs—upside down. The young hatch out in four to five days and will require infusoria or dried egg for a week and then larval brine shrimps.

INDEX

P

225

INDEX

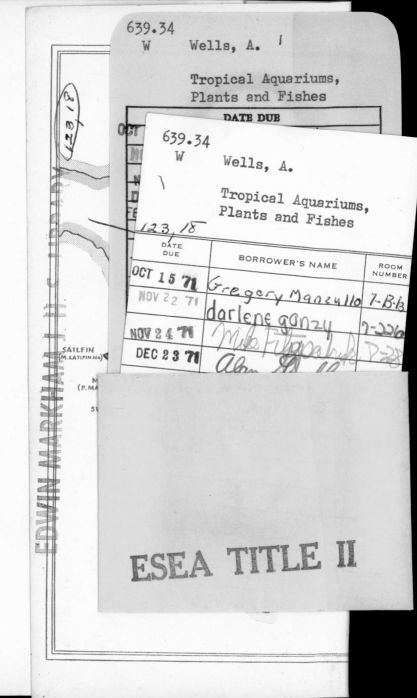

DATE DUE	BORROWER'S NAME	ROOM NUMBER
OCT 15 71	Gregory Manzullo	7-B-13
NOV 22 71	darlene ganzy	7-226
NOV 24 71	Mike Fitzpatrick	D-28
DEC 23 71	Alan	

ESEA TITLE II

EDWIN MARKHAM J.H.S. LIBRARY

123 18

SAILFIN
(M.LATIPINNA)

(P.MA

S\

TEXT PRINTED IN GREAT BRITAIN
BY EBENEZER BAYLIS AND SON, LTD., THE
TRINITY PRESS, WORCESTER, AND LONDON
PLATES PRINTED IN GREAT BRITAIN BY
HENRY STONE & SON (PRINTERS) LTD.
BANBURY
138.766

right away. Do you mind? Finish your tea, of course, and stay here as long as you like.'

He tore off his overalls, and, without attempting to tidy up the material of his painting, was gone almost immediately. I had never before seen him so agitated. The front door slammed. A sense of emptiness fell on the house.

In the circumstances, I could not possibly blame Barnby for absenting himself so precipitately, experiencing at the same time a distinct feeling of being left in a void, not less so on account of the substance of our conversation that had been in this way terminated so abruptly. I poured out another cup of tea, and thought over some of the things he had been saying. I could not help envying the opportune nature, so far as Barnby himself was concerned, of the telephone call, which seemed an outward indication of the manner in which he had—so it seemed to me in those days— imposed his will on the problem at hand.

His life's unusual variety of form provided a link between what I came, in due course, to recognise as the world of Power, as represented, for example, by the ambitions of Widmerpool and Truscott, and that imaginative life in which a painter's time is of necessity largely spent: the imagination, in such a case, being primarily of a visual kind. In the conquest of Mrs. Wentworth, however, other spheres —as the figures of Sir Magnus Donners and Prince Theodoric alone sufficiently illustrated—had inevitably to be invaded by him. These hinterlands are frequently, even compulsively, crossed at one time or another by almost all who practise the arts, usually in the need to earn a living; but the arts themselves, so it appeared to me as I considered the matter, by their ultimately sensual essence, are, in the long run, inimical to those who pursue power for its own sake. Conversely, the artist who traffics in power does so, if not necessarily disastrously, at least at considerable risk. I was making preparations to occupy my mind with such thoughts until it was time to proceed to the Widmerpools'; but the room was warm, and, for a time, I dozed.

Nothing in life can ever be entirely divorced from myriad other incidents; and it is remarkable, though no doubt logical, that action, built up from innumerable causes, each in itself allusive and unnoticed more often than not, is almost always provided with an apparently ideal moment for its final expression. So true is this that what has gone before is often, to all intents and purposes, swallowed up by the aptness of the climax; opportunity appearing, at least on the surface, to be the sole cause of fulfilment. The circumstances that had brought me to Barnby's studio supplied a fair example of this complexity of experience. There was, however, more to come.

When I awoke from these sleepy, barely coherent reflections, I decided that I had had enough of the studio, which merely reminded me of Barnby's apparent successes in a field in which I was then, generally speaking, feeling decidedly unsuccessful. Without any very clear idea of how I would spend my time until dinner, I set off down the stairs, and had just reached the door that led from the back of the shop to the foot of the staircase, when a female voice from the other side shouted: 'Who is that?'

My first thought was that Mr. Deacon's sister had returned to the house. After the cremation, she had announced herself as retiring for the rest of the day to her hotel in Bloomsbury, as she was suffering from a headache. I supposed now that she had changed her mind, and decided to continue the task of sorting her brother's belongings, regarding some of which she had already consulted Barnby, since there were books and papers among Mr. Deacon's property that raised a number of questions of disposal, sometimes of a somewhat delicate kind. She had probably come back to the shop and again sought guidance on some matter. It was to be hoped that the point would not prove an embarrassing one. However, when I said my name, the person beyond the door turned out to be Gypsy.

'Come in for a moment,' she called.

I turned the handle and entered. She was standing behind the screen, in the shadows, at the back of the shop. My first impression was that she had stripped herself stark naked. There was, indeed, good reason for this misapprehension; for a second look showed that she was wearing a kind of bathing-dress, flesh-coloured, and of unusually sparing cut. I must have showed my surprise, because she burst into a paroxysm of laughter.

'I thought you would like to see my dress for the Merry Thought fancy-dress party,' she said. 'I am going as Eve.'

She came closer.

'Where is Barnby?' she asked.

'He went out. Didn't you hear him go? After he spoke on the telephone.'

'I've only just come in,' she said. 'I wanted to try out my costume on both of you.'

She sounded disappointed at having missed such an opportunity to impress Barnby, though I thought the display would have annoyed rather than amused him; which was no doubt her intention.

'Won't you be cold?'

'The place is going to be specially heated. Anyway, the weather is mild enough. Still, shut the door. There's a bit of a draught.'

She sat down on the divan. That part of the shop was shut off from the rest by the screen in such a way as almost to form a cubicle. As Mr. Deacon had described, shawls

255

or draperies of some sort were spread over the surface of this piece of furniture.

'What do you think of the fig leaf?' she asked. 'I made it myself.'

I have already spoken of the common ground shared by conflicting emotions. As Barnby had remarked, the funeral had been 'hard on the nerves', and a consciousness of sudden relief from pressure was stimulating. Gypsy, somewhat altering the manner she had adopted on my first arrival in the shop, now managed to look almost prim. She had the air of waiting for something, of asking a question to which she already knew the answer. There was also something more than a little compelling about the atmosphere of the alcove: the operation perhaps of memories left over as a residue from former states of concupiscence, although so fanciful a condition could hardly be offered in extenuation. I asked myself whether this situation, or something not far from it, was not one often premeditated, and, although I still felt only half awake, not to be lightly passed by.

The lack of demur on her part seemed quite in accordance with the almost somnambulistic force that had brought me into that place, and also with the torpid, dreamlike atmosphere of the afternoon. At least such protests as she put forward were of so formal and artificial an order that they increased, rather than diminished, the impression that a long-established rite was to be enacted, among Staffordshire figures and *papier-mâché* trays, with the compelling, detached formality of nightmare. Perhaps some demand, not to be denied in its overpowering force, had occasioned simultaneously both this summons and Mrs. Wentworth's telephone call; each product of that slow process of building up of events, as already mentioned, coming at last to a head. I was conscious of Gypsy changing her individuality, though at the same time retaining her familiar form; this illusion almost conveying the extraordinary impression that there were really three of us—perhaps even four, because I was aware that alteration had taken place within myself too—of whom the pair of active participants had been, as it were, projected from out of our normally unrelated selves.

In spite of the apparently irresistible nature of the circumstances, when regarded through the larger perspectives that seemed, on reflection, to prevail—that is to say of a general subordination to an intricate design of cause and effect—I could not help admitting, in due course, the awareness of a sense of inadequacy. There was no specific suggestion that anything had, as it might be said, 'gone wrong'; it was merely that any wish to remain any longer present in those surroundings had suddenly and violently decreased, if not disappeared entirely. This feeling was, in its way, a shock. Gypsy, for her part, appeared far less impressed than myself by consciousness of anything, even relatively momentous, having occurred. In fact, after the brief interval of extreme animation, her subsequent indifference, which might almost have been called torpid, was, so it seemed to me, remarkable. This imperturbability was inclined to produce an impression that, so far from knowing each other a great deal better, we had progressed scarcely at all in that direction; even, perhaps, become more than ever, even irretrievably, alienated. Barbara's recurrent injunction to avoid any question of 'getting sentimental' seemed, here in the embodiment of Gypsy, now carried to lengths which might legitimately be looked upon as such a principle's logical conclusion.

This likeness to Barbara was more clearly indicated, however, than by a merely mental comparison of theory, because, while Gypsy lay upon the divan, her hands before her, looking, perhaps rather self-consciously, a little like Goya's *Maja nude*—or possibly it would be nearer the mark to cite that picture's derivative, Manet's *Olympia,* which I had, as it happened, heard her mention on some former occasion—she glanced down, with satisfaction, at her own extremities.

'How brown my leg is,' she said. 'Fancy sunburn lasting that long.'

Were Barbara and Gypsy really the same girl, I asked myself. There was something to be said for the theory; for I had been abruptly reminded of Barbara's remark, uttered under the trees of Belgrave Square earlier in the year: 'How blue my hand is in the moonlight.' Self-admiration apart, there could be no doubt now that they had a great deal in common. It was a concept that made me feel that, in so far as I was personally involved in matters of sentiment, the season was, romantically speaking, autumn indeed; and that the leaves had undeniably fallen from the trees so far as former views on love were concerned: even though such views had been held by me only so short a time before. Here, at least, at the back of Mr. Deacon's shop, some conclusion had been reached, though even that inference, too, might be found open to question. At the same time, I could not help being struck, not only by a kind of wonder that I now found myself, as it were, with Barbara in conditions once pictured as beyond words vain of achievement. but also at that same moment by a sense almost of solemnity at this latest illustration of the pattern that life forms. A new phase in conversation was now initiated by a question from Gypsy.

'What was the funeral like?' she asked, as if making a deliberate return to every-day conditions.

'Short.'

'I think I was right not to go.'

'You didn't miss much.'

'It was a matter of conscience.'

She developed for a time this line of thought, and I agreed that, regarded in the light of her convictions, her absence might be looked upon as excusable, if any such severity of doctrine was indeed insurmountable. I agreed further that Mr. Deacon himself might have appreciated such scruples.

'Max Pilgrim was there.'

'The man who sings the songs?'

'He didn't at the cremation.'

'There comes a moment when you've got to make a stand.'

I presumed that she had returned to the problems of her own conscience rather than to refer to Pilgrim's restraint in having kept himself from breaking into song at the crematorium.

'Where will you stay now that the shop is coming to an end?'

'Howard says he can put me up once in a way at the Vox Populi. They've got a camp-bed there. He's taking me to the party tonight.'

'What's he going as?'

'Adam.'

'Is he arriving here in that guise?'

'We're dining early, and going back to his place to dress up. Only I thought I must try out my costume first. As a matter of fact he is picking me up here fairly soon.'

She looked rather doubtful, and I saw that I must not overstay my welcome. There was nothing to be said for allowing time to slip by long enough for Craggs to arrive. It appeared that Gypsy was going to the country—it was to be presumed with Craggs—in the near future. We said good-bye. Later, as I made my way towards the Widmer-pools', association of ideas led inevitably to a reminder, not a specially pleasant one, of Widmerpool himself and his desires; parallel, it appeared, in their duality, with my own: and fated to be defrauded a second time. The fact that I was dining at his flat that evening in no way reduced the accentuation given by events to that sense of design already mentioned. Whatever the imperfections of the situation from which I had just emerged, matters could be considered with justice only in relation to a much larger configuration, the vast composition of which was at present —that at least was clear—by no means even nearly completed.

There is a strong disposition in youth, from which some individuals never escape, to suppose that everyone else is having a more enjoyable time than we are ourselves; and, for some reason, as I moved southwards across London, I was that evening particularly convinced that I had not yet succeeded in striking a satisfactory balance in my manner of conducting life. I could not make up my mind whether the deficiencies that seemed so stridently to exist were attributable to what had already happened that day, or to a growing certainty in my own mind that I should much prefer to be dining elsewhere. The Widmerpools—for I felt that I had already heard so much of Widmerpool's mother that my picture of her could not be far from the truth—were the last persons on earth with whom I wished to share the later part of the evening. I suppose I could have had a meal by myself, thinking of some excuse later to explain my absence; but the will to take so decisive a step seemed to have been taken physically from me.

They lived, as Widmerpool had described, on the top floor of one of the smaller erections of flats in the neighbourhood of Westminster Cathedral. The lift, like an ominously creaking funicular, swung me up to these mountainous regions, and to a landing where light shone through frosted panes of glass. The door was opened by a depressed elderly maid, wearing cap and pince-nez, who showed me into a drawing-room, where Widmerpool was sitting alone, reading *The Times*. I was dimly aware of a picture called *The Omnipresent* hanging on one of the walls, in which three figures in bluish robes stand or kneel on the edge of a precipice. Widmerpool rose, crumpling the paper, as if he were surprised to see me, so that for a painful moment I wondered whether, by some unhappy mistake, I had arrived on the wrong night. However, a second later, he made some remark to show I was expected, and asked me to sit down, explaining that 'in a minute or two' his mother would be ready.

'I am very much looking forward to your meeting my mother,' he said.

He spoke as if introduction to his mother was an experience, rather a vital one, that every serious person had, sooner or later, to undergo. I became all at once aware that this was the first occasion upon which he and I had met anywhere but on neutral ground. I think that Widmerpool, too, realised that a new relationship had immediately risen between us from the moment when I had entered the drawing-room; for he smiled in a rather embarrassed way, after making this remark about his mother, and seemed to make an effort, more conscious than any he had ever shown before, to appear agreeable. In view of the embarrassments he had spoken of when we had last met—and their apparent conclusion so far as he were concerned—I had expected to find him depressed. On the contrary, he was in unusually high spirits.

'Miss Walpole-Wilson is supping with us,' he said.

'Eleanor?'

'Oh, no,' he said, as if such a thing were unthinkable. 'Her aunt. Such a knowledgeable woman.'

Before any comment were possible, Mrs. Widmerpool herself came through the door, upon the threshold of which she paused for a moment, her head a little on one side.

'Why, Mother,' said Widmerpool, speaking with approval, 'you are wearing your bridge-coat.'

We shook hands, and she began to speak at once, before I could take in her appearance.

'And so you were both at Mr. Le Bas's house at school,' she said. 'I never really cared for him as a man. I expect he had his good qualities, but he never quite appreciated Kenneth.'

'He was an odd man in many ways.'

'Kenneth so rarely brings the friends of his school days here.'

I said that we had also stayed together with the same French family in Touraine; for, if I had to be regarded as a close friend of her son's, it was at La Grenadière that I had come to know him best: rather than at school, where he had always seemed a figure almost too grotesque to take seriously.

'At the Leroys'?' she asked, as if amazed at the brilliance of my parents in having hit on the only possible household in the whole of France.

'For six weeks or so.'

She turned to Widmerpool.

'But you never told me that,' she said. 'That was naughty of you!'

'Why should I?' said Widmerpool. 'You didn't know him.'

Mrs. Widmerpool clicked her tongue against the roof of her mouth. Her large features distinctly recalled the linea-

262

ments of her son, though she had perhaps been good looking when younger. Even now she seemed no more than
in her late forties, though I believe she was, in fact, older
than that. However, her well-preserved appearance was in
striking contrast with Widmerpool's own somewhat decaying youth, so that the pair of them appeared almost more
like contemporaries, even husband and wife, rather than
mother and son. Her eyes were brighter than his, and she
rolled them, expanding the pupils, in comment to any
remark that might be thought at all out of the ordinary.
Her double row of firm teeth were set between cheeks
of brownish red, which made her a little resemble Miss
Walpole-Wilson, with whom she clearly possessed something discernibly in common that explained their friendly
connexion. She seemed a person of determination, from
whom no doubt her son derived much of his tenacity of
purpose. The garment to which he referred was of
flowered velvet, with a fringe, and combined many colours
in its pattern.

'I hear you know the Gorings,' she said. 'It seems such
a pity they have allowed Barbara to run so wild. She used
to be such a dear little girl. There really appears to be
something a trifle queer about Lord Aberavon's grand-
children.'

'Oh, shut up, Mother,' said Widmerpool, changing his
almost amatory manner unexpectedly. 'You don't know
anything about it.'

He must have felt, not entirely without reason, that his
mother was on delicate ground in bringing up so early,
and in such a critical spirit, the subject of Gorings and
Walpole-Wilsons. Mrs. Widmerpool seemed not at all put
out by the brusque form of address used by her son; continuing to express herself freely on the characteristics, in
her eyes, good, bad and indifferent, of Barbara and Eleanor,

adding that she understood that neither of the Goring sons were 'very much of a hand at their books'. She felt perhaps that now was the time to unburden herself upon matters hardly to be pursued with the same freedom after the arrival of Miss Janet Walpole-Wilson. From her comments, I supposed that Widmerpool must have given his mother, perhaps involuntarily, some indication that the Gorings were out of favour with him; although it was impossible to guess how accurately she might be informed about her son's former feelings for Barbara: even if she knew of them at all. It was possible that she had attributed the anxiety he had gone through with Gypsy Jones to a later aggravation of his entanglement with Barbara: in fact, the same conclusion to which I had myself first arrived, when, at Stourwater, he had spoken of the troubles that were oppressing him.

'There doesn't seem any sign of Eleanor getting married yet,' said Mrs. Widmerpool, almost dreamily, as if she were decrying in the depths of the gas-fire a vision invisible to the rest of us, revealing the unending cavalcade of Eleanor's potential suitors.

'Perhaps she doesn't want to,' said Widmerpool, in a tone evidently intended to close the subject. 'I expect you two will like a talk on books before the end of the evening.'

'Yes, indeed, for I hear you are in the publishing trade,' said his mother. 'You know, I have always liked books and bookish people. It is one of my regrets that Kenneth is really too serious-minded to enjoy reading for its own sake. I expect you are looking forward to those articles in *The Times* by Thomas Hardy's widow. I know I am.'

While I was making some temporising answer to these reassurances on Mrs. Widmerpool's part regarding her inclination towards literature, Miss Walpole-Wilson was announced, who excused her lateness on the grounds of the chronic irregularity of the bus service from Chelsea, where her flat was situated. She was wearing a mackintosh, of which, for some reason, she had refused to divest herself in the hall; exemplifying in this manner a curious trait common to some persons of wilful nature, whose egotism seems often to make them unwilling, even incapable, of shedding anything of themselves until they can feel that they have safely reached their goal. She now removed this waterproof, folding and establishing it upon a chair—an act watched by her hostess with a fixed smile that might have signified disapproval—revealing that she, too, was wearing a richly-coloured coat. It was made of orange, black, and gold silk: a mandarin's coat, so she explained, that Sir Gavin had given her years before.

The relationship between Mrs. Widmerpool and Miss Walpole-Wilson, in general an amicable one, gave the impression of resting not exactly upon planned alliance so much as community of interest, unavoidable from the nature of the warfare both waged against the rest of the world. Miss Walpole-Wilson was, of course, as she sometimes described herself, 'a woman of wide interests', while Mrs. Widmerpool concerned herself with little that had not some direct reference to the career of her son. At the same time there was an area of common ground where disparagement of other people brought them close together, if only on account of the ammunition with which each was able to provide the other: mutual aid that went far to explain a friendship long established.

Miss Walpole-Wilson's manner that evening seemed intended to notify the possession of some important piece of news to be divulged at a suitable moment. She had, indeed, the same air as Widmerpool: one, that is to say, suggesting that she was unusually pleased with herself. We talked for a time, until the meal was despondently

265

announced by the decrepit house-parlourmaid, who, a minute or two later, after we had sat down to cold food in a neighbouring room, hurried plates and dishes round the table with reckless speed, as if she feared that death—with which the day seemed still associated in my mind—would intervene to terminate her labours. There was a bottle of white wine. I asked Miss Walpole-Wilson whether she had been seeing much of Eleanor.

'Eleanor and I are going for a sea trip together,' she said. 'A banana boat to Guatemala.'

'Rather wise to get her away from her family for a bit,' said Mrs. Widmerpool, making a grimace.

'Her father is full of old-fashioned ideas,' said Miss Walpole-Wilson, 'and he won't be laughed out of them.'

'Eleanor will enjoy the free life of the sea,' Mrs. Widmerpool agreed.

'Of course she will,' said Miss Walpole-Wilson; and, pausing for a brief second to give impetus to her question, added: 'You have heard, I expect, about Barbara?'

It was clear from the way she spoke that she felt safe in assuming that none of us could possibly have heard already whatever her news might be. I thought, though the supposition may have been entirely mistaken, that for an instant she fixed her eyes rather malignantly on Widmerpool; and certainly there was no reason to suggest that she knew anything of his former interest in Barbara. However, if she intended to tease him, she scored a point, for at mention of the name his face at once took on a somewhat guilty expression. Mrs. Widmerpool enquired curtly what had happened. She also seemed to feel that Miss Walpole-Wilson might be trying to provoke her son.

'Barbara is engaged,' said Miss Walpole-Wilson, smiling, though without good-humour.

'Who to?' asked Widmerpool, abruptly.

'I can't remember whether you know him,' she said. 'He is a young man in the Guards. Rich, I think.'

I felt certain, immediately, that she must refer to someone I had never met. Many people can never hear of any engagement without showing envy; and no one can be quite disinterested who has been at one time an implicated party. The thought that the man would turn out to be unknown to me was, therefore, rather a relief.

'But what is the name?' said Widmerpool, insistently.

He was already nettled. There could be no doubt that Miss Walpole-Wilson was deliberately tormenting him, although I could not decide whether this was simply her usual technique in delaying the speed at which she passed on gossip with the object of making it more appetising, or because she knew, either instinctively or from specific information in her possession, that he had been concerned with Barbara. For a moment or two she smiled round the table frostily.

'He is called Pardoe,' she said, at last. 'I think his other name is John.'

'Her parents *must* be pleased,' said Mrs. Widmerpool. 'I always thought that Barbara was becoming—well— almost a problem in a small way. She got so noisy. Such a pity when that happens to a girl.'

I could see from Widmerpool's pursed lips and glassy eyes that he was as astonished as myself. The news went some way to dispel his air of self-satisfaction, that had seemed only momentarily displaced by irritation with Miss Walpole-Wilson before this announcement. I was myself conscious of a faint sense of bitterness, rather indefinite in its application. Among the various men who had, at one time or another, caused me apprehension, just or unjust, in connexion with Barbara, Pardoe had never, at any moment, figured in the smallest degree. Why this immunity from my jealousy should have attached to him, I was now quite unable to understand, when, in the light of the information just imparted, I considered past incidents. Even after deciding that I was no longer in love with Barbara, I could still slightly resent her attitude towards Tompsitt; but objection—like Widmerpool's—to her crossing the supper-room to sit with Pardoe would never have entered my mind.

In fact, Widmerpool's instinct on the matter, if not his action, had, in one sense, been sound, so it now appeared; though it was true that his own emotions were still at that time deeply involved: a condition having a natural tendency to sharpen all perceptions in that particular direction. The manner in which jealousy operates is, indeed, curious enough: having perhaps relatively little bearing on the practical menace offered by a rival. Barnby used to describe a husband and lover known to him, who had both combined against a third—or rather fourth—party, found to be intervening. However, that situation was, of course, poles apart from the one under examination. Widmerpool now made an effort to control his voice.

'When did this happen?' he asked, speaking casually.

'I think they actually became engaged in Scotland,' said Miss Walpole-Wilson, pleased with the impression she had made. 'But it has not been made public yet.'

There was a pause. Widmerpool had failed to rise above the situation. For the moment he had lost all his good-humour. I think he was cross not only at Barbara's engagement, but also at the inability he was experiencing to conceal his own annoyance. I felt a good deal of sympathy for him in what he was going through.

'Rather a ridiculous little man,' he said, after a time. 'Still the fortune is a large one, and I have been told it is a nice house. I hope she will be very happy.'

'Barbara has great possibilities,' said Miss Walpole-Wilson. 'I don't know how she will like being an officer's wife. Personally, I always find soldiers so dull.'

'Oh, not in the *Guards*, surely?' said Mrs. Widmerpool, baring her teeth, as if in expectation, or memory, of behaviour on the part of Guardsmen infinitely removed from anything that could be regarded as dull, even by the most satiated.

'Of course, one of Barbara's brothers went into the Army,' said Miss Walpole-Wilson, as if that might be calculated to soften the blow.

Discussion of the engagement continued in a desultory manner. Such matters are habitually scrutinised from angles that disregard almost everything that might be truly looked upon as essential in connexion with a couple's married life together; so that, as usual, it was hard to think with even moderate clearness how the marriage would turn out. The issues were already hopelessly confused, not only by Miss Walpole-Wilson and Mrs. Widmerpool, but also by the anarchical litter enveloping the whole subject, more especially in the case of the particular pair concerned: a kind of phantasmagoria taking possession of the mind at the thought of them as husband and wife; for the surroundings provided by the Widmerpool flat were such as to encourage, for some reason, the worst flights of imagination, possibly on account of some inexplicable moral inadequacy in which its inhabitants seemed themselves to exist. Barbara's engagement lasted as a topic throughout the meal.

'Shall we leave the gentlemen to their port?' said Mrs. Widmerpool, when finally the subject had been picked bone-dry.

She mouthed the words 'gentlemen' and 'port' as if they might be facetiously disputable as strictly literal descriptions in either case. Widmerpool shut the door, evidently glad to be rid of both women for the time being. I wondered whether he would begin to speak of Barbara or Gypsy. To my surprise, neither girl turned out to be his reason for his so impatiently desiring a *tête-à-tête* conversation.

'I say, I've had an important move up at Donners-Brebner,' he said. 'That speech at the Incorporated Metals dinner had repercussions. The Chief was pleased about it.'

'Did he forgive you for knocking his garden about?'

Widmerpool laughed aloud at the idea that such a matter should have been brought up against him.

'You know,' he said, 'you sometimes make me feel that you must live completely out of the world. A man like Sir Magnus Donners does not bother about an accident of that sort. He has something more important to worry about. For example, he said to me the other day that he did not give tuppence what degrees a man had. What he wanted was someone who knew the ropes and could think and act quickly.'

'I remember him saying something of the sort when Charles Stringham went into Donners-Brebner.'

'Stringham is leaving us now that he is married. Just as well, in my opinion. I believe Truscott really thinks so too. People talk a great deal about "charm", but something else is required in business, I can assure you. Perhaps Stringham will settle down now. I believe he had some rather undesirable connexions.'

I enquired what Stringham was going to do now that he was departing from Donners-Brebner, but Widmerpool was ignorant on that point. I was unable to gather from him precisely what form his own promotion, with which he was so pleased, would take, though he implied that he would probably go abroad in the near future.

'I think I may be seeing something of Prince Theodoric,' he said. 'I believe you just met him.'

'Sir Gavin Walpole-Wilson could tell you all about Theodoric.'

'I think I may say I have better sources of information at hand than that to be derived from diplomats who have been "unstuck",' said Widmerpool, with complacency. 'I have been brought in touch recently with a man you probably know from your university days, Sillery—"Sillers"— I find him quite a character in his way.'

Feeling in no mood to discuss Sillery with Widmerpool, I asked him what he thought about Barbara and Pardoe.

'I suppose it was only to be expected,' he said, reddening a bit.

'But had you any idea?'

'I really do not devote my mind to such matters.'

In saying this, I had no doubt that he was speaking the truth. He was one of those persons capable of envisaging others only in relation to himself, so that, when in love with Barbara, it had been apparently of no interest to him to consider what other men might stand in the way. Barbara was either in his company, or far from him; the latter state representing a kind of void in which he was uninterested except at such a moment as that at the Huntercombes', when her removal was brought painfully to his notice. Turning things over in my mind, I wondered whether I could be regarded as having proved any more sentient myself. However, I felt now that the time had come to try and satisfy my curiosity about the other business.

'What about the matter you spoke of at Stourwater?'

Widmerpool pushed back his chair. He took off his spectacles and rubbed the lenses. I had the impression that he was about to make some important pronouncement: rather in the manner of the Prime Minister allowing some aspect of governmental policy to be made known at the Lord Mayor's Banquet or Royal Academy Dinner.

'I am rather glad you asked that,' he said, slowly. 'I wondered if you would. Will you do me a great favour?'

'Of course—if I can.'

'Never mention the subject again.'

'All right.'

'I behaved unwisely, perhaps, but I gained something.'

'You did?'

I had accented the question in the wrong manner. Widmerpool blushed again.

'Possibly we do not mean the same thing,' he said. 'I referred to being brought in touch with a new side of life—even new political opinions.'

'I see.'

'I am going to tell you something else about myself.'

'Go ahead.'

'No woman who takes my mind off my work is ever to play a part in my life in the future.'

'That sounds a wise decision so far as it goes.'

'And another thing . . .'

'Yes?'

'If I were you, Nicholas—I hope, by the way, you will call me Kenneth in future, we know each other well enough by now to use Christian names—I should avoid all that set. Deacon and the whole lot of them. You won't get any good out of it.'

'Deacon is dead.'

'What?'

'I went to the funeral this afternoon. He was cremated.'

'Really,' said Widmerpool.

He demanded no details, so I supplied none. I felt now that we were, in a curious way, fellow-conspirators, even

272

though Widmerpool might be unaware of this; and I was myself not unwilling to connive at his desire to draw a veil over the matter of which we had spoken. For a time we talked of other things, such as the arrangements to be made when he went abroad. After a while we moved into the next room, where Miss Walpole-Wilson was describing experiences in the Far East. When I left, at a comparatively early hour, she was still chronicling the occasion when she had trudged across the face of Asia.

'You must come again soon,' said Mrs. Widmerpool. 'We never managed to have our chat about books.'

During the descent in the lift, still groaning precariously, thinking over Widmerpool and his mother, and their life together, it came to me in a flash who it was Mrs. Andriadis had resembled when I had seen her at the party in Hill Street. She recalled, so I could now see, two persons I had met; and although these two were different enough from each other, their elements, or at least some of them, were combined in her. These two were Stringham's mother and her former secretary, Miss Weedon. I remembered the dialogue that had taken place when Stringham had quarrelled with Mrs. Andriadis at the end of that night. 'As you wish, Milly,' he had said; just as I could imagine him, in his younger days, saying to Miss Weedon: 'As you wish, Tuffy', at the termination of some trivial dispute at his home.

It was a moonlight night. That region has an atmosphere peculiar to itself, separated in spirit as far from the historic gloom of Westminster's more antique streets as from the *louche* seediness and Victorian decay of the wide squares of Pimlico beyond Vauxhall Bridge Road. For some reason, perhaps the height of the tower, or more probably the prodigal inappropriateness to London of the whole structure's architectural style, the area immediately adjacent to the cathedral imparts a sense of vertigo, a dizziness almost alarming in its intensity: lines and curves of red brick appearing to meet in a kind of vortex, rather than to be ranged in normal forms of perspective. I had noticed this before when entering the terrain from the north, and now the buildings seemed that evening almost as if they might swing slowly forward from their bases, and downward in complete prostration.

Certain stages of experience might be compared with the game of Russian billiards, played (as I used to play with Jean, when the time came) on those small green tables, within the secret recesses of which, at the termination of a given passage of time—a quarter of an hour, I think— the hidden gate goes down; after the descent of which, the coloured balls return no longer to the slot to be replayed; and all scoring is doubled. This is perhaps an image of how we live. For reasons not always at the time explicable, there are specific occasions when events begin suddenly to take on a significance previously unsuspected; so that, before we really know where we are, life seems to have begun in earnest at last, and we ourselves, scarcely aware that any change has taken place, are careering uncontrollably down the slippery avenues of eternity.

The Acceptance World

For
Adrian

1.

ONCE in a way, perhaps as often as every eighteen months, an invitation to Sunday afternoon tea at the Ufford would arrive on a postcard addressed in Uncle Giles's neat, constricted handwriting. This private hotel in Bayswater, where he stayed during comparatively rare visits to London, occupied two corner houses in a latent, almost impenetrable region west of the Queen's Road. Not only the battleship-grey colour, but also something at once angular and top-heavy about the block's configuration as a whole, suggested a large vessel moored in the street. Even within, at least on the ground floor, the Ufford conveyed some reminder of life at sea, though certainly of no luxuriously equipped liner; at best one of those superannuated schooners of Conrad's novels, perhaps decorated years before as a rich man's yacht, now tarnished by the years and reduced to ignoble uses like traffic in tourists, pilgrims, or even illegal immigrants; pervaded—to borrow an appropriately Conradian mannerism—with uneasy memories of the strife of men. That was the feeling the Ufford gave, riding at anchor on the sluggish Bayswater tides.

To this last retrospective, and decidedly depressing, aspect of the hotel's character, Uncle Giles himself had no doubt in a small degree contributed. Certainly he had done nothing to release the place from its air of secret, melancholy guilt. The passages seemed catacombs of a hell assigned to the subdued regret of those who had lacked in life the income to which they felt themselves entitled; this suspicion that the two houses were an abode of the dead being increased by the fact that no one was ever to be seen about, even at the reception desk. The floors of the formerly separate buildings, constructed at different levels, were now joined by unexpected steps and narrow, steeply slanting passages. The hall was always wrapped in silence; letters in the green baize board criss-crossed with tape remained yellowing, for ever unclaimed, unread, unchanged.

However, Uncle Giles himself was attached to these quarters. 'The old pub suits me,' I had once heard him mutter thickly under his breath, high commendation from one so sparing of praise; although of course the Ufford, like every other institution with which he came in contact, would fall into disfavour from time to time, usually on account of some 'incivility' offered him by the management or staff. For example, Vera, a waitress, was an old enemy, who would often attempt to exclude him from his favourite table by the door 'where you could get a breath of air'. At least once, in a fit of pique, he had gone to the De Tabley across the road; but sooner or later he was back again, grudgingly admitting that the Ufford, although going downhill from the days when he had first known the establishment, was undoubtedly convenient for the purposes of his aimless, uncomfortable, but in a sense dedicated life.

Dedicated, it might well be asked, to what? The question would not be easy to answer. Dedicated, perhaps, to his own egotism; his determination to be—without adequate moral or intellectual equipment—absolutely different from everybody else. That might offer one explanation of his behaviour. At any rate, he was propelled along from pillar to post by some force that seemed stronger than a mere instinct to keep himself alive; and the Ufford was the nearest thing he recognised as a home. He would leave his luggage there for weeks, months, even years on end; complaining afterwards, when he unpacked, that dinner-

2

jackets were not only creased but also ravaged by moth, or
that oil had been allowed to soak through the top of his
cane trunk and ruin the tropical clothing within; still worse
—though exact proof was always lacking—that the pieces
left in the hotel's keeping had actually been reduced in
number by at least one canvas valise, leather hat-box, or
uniform-case in black tin.

On most of the occasions when I visted the Ufford, halls
and reception rooms were so utterly deserted that the
interior might almost have been Uncle Giles's private
residence. Had he been a rich bachelor, instead of a poor
one, he would probably have lived in a house of just that
sort: bare: anonymous: old-fashioned: draughty: with
heavy mahogany cabinets and sideboards spaced out at
intervals in passages and on landings; nothing that could
possibly commit him to any specific opinion, beyond general
disapproval of the way the world was run.

We always had tea in an apartment called 'the lounge',
the back half of a large double drawing-room, the inner
doors of which were kept permanently closed, thus detaching 'the lounge' from 'the writing-room', the half over-
looking the street. (Perhaps, like the doors of the Temple
of Janus, they were closed only in time of Peace; because,
years later, when I saw the Ufford in war-time these particular doors had been thrown wide open.) The lace-
curtained windows of the lounge gave on to a well; a bleak
outlook, casting the gloom of perpetual night, or of a sky
for ever dark with rain. Even in summer the electric light
had to be switched on during tea.

The wallpaper's intricate floral design in blue, grey and
green ran upwards from a cream-coloured lincrusta dado
to a cornice also of cream lincrusta. The pattern of flowers,
infinitely faded, closely matched the chintz-covered sofa
and armchairs, which were roomy and unexpectedly com-

fortable. A palm in a brass pot with ornamental handles stood in one corner: here and there were small tables of Moorish design upon each of which had been placed a heavy white globular ash-tray, equipped with an attachment upon which to rest a cigar or cigarette. Several circular gilt looking-glasses hung about the walls, but there was only one picture, an engraving placed over the fireplace, of Landseer's *Bolton Abbey in the Olden Time*. Beneath this crowded scene of medieval plenty—presenting a painful contrast with the Ufford's *cuisine*—a clock, so constructed that pendulum and internal works were visible under its glass dome, stood eternally at twenty minutes past five. Two radiators kept the room reasonably warm in winter, and the coal, surrounded in the fireplace with crinkled pink paper, was never alight. No sign of active life was apparent in the room except for several much-thumbed copies of *The Lady* lying in a heap on one of the Moorish tables.

'I think we shall have this place to ourselves,' Uncle Giles used invariably to remark, as if we had come there by chance on a specially lucky day, 'so that we shall be able to talk over our business without disturbance. Nothing I hate more than having some damn'd fellow listening to every word I say.'

Of late years his affairs, in so far as his relatives knew anything of them, had become to some extent stabilised, although invitations to tea were inclined to coincide with periodical efforts to extract slightly more than his agreed share from 'the Trust'. Either his path had grown more tranquil than formerly, or crises were at longer intervals and apparently less violent. This change did not imply that he approached life itself in a more conciliatory spirit, or had altered his conviction that worldly success was a matter of 'influence'. The country's abandondment of the Gold Standard at about this time—and the formation of the

4

National Government—had particularly annoyed him. He propagated contrary, and far more revolutionary, economic theories of his own as to how the European monetary situation should be regulated.

He was, however, a shade less abrupt in personal dealings. The anxiety of his relations that he might one day get into a really serious financial tangle, never entirely at rest, had considerably abated in comparison with time past; nor had there been recently any of those once recurrent rumours that he was making preparations for an unsuitable marriage. He still hovered about the Home Counties, seen intermittently at Reading, Aylesbury, Chelmsford, or Dover —and once so far afield as the Channel Islands—his 'work' now connected with the administration of some charitable organisation which paid a small salary and allowed a reasonably high expense account.

I was not sure, however, in the light of an encounter during one of my visits to the Ufford, that Uncle Giles, although by then just about in his sixties, had wholly relinquished all thought of marriage. There were circumstances that suggested a continued interest in such a project, or at least that he still enjoyed playing with the idea of matrimony when in the company of the opposite sex.

On that particular occasion, the three fish-paste sandwiches and slice of seed cake finished, talk about money was about to begin. Uncle Giles himself never ate tea, though he would usually remove the lid of the teapot on its arrival and comment: 'A good sergeant-major's brew you've got there,' sometimes sending the tea back to the kitchen if something about the surface of the liquid specially displeased him. He had blown his nose once or twice as a preliminary to financial discussion, when the door of the lounge quietly opened and a lady wearing a large hat and purple dress came silently into the room.

5

She was between forty and fifty, perhaps nearer fifty, though possibly her full bosom and style of dress, at a period when it was fashionable to be thin, made her seem a year or two older than her age. Dark red hair piled high on her head in what seemed to me an outmoded style, and good, curiously blurred features from which looked out immense, misty, hazel eyes, made her appearance striking. Her movements, too, were unusual. She seemed to glide rather than walk across the carpet, giving the impression almost of a phantom, a being from another world; this illusion no doubt heightened by the mysterious, sombre *ambiance* of the Ufford, and the fact that I had scarcely ever before seen anybody but Uncle Giles himself, or an occasional member of the hotel's staff, inhabit its rooms.

'Why, Myra,' said Uncle Giles, rising hurriedly, and smoothing the worn herring-bone tweed of his trouser leg, 'I thought you said you were going to be out all day.'

He sounded on the whole pleased to see her, although perhaps a trifle put out that she should have turned up just at that moment. He would very occasionally, and with due warning, produce an odd male acquaintance for a minute or two, never longer, usually an elderly man, probably a retired accountant, said to possess 'a very good head for business', but never before had I seen him in the company of a woman not a member of the family. Now as usual his habitual air of hardly suppressed irritation tended to cloak any minor emotion by the strength of its cosmic resentment. All the same, a very rare thing with him, faint patches of colour showed for a moment in his cheeks, disappearing almost immediately, as he fingered his moustache with a withered, skinny hand, as if uncertain how best to approach the situation.

'This is my nephew Nicholas,' he said; and to me: 'I don't think you have met Mrs. Erdleigh.'

6

He spoke slowly, as if, after much thought, he had chosen me from an immense number of other nephews to show her at least one good example of what he was forced to endure in the way of relatives. Mrs. Erdleigh gazed at me for a second or two before taking my hand, continuing to encircle its fingers even after I had made a slight effort to relax my own grasp. Her palm felt warm and soft, and seemed to exude a mysterious tremor. Scent, vaguely Oriental in its implications, rolled across from her in great stifling waves. The huge liquid eyes seemed to look deep down into my soul, and far, far beyond towards nameless, unexplored vistas of the infinite.

'But he belongs to another order,' she stated at once.

She spoke without surprise and apparently quite decisively; indeed as if the conclusion had been the logical inference of our hands' prolonged contact. At the same time she turned her head towards Uncle Giles, who made a deprecatory sound in his throat, though without venturing to confirm or deny her hypothesis. It was evident that he and I were placed violently in contrast together in her mind, or rather, I supposed, her inner consciousness. Whether she referred to some indefinable difference of class or bearing, or whether the distinction was in moral standards, was not at all clear. Nor had I any idea whether the comparison was in my uncle's favour or my own. In any case I could not help feeling that the assertion, however true, was untimely as an opening gambit after introduction.

I had half expected Uncle Giles to take offence at the words, but, on the contrary, he seemed not at all annoyed or surprised; even appearing rather more resigned than before to Mrs. Erdleigh's presence. It was almost as if he now knew that the worst was over; that from this moment relations between the three of us would grow easier.

'Shall I ring for some more tea?' he asked, without in any way pressing the proposal by tone of voice.

Mrs. Erdleigh shook her head dreamily. She had taken the place beside me on the sofa.

'I have already had tea,' she said softly, as if that meal had been for her indeed a wonderful experience.

'Are you sure?' asked my uncle, wonderingly; confirming by his manner that such a phenomenon was scarcely credible.

'Truly.'

'Well, I won't, then.'

'No, please, Captain Jenkins.'

I had the impression that the two of them knew each other pretty well; certainly much better than either was prepared at that moment to admit in front of me. After the first surprise of seeing her, Uncle Giles no longer called Mrs. Erdleigh 'Myra', and he now began to utter a disconnected series of conventional remarks, as if to display how formal was in fact their relationship. He explained for the hundredth time how he never took tea as a meal, however much encouraged by those addicted to the habit, commented in desultory phrases on the weather, and sketched in for her information a few of the outward circumstances of my own life and employment.

'Art books, is it?' he said. 'Is that what you told me your firm published?'

'That's it.'

'He sells art books,' said Uncle Giles, as if he were explaining to some visitor the strange habits of the aborigines in the land where he had chosen to settle.

'And other sorts too,' I added, since he made the publication of art books sound so shameful a calling.

In answering, I addressed myself to Mrs. Erdleigh, rather in the way that a witness, cross-questioned by counsel,

8

replies to the judge. She seemed hardly to take in these trivialities, though she smiled all the while, quietly, almost rapturously, rather as if she were enjoying a warm bath after a trying day's shopping. I noticed that she wore no wedding ring, carrying in its place on her third finger a large opal, enclosed by a massive gold serpent swallowing its own tail.

'I see you are wondering about my opal,' she said, suddenly catching my eye.

'I was admiring the ring.'

'Of course I was born in October.'

'Otherwise it would be unlucky?'

'But *not* under the Scales.'

'I am the Archer.'

I had learned that fact a week or two before from the astrological column of a Sunday newspaper. This seemed a good moment to make use of the knowledge. Mrs. Erdleigh was evidently pleased even with this grain of esoteric apprehension. She took my hand once more, and held the open palm towards the light.

'You interest me,' she said.

'What do you see?'

'Many things.'

'Nice ones?'

'Some good, some less good.'

'Tell me about them.'

'Shall I?'

Uncle Giles fidgeted. I thought at first he was bored at being momentarily out of the conversation, because, in his self-contained, unostentatious way, he could never bear to be anything less than the centre of interest; even when that position might possess an unpleasant significance as sometimes happened at family gatherings. However, another matter was on his mind.

9

'Why not put the cards out?' he broke in all at once with forced cheerfulness. 'That is, if you're in the mood.'

Mrs. Erdleigh did not reply immediately to this suggestion. She continued to smile, and to investigate the lines of my palm.

'Shall I?' she again said softly, almost to herself. 'Shall I ask the cards about you both?'

I added my request to my uncle's. To have one's fortune told gratifies, after all, most of the superficial demands of egotism. There is no mystery about the eternal popularity of divination. All the same, I was surprised that Uncle Giles should countenance such pursuits. I felt sure he would have expressed loud contempt if anyone else had been described to him as indulging in efforts to foretell the future. Mrs. Erdleigh pondered a few seconds, then rose, still smiling, and glided away across the room. When she had shut the door we remained in silence for some minutes. Uncles Giles grunted several times. I suspected he might be feeling rather ashamed of himself for having put this request to her. I made some enquiries about his friend.

'Myra Erdleigh?' he said, as if it were strange to meet anyone unaware of Mrs. Erdleigh's circumstances. 'She's a widow, of course. Husband did something out in the East. Chinese Customs, was it? Burma Police? Something of the sort.'

'And she lives here?'

'A wonderful fortune-teller,' said Uncle Giles, ignoring the last question. 'Really wonderful. I let her tell mine once in a while. It gives her pleasure, you know—and it interests me to see how often she is right. Not that I expect she will have much to promise me at my time of life.'

He sighed; though not, I thought, without a certain self-satisfaction. I wondered how long they had known one another. Long enough, apparently, for the question of fortune-telling to have cropped up between them a number of times.

'Does she tell fortunes professionally?'

'Has done, I believe, in the past,' Uncle Giles admitted. 'But of course there wouldn't be any question of a five guinea consultation fee this evening.'

He gave a short, angry laugh to show that he was joking, adding rather guiltily: 'I don't think anyone is likely to come in. Even if they did, we could always pretend we were taking a hand at cut-throat.'

I wondered if Mrs. Erdleigh used Tarot cards. If so, three-handed bridge might not look very convincing to an intruder; for example, should one of us try to trump 'the drowned Phœnician Sailor' with the Hanged Man'. In any case, there seemed no reason why we should not have our fortunes told in the lounge. That would at least be employing the room to some purpose. The manner in which Uncle Giles had spoken made me think he must enjoy 'putting the cards out' more than he cared to acknowledge.

Mrs. Erdleigh did not come back to the room immediately. We awaited her return in an atmosphere of expectancy induced by my uncle's unconcealed excitement. I had never before seen him in this state. He was breathing heavily. Still Mrs. Erdleigh did not appear. She must have remained away at least ten minutes or a quarter of an hour. Uncle Giles began humming to himself. I picked up one of the tattered copies of *The Lady*. At last the door opened once more. Mrs. Erdleigh had removed her hat, renewed the blue make-up under her eyes, and changed into a dress of sage green. She was certainly a conspicuous, perhaps even a faintly sinister figure. The cards she brought with her were grey and greasy with use. They were not a Tarot pack. After a brief discussion it was agreed that Uncle Giles should be the first to look into the future.

'You don't think it has been too short an interval?' he asked, obviously with some last-moment apprehensions.

'Nearly six months,' said Mrs. Erdleigh, in a more matter-of-fact voice than that she had used hitherto; adding, as she began to shuffle the pack: 'Although, of course, one should not question the cards too often, as I have sometimes warned you.'

Uncle Giles slowly rubbed his hands together, watching her closely as if to make certain there was no deception, and to ensure that she did not deliberately slip in a card that would bring him bad luck. The rite had something solemn about it: something infinitely ancient, as if Mrs. Erdleigh had existed long before the gods we knew, even those belonging to the most distant past. I asked if she always used the same pack.

'Always the same dear cards,' she said, smiling; and to my uncle, more seriously: 'Was there anything special?'

'Usually need to look ahead in business,' he said, gruffly. 'That would be Diamonds, I suppose. Or Clubs?'

Mrs. Erdleigh continued to smile without revealing any of her secrets, while she set the cards in various small heaps on one of the Moorish tables. Uncle Giles kept a sharp eye on her, still rubbing his hands, making me almost as nervous as himself at the thought of what the predictions could involve. There might always be grave possibilities to be faced for someone of his erratic excursion through life. However, I was naturally much more interested in what she would say about myself. Indeed, I was then so far from grasping the unchanging mould of human nature that I found it even surprising that at his age he could presuppose anything to be called 'a future'. So far as I myself was concerned, on the other hand, there seemed no reason to curb the wildest absurdity of fancy as to what might happen the very next moment.

However, when Uncle Giles's cards were examined, their secrets did not appear to be anything like so ominous as might have been feared. There was a good deal of opposition to his 'plans', perhaps not surprisingly; also, it was true, much gossip, even some calumny surrounded him.

'Don't forget you have Saturn in the Twelfth House,' Mrs. Erdleigh remarked in an aside. 'Secret enemies.'

As against these threatening possibilities, someone was going to give him a present, probably money; a small sum, but acceptable. It looked as if this gift might come from a woman. Uncle Giles, whose cheeks had become furrowed at the thought of all the gossip and calumny, cheered up a little at this. He was told he had a good friend in a woman —possibly the one who was to make him a present—the Queen of Hearts, in fact. This, too, Uncle Giles accepted willingly enough.

'That was the marriage card that turned up, wasn't it?' he asked at one point.

'Could be.'

'Not necessarily?'

'Other influences must be taken into consideration.'

Neither of them commented on this matter, though their words evidently had regard to a question already reconnoitred in the past. For a moment or two there was perhaps a faint sense of additional tension. Then the cards were collected and shuffled again.

'Now let's hear about *him*,' said Uncle Giles.

He spoke more with relief that his own ordeal was over, rather than because he was seriously expressing any burning interest in my own fate.

'I expect *he* wants to hear about *love*,' said Mrs. Erdleigh, beginning to titter to herself again.

13

Uncle Giles, to show general agreement with this sup-position, grunted a disapproving laugh. I attempted some formal denial, although it was perfectly true that the thought was uppermost in my mind. The situation in that quarter was at the moment confused. In fact, so far as 'love' was concerned, I had been living for some years past in a rather makeshift manner. This was not because I felt the matter to be of little interest, like a man who hardly cares what he eats provided hunger is satisfied, or one prepared to discuss painting, should the subject arise, though never tempted to enter a picture gallery. On the contrary, my interest in love was keen enough, but the thing itself seemed not particularly simple to come by. In that direction, other people appeared more easily satisfied than myself. That at least was how it seemed to me. And yet, in spite of some show of picking and choosing, my experiences, on subsequent examination, were certainly no more admirable than those to which neither Templer nor Barnby, for example, would have given a second thought; they were merely fewer in number. I hoped the cards would reveal nothing too humiliating to my own self-esteem.

'There is a link between us,' said Mrs. Erdleigh, as she set out the little heaps. 'At present I cannot see what it is—but there is a link.'

This supposed connexion evidently puzzled her.

'You are musical?'

'No.'

'Then you write—I think you have written a book?'

'Yes.'

'You live between two worlds,' she said. 'Perhaps even more than two worlds. You cannot always surmount your feelings.'

I could think of no possible reply to this indictment.

'You are thought cold, but you possess deep affections,

sometimes for people worthless in themselves. Often you are at odds with those who might help you. You like women, and they like you, but you often find the company of men more amusing. You expect too much, and yet you are also too resigned. You must try to understand life.'

Somewhat awed by this searching, even severe analysis, I promised I would do better in future.

'People can only be themselves,' she said. 'If they possessed the qualities you desire in them, they would be different people.'

'That is what I should like them to be.'

'Sometimes you are too serious, sometimes not serious enough.'

'So I have been told.'

'You must make a greater effort in life.'

'I can see that.'

These strictures certainly seemed just enough; and yet any change of direction would be hard to achieve. Perhaps I was irrevocably transfixed, just as she described, half-way between dissipation and diffidence. While I considered the matter, she passed on to more circumstantial things. It turned out that a fair woman was not very pleased with me; and a dark one almost equally vexed. Like my uncle—perhaps some family failing common to both of us—I was encompassed by gossip.

'They do not signify at all,' said Mrs. Erdleigh, referring thus rather ruthlessly to the women of disparate colouring. 'This is a much more important lady—medium hair, I should say—and I think you have run across her once or twice before, though not recently. But there seems to be another man interested, too. He might even be a husband. You don't like him much. He is tallish, I should guess. Fair, possibly red hair. In business. Often goes abroad.'

I began to turn over in my mind every woman I had ever met.

'There is a small matter in *your* business that is going to cause inconvenience,' she went on. 'It has to do with an elderly man—and two young ones connected with him.'

'Are you sure it is not two elderly men and one young man?'

It had immediately struck me that she might be *en rapport* with my firm's growing difficulties regarding St. John Clarke's introduction to *The Art of Horace Isbister*. The elderly men would be St. John Clarke and Isbister themselves—or perhaps St. John Clarke and one of the partners—and the young man was, of course, St. John Clarke's secretary, Mark Members.

'I see the two young men quite plainly,' she said. 'Rather a troublesome couple, I should say.'

This was all credible enough, including the character sketch, though perhaps not very interesting. Such trivial comment, mixed with a few home truths of a personal nature, provide, I had already learnt, the commonplaces of fortune-telling. Such was all that remained in my mind of what Mrs. Erdleigh prophesied on that occasion. She may have foretold more. If so, her words were forgotten by me. Indeed, I was not greatly struck by the insight she had shown; although she impressed me as a woman of dominant, even oddly attractive personality, in spite of a certain absurdity of demeanour. She herself seemed well pleased with the performance.

At the end of her sitting it was time to go. I was dining that evening with Barnby, picking him up at his studio. I rose to say good-bye, thanking her for the trouble she had taken.

'We shall meet again.'

'I hope so.'

'In about a year from now.'

'Perhaps before.'

'No,' she said, smiling with the complacence of one to whom the secrets of human existence had been long since occultly revealed. 'Not before.'

I did not press the point. Uncle Giles accompanied me to the hall. He had by then returned to the subject of money, the *mystique* of which was at least as absorbing to him as the rites upon which we had been engaged.

'. . . and then one could not foresee that San Pedro Warehouses Deferred would become entirely valueless,' he was saying. 'The expropriations were merely the result of a liberal dictator coming in—got to face these changes. There was one of those quite natural revulsions against foreign capital. . . .'

He broke off. Supposing our meeting now at an end, I turned from him, and made preparations to plunge through the opaque doors into the ocean of streets, in the grey ebb and flow of which the Ufford floated idly upon the swell. Uncle Giles put his hand on my arm.

'By the way,' he said, 'I don't think I should mention to your parents the matter of having your fortune told. I don't want them to blame me for leading you into bad habits, superstitious ones, I mean. Besides, they might not altogether approve of Myra Erdleigh.'

His brown, wrinkled face puckered slightly. He still retained some vestige of good looks, faintly military in character. Perhaps this hint, increased with age, of past regimental distinction in some forgotten garrison town was what Mrs. Erdleigh admired in him. Neither my parents, nor any of the rest of Uncle Giles's relations, were likely to worry about his behaviour if the worst he ever did was to persuade other members of the family to have their fortunes told. However, recognising that silence upon the

17

subject of Mrs. Erdleigh might be a reasonable request, I assured him that I would not speak of our meeting.

I was curious to know what their relationship might be. Possibly they were planning marriage. The 'marriage card' had clearly been of interest to my uncle. There was something vaguely 'improper' about Mrs. Erdleigh, almost deliberately so; but impropriety of an unremembered, Victorian kind: a villa in St. John's Wood, perhaps, and eccentric doings behind locked doors and lace curtains on sultry summer afternoons. Uncle Giles was known to possess a capacity for making himself acceptable to ladies of all sorts, some of whom had even been rumoured to contribute at times a trifle towards his expenses; those many expenses to which he was subject, and never tired of detailing. Mrs. Erdleigh looked not so much 'well off' as eminently capable of pursuing her own interests effectively. Possibly Uncle Giles considered her a good investment. She, on her side, no doubt had her uses for him. Apart from material considerations, he was obviously fascinated by her occult powers, with which he seemed almost religiously preoccupied. Like all such associations, this one probably included a fierce struggle of wills. It would be interesting to see who won the day. On the whole, my money was on Mrs. Erdleigh. I thought about the pair of them for a day or two, and then they both passed from my mind.

As I made my way towards the neighbourhood of Fitzroy Square, experiencing as usual that feeling of release that always followed parting company with Uncle Giles, I returned to the subject of future business difficulties foretold in the cards. These, as I have said, had seemed to refer to St. John Clarke's introduction to *The Art of Horace Isbister,* already a tiresome affair, quite likely to pass from bad to worse. The introduction had been awaited for at least a year now, and we seemed no nearer getting the manuscript. The delay caused inconvenience at the office, since blocks had been made for a series of forty-eight monochrome plates and four three-colour half-tones; to which St. John Clarke was to add four or five thousand words of biographical reminiscence.

Isbister himself had been ill, on and off, for some little time, so that it had not been possible through him to bring pressure to bear on St. John Clarke, although the painter was the novelist's old friend. They may even have been at school together. Isbister had certainly executed several portraits of St. John Clarke, one of them (the sitter in a high, stiff collar and limp spotted bow tie) showing him as quite a young man. The personal legend of each, for publicity purposes, took the form of a country lad who had 'made good', and they would occasionally refer in print to their shared early struggles. St. John Clarke, in the first instance, had positively gone out of his way to arrange that the introduction should be written by himself, rather than by some suitable hack from amongst the Old Guard of the art critics, several of whom were in much more need of the fee, not a very princely one, that my firm was paying for the work.

That a well-known novelist should take on something that seemed to call in at least a small degree for an accredited expert on painting was not so surprising as might at first sight have appeared, because St. John Clarke, although certainly quieter of late years, had in the past often figured in public controversy regarding the arts. He had been active, for example, in the years before the war in supporting the erection of the Peter Pan statue in Kensington Gardens: a dozen years later, vigorously opposing the establishment of Rima in the bird sanctuary of the same neighbourhood. At one of the Walpole-Wilsons' dinner parties I could remember talk of St. John Clarke's intervention in the question of the Haig memorial, then much discussed. These examples suggest a special interest in sculpture, but St. John Clarke often expressed himself with equal force regarding painting and music. He had certainly been associated with opposition to the Post-Impressionists in 1910: also in leading some minor skirmish in operatic circles soon after the Armistice.

I myself could not have denied a taste for St. John Clarke's novels at about the period when leaving school. In fact Le Bas, my housemaster, finding me reading one of them, had taken it from my hand and glanced through the pages.

'Rather morbid stuff, isn't it?' he had remarked.

It was a statement rather than a question, though I doubt whether Le Bas had ever read any of St John Clarke's novels himself. He merely felt, in one sense correctly, that there was something wrong with them. At the same time he made no attempt to disallow, or confiscate, the volume. However, I had long preferred to forget the days when I had regarded St. John Clarke's work as fairly daring. In fact I had become accustomed to refer to him and his books with the savagery which, when one is a young man, seems—perhaps rightly—the only proper and serious attitude towards anyone, most of all an older person, practising the arts in an inept or outworn manner.

Although a few years younger than the generation of H. G. Wells and J. M. Barrie, St. John Clarke was connected in my mind with those two authors, chiefly because I had once seen a snapshot of the three of them reproduced in the memoirs of an Edwardian hostess. The photograph had probably been taken by the lady herself. The writers were standing in a group on the lawn of a huge, rather gracelessly pinnacled country seat. St. John Clarke was a little to one side of the picture. A tall, cadaverous man, with spectacles and long hair, a panama hat at the back of his head, he leant on a stick, surveying his more diminutive fellow guests with an expression of uneasy interest; rather as if he were an explorer or missionary, who had just coaxed from the jungle these powerful witch-doctors of some neighbouring, and on the whole unfriendly, tribe. He seemed, by his expression, to feel that constant supervision of the other two was necessary to foil misbehaviour or escape. There was something of the priest about his appearance.

The picture had interested me because, although I had already read books by these three writers, all had inspired me with the same sense that theirs was not the kind of writing I liked. Later, as I have said, I came round for a time to St. John Clarke with that avid literary consumption of the immature which cannot precisely be regarded either as enjoyment or the reverse. The flavour of St. John Clarke's novels is hard to describe to those unfamiliar with them, perhaps on account of their own inexactitudes of thought and feeling. Although no longer looked upon as a 'serious' writer, I believe he still has his readers in number not to be disregarded. In his early years he had been treated with respect by most of the eminent critics of his time, and to the day of his death he hoped in vain for the Nobel Prize. Mark Members, his secretary, used to say that once, at least, that award had seemed within his grasp.

We had never met, but I had seen him in Bond Street, walking with Members. Though his hair was by then white and straggling, he still looked remarkably like his picture in the book of memoirs. He was wearing a grey soft hat, rather high in the crown with a band of the same colour, a black suit and buff double-breasted waistcoat. As he strolled along he glanced rather furtively about him, seeming scarcely aware of Members, sauntering by his side. His features bore that somewhat exasperated expression that literary men so often acquire in middle life. For a second I had been reminded of my old acquaintance, Mr. Deacon, but a Mr. Deacon far more capable of coping with the world. Members, in his black homburg, swinging a rolled umbrella, looked quite boyish beside him.

St. John Clarke's reputation as a novelist had been made by the time he was in his thirties. For many years past he had lived the life of a comparatively rich bachelor, able to indulge most of his whims, seeing only the people who suited him, and making his way in what he used to call, 'rather lovingly', so Members said, the *'beau monde'*. Even in those days, critics malicious enough to pull his books to pieces in public were never tired of pointing out that investigations of human conduct, based on assumptions accepted when St. John Clarke was a young man, were hopelessly out of date. However, fortunately his sales did not depend on favourable reviews, although, in spite of this, he was said to be—like so many financially successful writers—painfully sensitive to hostile criticism. It was perhaps partly for the reason that he felt himself no longer properly appreciated that he had announced he would write no more novels. In due course memoirs would appear, though he confessed he was in no hurry to compose them.

His procrastination regarding the introduction had, therefore, nothing to do with pressure of work. Putting the Isbister task in its least idealistic and disinterested light, it would give him a chance to talk about himself, a perfectly legitimate treat he was as a rule unwilling to forgo. Friendship made him a suitable man for the job. Those who enjoy finding landmarks common to different forms of art might even have succeeded in tracing a certain similarity of approach tenuously relating the novels of St. John Clarke with the portrait painting of Isbister. The delay was, indeed, hard to explain.

There had been, however, various rumours recently current regarding changes supposedly taking place in St. John Clarke's point of view. Lately, he had been seen at parties in Bloomsbury, and elsewhere, surrounded by people who were certainly not readers of his books. This was thought to show the influence of Members, who was said to be altering his employer's outlook. Indeed, something suggesting a change of front in that quarter had been brought to my own notice in a very personal manner.

St. John Clarke had contributed an article to a New York paper in which he spoke of the younger writers of that moment. Amongst a rather oddly assorted collection of names, he had commented, at least by implication favourably, upon a novel of my own, published a month or two before—the 'book' to which Mrs. Erdleigh had referred. Latterly, St. John Clarke had rarely occupied himself with occasional journalism, and in print he had certainly never before shown himself well disposed towards a younger generation. His remarks, brief and relatively guarded though they had been, not unnaturally aroused my interest, especially because any recommendation from that quarter was so entirely unexpected. I found myself looking for excuses to cover what still seemed to me his own shortcomings as a novelist.

As I turned over these things in my mind, on the way to Barnby's studio, it struck me that Barnby himself might be able to tell me something of St. John Clarke as a person; for, although unlikely it was that Barnby had read the novels, the two of them might well have met in the widely different circles Barnby frequented. I began to make enquiries soon after my arrival there.

Barnby rubbed his short, stubby hair, worn *en brosse,* which, with his blue overalls, gave him the look of a *sommelier* at an expensive French restaurant. By then we had known each other for several years. He had moved house more than once since the days when he had lived above Mr. Deacon's antique shop, emigrating for a time as far north as Camden Town. Still unmarried, his many adventures with women were a perpetual topic between us. In terms of literature, Barnby might have found a place among Stendhal's heroes, those power-conscious young men, anxious to achieve success with women without the banal expedient of 'falling in love': a state, of course, necessarily implying, on the part of the competitor, a depletion, if not entire abrogation, of 'the will'. Barnby was, on the whole, more successful than his Stendhalian prototypes, and he was certainly often 'in love'. All the same, he belonged in that group. Like Valmont in *Les Liaisons Dangereuses,* he set store 'upon what terms' he possessed a woman, seeking a relationship in which sensuality merged with power, rather than engaging in their habitual conflict.

Like everyone else, at that moment, Barnby was complaining of 'the slump', although his own reputation as a painter had been rising steadily during the previous two or three years. The murals designed by him for the Donners-Brebner Building had received, one way and another, a great deal of public attention; the patronage of Sir Magnus Donners himself in this project having even survived Barnby's love affair with Baby Wentworth, supposed mistress of Sir Magnus. Indeed, it had been suggested that 'the Great Industrialist', as Barnby used to call him, had been glad to make use of that or some other indiscretion, soon after the completion of the murals, as an excuse for bringing to an end his own association with Mrs. Wentworth. There appeared to be no bad feeling between any of the persons concerned in this triangular adjustment. Sir Magnus was now seen about with a *jolie laide* called Matilda Wilson; although, as formerly in the Baby Wentworth connexion, little or nothing definite was known of this much discussed liaison. Baby herself had married an Italian and was living in Rome.

'You'll never get that introduction now,' Barnby said, after listening to my story. 'St. John Clarke in these days would think poor old Isbister much too *pompier.*'

'But they are still great friends.'

'What does that matter?'

'Besides, St. John Clarke doesn't know a Van Dyck from a Van Dongen.'

'Ah, but he does now,' said Barnby. 'That's where you are wrong. You are out of date. St. John Clarke has undergone a conversion.'

'To what?'

'Modernism.'

'Steel chairs?'

'No doubt they will come.'

'Pictures made of shells and newspaper?'

'At present he is at a slightly earlier stage.'

I asked for further details.

'The outward and visible sign of St. John Clarke's conversion,' said Barnby, portentously, 'is that he has indeed become a collector of modern pictures—though, as I understand it, he still loves them on this side Surrealism. As a matter of fact he bought a picture of mine last week.'

'This conversion explains his friendly notice of my book.'

'It does.'

'I see.'

'You yourself supposed that something unusual in the quality of your writing had touched him?'

'Naturally.'

'I fear it is all part of a much larger design.'

'Just as good for me.'

'Doubtless.'

All the same, I felt slightly less complimented than before. The situation was now clear. The rumours already current about St. John Clarke, less explicit than Barnby's words, had equally suggested some kind of intellectual upheaval. Isbister's portraits of politicians, business men and ecclesiastics, executed with emphatic, almost aggressive disregard for any development of painting that could possibly be called 'modern', would now certainly no longer appeal to his old friend. At the same time the ray of St. John Clarke's approval directed towards myself, until then so phenomenal, was in fact only one minute aspect of the novelist's new desire to ally himself with forces against which, for many years, he had openly warred.

'That secretary of his even suggested Clarke might commission a portrait.'

'It is Members, of course, who has brought this about.'

'Oh, I don't know,' said Barnby. 'This sort of thing often happens to successful people when they begin to get old. They suddenly realise what dull lives they have always led.'

'But St. John Clarke hasn't led a dull life. I should have thought he had done almost everything he wanted—with just sufficient heights still to climb to give continued zest to his efforts.'

'I agree in one sense,' said Barnby. 'But for a man of his comparative intelligence, St. John Clarke has always limited himself to the dullest of dull ideas—in order to make money, of course, a very reasonable aim, thereby avoiding giving offence to his public. Think of the platitudes of his books. True, I have only read a few pages of one of them, but that was sufficient. And then that professional world of bogus artists and bogus writers which he himself frequents. No wonder he wants to escape from it once in a while, and meet an occasional duchess. Men like him always feel they have missed something. You can leave the arts alone, but it is very dangerous to play tricks with them. After all, you yourself tell me he has agreed to write an introduction to the work of Isbister—and then you ask me why I consider St. John Clarke leads a dull life.'

'But will this new move make his life any better?'

'Why not?'

'He must always have been picture-blind.'

'Some of my best patrons are that. Don't be so idealistic.'

'But if you are not really interested in pictures, liking a Bonnard doesn't make you any happier than liking a Bouguereau.'

'The act of conversion does, though.'

'Besides, this will open up a new, much more lively world of social life. One must admit that.'

'Of course.'

'You are probably right.'

Perhaps it was surprising that nothing of the kind had happened earlier, because St. John Clarke had employed a whole dynasty of secretaries before Members. But former secretaries had been expected to work hard in the background, rather than to exist as an important element in the household. Members had built up the post to something far more influential than anything achieved by those who had gone before him. The fact was that, as St. John Clarke grew older, he wrote less, while his desire to cut a

27

social figure gained in volume. He began to require a secretary who was something more than a subordinate to answer the telephone and remember the date of invitations. It was natural enough that St. John Clarke, who was unmarried, should wish to delegate power in his establishment, and rely on someone to help him plan his daily life. He was fortunate in finding a young man so well equipped for the job; for even those who did not much care for Members personally had to admit that his methods, often erratic, were on the whole admirably suited to the life St. John Clarke liked to lead.

'Nothing equivocal about the position of Members in that *ménage,* do you think?' said Barnby.

'Not in the least.'

'I don't think St. John Clarke is interested in either sex,' said Barnby. 'He fell in love with himself at first sight and it is a passion to which he has always remained faithful.'

'Self-love seems so often unrequited.'

'But not in the case of St. John Clarke,' said Barnby. 'He is entirely capable of getting along without what most of the rest of us need.'

I had often heard that particular question discussed. Although his novels not uncommonly dealt with the intricate problems of married life, St. John Clarke did not, in general, greatly care for the society of women, except that of ladies in a position to invite him to agreeable dinners and week-end parties. Such hospitality was, after all, no more than a small and fitting return for the labours of a lifetime, and one that few but the envious would have begrudged him. However, this lack of interest in the opposite sex had from time to time given rise to gossip. Those persons who make a hobby, even a kind of duty, of tracking down malicious whispers to their source were forced to report in the case of St. John Clarke that nothing

28

in the smallest degree reprobate could be confirmed. This did not prevent the circulation of a certain amount of rather spiteful badinage on the subject of his secretary. Members was impervious to any such innuendo, perhaps even encouraging it to screen his own affairs with women. St. John Clarke, indifferent to this indulgence himself, naturally disapproved of an irregular life in others: especially in someone at such close quarters.

'So there he goes,' said Barnby. 'Head-first into the contemporary world.'

He hunched his shoulders, and made a grimace, as if to express the violence, even agony, that had accompanied St. John Clarke's æsthetic metamorphosis. By easy stages we moved off to dinner at Foppa's.

2.

A YEAR or more later Isbister died. He had been in bad health for some little time, and caught pneumonia during a period of convalescence. The question of the introduction, pigeon-holed indefinitely, since St. John Clarke utterly refused to answer letters on the subject, was now brought into the light again by the obituaries. Little or no general news was about at the time, so these notices were fuller than might have been expected. One of them called Isbister 'the British Franz Hals'. There were photographs of him, with his Van Dyck beard and Inverness cape, walking with Mrs. Isbister, a former model, the 'Morwenna' of many of his figure subjects. This was clearly the occasion to make another effort to complete and publish *The Art of Horace Isbister*. Artists, especially academic artists, can pass quickly into the shadows: forgotten as if they had never been.

Almost as a last resort, therefore, it had been arranged that I should meet Mark Members out of office hours, and talk things over 'as man to man'. For this assignation Members had chosen—of all places—the Ritz. Since becoming St. John Clarke's secretary he had acquired a taste for rich surroundings. It was that prolonged, flat, cheerless week that follows Christmas. My own existence seemed infinitely stagnant, relieved only by work on another book. Those interminable latter days of the dying year create an interval, as it were, of moral suspension: one form of life already passed away before another has had time to assert some new, endemic characteristic. Imminent change of direction is for some reason often foreshadowed by such colourless patches of time.

Along Piccadilly a north wind was blowing down the side streets, roaring hoarsely for a minute or two at a time, then dropping suddenly into silence; and then again, after a brief pause, beginning to roar once more, as if perpetually raging against the inconsistency of human conduct. The arches of the portico gave some shelter from this hurricane, at the same time forming a sort of ante-chamber leading on one side, through lighted glass, into another, milder country, where struggle against the forces of nature was at least less explicit than on the pavements. Outside was the northern winter; here among the palms the climate was almost tropical.

Although a Saturday evening, the place was crowded. A suggestion of life in warmer cities, far away from London, was increased by the presence of a large party of South Americans camped out not far from where I found a seat at one of the grey marble-topped tables. They were grouped picturesquely beneath the figure of the bronze nymph perched in her grotto of artificial rocks and fresh green ferns, a large family spreading over three or four of the tables while they chatted amicably with one another. There were swarthy young men with blue chins and pretty girls in smart frocks, the latter descending in point of age to mere children with big black eyes and brightly coloured bows in their hair. A bald, neat, elderly man, the rosette of some order in his buttonhole, his grey moustache closely clipped, discoursed gravely with two enormously animated ladies, both getting a shade plump in their black dresses.

Away on her pinnacle, the nymph seemed at once a member of this Latin family party, and yet at the same time morally separate from them: an English girl, perhaps, staying with relations possessing business interests in South

America, herself in love for the first time after a visit to some neighbouring estancia. Now she had strayed away from her hosts to enjoy delicious private thoughts in peace while she examined the grimacing face of the river-god carved in stone on the short surface of wall by the grotto. Pensive, quite unaware of the young tritons violently attempting to waft her away from the fountain by sounding their conches at full blast, she gazed full of wonder that no crystal stream gushed from the water-god's contorted jaws. Perhaps in such a place she expected a torrent of champagne. Although stark naked, the nymph looked immensely respectable; less provocative, indeed, than some of the fully dressed young women seated below her, whose olive skins and silk stockings helped to complete this most unwintry scene.

Waiting for someone in a public place develops a sense of individual loneliness, so that amongst all this pale pink and sage green furniture, under decorations of rich cream and dull gold, I felt myself cut off from the rest of the world. I began to brood on the complexity of writing a novel about English life, a subject difficult enough to handle with authenticity even of a crudely naturalistic sort, even more to convey the inner truth of the things observed. Those South Americans sitting opposite, coming from a Continent I had never visited, regarding which I possessed only the most superficial scraps of information, seemed in some respects easier to conceive in terms of a novel than most of the English people sitting round the room. Intricacies of social life make English habits unyielding to simplification, while understatement and irony—in which all classes of this island converse—upset the normal emphasis of reported speech.

How, I asked myself, could a writer attempt to describe in a novel such a young man as Mark Members, for example, possessing so much in common with myself, yet so different? How could this difference be expressed to that grave middle-aged South American gentleman talking to the plump ladies in black? Viewed from some distance off, Members and I might reasonably be considered almost identical units of the same organism, scarcely to be differentiated even by the sociological expert. We were both about the same age, had been to the same university, and were committed to the same profession of literature; though Members could certainly claim in that sphere a more notable place than myself, having by then published several books of poems and made some name for himself as a critic.

Thinking about Members that evening, I found myself unable to consider him without prejudice. He had been, I now realised, responsible for preventing St. John Clarke from writing the Isbister introduction. That was in itself understandable. However, he had also prevaricated about the matter in a way that showed disregard for the fact that we had known each other for a long time; and had always got along together pretty well. There were undoubtedly difficulties on his side too. Prejudice was to be avoided if— as I had idly pictured him—Members were to form the basis of a character in a novel. Alternatively, prejudice might prove the very element through which to capture and pin down unequivocally the otherwise elusive nature of what was of interest, discarding by its selective power the empty, unprofitable shell making up that side of Members untranslatable into terms of art; concentrating his final essence, his position, as it were, in eternity, into the medium of words.

Any but the most crude indication of my own personality would be, I reflected, equally hard to transcribe; at any rate one that did not sound a little absurd. It was all very well for Mrs. Erdleigh to generalise; far less easy to take an objective view oneself. Even the bare facts had an unreal, almost satirical ring when committed to paper, say in the manner of innumerable Russian stories of the nineteenth century: 'I was born in the city of L——, the son of an infantry officer . . .' To convey much that was relevant to the reader's mind by such phrases was in this country hardly possible. Too many factors had to be taken into consideration. Understatement, too, had its own banality; for, skirting cheap romanticism, it could also encourage evasion of unpalatable facts.

However, these meditations on writing were dispersed by the South Americans, who now rose in a body, and, with a good deal of talking and shrill laughter, trooped down the steps, making for the Arlington Street entrance. Their removal perceptibly thinned the population of the palm court. Among a sea of countenances, stamped like the skin of Renoir's women with that curiously pink, silky surface that seems to come from prolonged sitting about in Ritz hotels, I noticed several familiar faces. Some of these belonged to girls once encountered at dances, now no longer known, probably married; moving at any rate in circles I did not frequent.

Margaret Budd was there, with a lady who looked like an aunt or mother-in-law. In the end this 'beauty' had married a Scotch landowner, a husband rather older than might have been expected for such a lovely girl. He was in the whisky business, said to be hypochondriacal and bad-tempered. Although by then mother of at least two children, Margaret still looked like one of those golden-haired, blue-eyed dolls which say, 'Ma-Ma' and 'Pa-Pa', closing their eyes when tilted backward: unchanged in her possession of that peculiarly English beauty, scarcely to be altered by grey hair or the pallor of age. Not far from

34

her, on one of the sofas, sandwiched between two men, both of whom had the air of being rather rich, sat a tall, blonde young woman I recognised as Lady Ardglass, popularly supposed to have been for a short time mistress of Prince Theodoric. Unlike Margaret Budd—whose married name I could not remember—Bijou Ardglass appeared distinctly older: more than a little ravaged by the demands of her strenuous existence. She had lost some of that gay, energetic air of being ready for anything which she had so abundantly possessed when I had first seen her at Mrs. Andriadis's party. That occasion seemed an eternity ago.

As time passed, people leaving, others arriving, I began increasingly to suspect that Members was not going to show up. That would not be out of character, because cutting appointments was a recognised element in his method of conducting life. This habit—to be in general associated with a strong, sometimes frustrated desire to impose the will—is usually attributed on each specific occasion to the fact that 'something better turned up'. Such defaulters are almost as a matter of course reproached with trying to make a more profitable use of their time. Perhaps, in reality, self-interest in its crudest form plays less part in these deviations than might be supposed. The manœuvre may often be undertaken for its own sake. The person awaited deliberately withholds himself from the person awaiting. Mere absence is in this manner turned into a form of action, even potentially violent in its consequences.

Possibly Members, from an inner compulsion, had suddenly decided to establish ascendancy by such an assertion of the will. On the other hand, the action would in the circumstances represent such an infinitesimal score against life in general that his absence, if deliberate, was probably attributable to some minor move in domestic politics vis-à-

35

vis St. John Clarke. I was thinking over these possibilities, rather gloomily wondering whether or not I would withdraw or stay a few minutes longer, when an immensely familiar head and shoulders became visible for a second through a kind of window, or embrasure, looking out from the palm court on to the lower levels of the passage and rooms beyond. It was Peter Templer. A moment later he strolled up the steps.

For a few seconds Templer gazed thoughtfully round the room, as if contemplating the deterioration of a landscape, known from youth, once famed for its natural beauty, now ruined beyond recall. He was about to turn away, when he caught sight of me and came towards the table. It must have been at least three years since we had met. His sleekly brushed hair and long, rather elegant stride were just the same. His face was perhaps a shade fuller, and his eyes at once began to give out that familiar blue mechanical sparkle that I remembered so well from our schooldays. With a red carnation in the buttonhole of his dark suit, his shirt cuffs cut tightly round the wrist so that somehow his links asserted themselves unduly, Templer's air was distinctly prosperous. But he also looked as if by then he knew what worry was, something certainly unknown to him in the past.

'I suppose you are waiting for someone, Nick,' he said, drawing up a chair. 'Some ripe little piece?'

'You're very wide of the mark.'

'Then a dowager is going to buy your dinner—after which she will make you an offer?'

'No such luck.'

'What then?'

'I'm waiting for a man.'

'I say, old boy, sorry to have been so inquisitive. Things have come to that, have they?'

'You couldn't know.'

'I should have guessed.'

'Have a drink, anyway.'

I remembered reading, some years before, an obituary notice in the *Morning Post,* referring to his father's death. This paragraph, signed 'A.S.F.', was, in fact, a brief personal memoir rather than a bald account of the late Mr. Templer's career. Although the deceased's chairmanship of various companies was mentioned—his financial interests had been chiefly in cement—more emphasis was laid on his delight in sport, especially boxing, his many undisclosed benefactions to charity, and the kind heart within him, always cloaked by a deceptively brusque manner. The initials, together with a certain banality of phrasing, suggested the hand of Sunny Farebrother, Mr. Templer's younger City associate I had met at their house. That visit had been the sole occasion when I had seen Templer's father. I had wondered vaguely—to use a favourite expression of his son's—'how much he had cut up for'. Details about money are always of interest; even so, I did not give the matter much thought. Already I had begun to think of Peter Templer as a friend of my schooldays rather than one connected with that more recent period of occasional luncheons together, during the year following my own establishment in London after coming down from the university. When, once in a way, I had attended the annual dinner for members of Le Bas's House, Templer had never been present.

That we had ceased to meet fairly regularly was due no doubt to some extent to Templer's chronic inability—as our housemaster Le Bas would have said—to 'keep up' a friendship. He moved entirely within the orbit of events of the moment, looking neither forward nor backward. If we happened to run across each other, we arranged to do something together; not otherwise. This mutual detachment had been brought about also by the circumstances of my own life. To be circumscribed by people constituting the same professional community as myself was no wish of mine; rather the contrary. However, an inexorable law governs all human existence in that respect, ordaining that sooner or later everyone must appear before the world as he is. Many are not prepared to face this sometimes distasteful principle. Indeed, the illusion that anyone can escape from the marks of his vocation is an aspect of romanticism common to every profession; those occupied with the world of action claiming their true interests to lie in the pleasure of imagination or reflection, while persons principally concerned with reflective or imaginative pursuits are for ever asserting their inalienable right to participation in an active sphere.

Perhaps Templer himself lay somewhere within the range of this definition. If so, he gave little indication of it. In fact, if taxed, there can be no doubt that he would have denied any such thing. The outward sign that seemed to place him within this category was his own unwillingness ever wholly to accept the people amongst whom he had chosen to live. A curious streak of melancholy seemed to link him with a less arid manner of life than that to which he seemed irrevocably committed. At least I supposed something of that sort could still be said of his life; for I knew little or nothing of his daily routine, in or out of the office, though suspecting that neither his activities, nor his friends, were of a kind likely to be very sympathetic to myself.

However, various strands, controlled without much method and then invisible to me, imparted a certain irregular pattern to Templer's personal affairs. For example, he liked his friends to be rich and engrossed in whatever business occupied them. They had to be serious about money, though relatively dissipated in their private lives; to possess no social ambitions whatever, though at the same time to be disfigured by no grave social defects. The women had to be good-looking, the men tolerably proficient at golf and bridge, without making a fetish of those pastimes. Both sexes, when entertained by him, were expected to drink fairly heavily; although, here again, intoxication must not be carried to excess. In fact, broadly speaking, Templer disliked anything that could be labelled 'bohemian', as much as anything with claims to be 'smart'. He did not fancy even that sort of 'smartness' to be found to a limited extent in the City, a form of life which had, after all, so much in common with his own tastes.

'You know, I really rather hate the well-born,' he used to say. 'Not that I see many of them these days.'

Nothing might be thought easier than gratification of these modest requirements among a circle of intimates; and the difficulty Templer found in settling down to any one set of persons limited by these terms of reference, and at the same time satisfactory to himself, was really remarkable. This side of him suggested a kind of 'spoiled intellectual'. There was also the curious sympathy he could extend to such matters as the story of the St. John Clarke introduction, which he now made me outline after I had explained my purpose in the Ritz. The facts could scarcely have been very interesting to him, but he followed their detail as if alteration of the bank rate or fluctuations of the copper market were ultimately concerned. Perhaps this capacity for careful attention to other people's affairs was the basis of his own success in business.

'Of course I know about Isbister, R.A.,' he said. 'He painted that shocking picture of my old man. I tried to pop it when he dropped off the hooks, but there were no takers. I know about St. John Clarke, too. Mona reads his books. Absolutely laps them up, in fact.'

'Who is Mona?'

'Oh, yes, you haven't met her yet, have you? Mona is my wife.'

'But, my dear Peter, I had no idea you were married.'

'Strange, isn't it? Our wedding anniversary, matter of fact. Broke as I am, I thought we could gnaw a cutlet at the Grill to celebrate. Why not join us? Your chap is obviously not going to turn up.'

He began to speak of his own affairs, talking in just the way he did when we used to have tea together at school. Complaining of having lost a lot of money in 'the slump', he explained that he still owned a house in the neighbourhood of Maidenhead.

'More or less camping out there now,' he said. 'With a married couple looking after us. The woman does the cooking. The man can drive a car and service it pretty well, but he hasn't the foggiest idea about looking after my clothes.'

I asked about his marriage.

'We met first at a road-house near Staines. Mona was being entertained there by a somewhat uncouth individual called Snider, an advertising agent. Snider's firm was using her as a photographer's model. You'll know her face when you see her. Laxatives—halitosis—even her closest friend wouldn't tell her—and so on.'

I discovered in due course that Mona's chief appearance on the posters had been to advertise toothpaste; but both she and her husband were inclined to emphasise other more picturesque possibilities.

'She'd already had a fairly adventurous career by then,' Templer said.

He began to enlarge on this last piece of information,

40

like a man unable to forgo irritating the quiescent nerve of a potentially aching tooth. I had the impression that he was still very much in love with his wife, but that things were perhaps not going as well as he could wish. That would explain a jerkiness of manner that suggested worry. The story itself seemed commonplace enough, yet containing implications of Templer's own recurrent desire to escape from whatever world enclosed him.

'She *says* she's partly Swiss,' he said. 'Her father was an engineer in Birmingham, always being fired for being tight. However, both parents are dead. The only relation she's got is an aunt with a house in Worthing—a boarding-house, I think.'

I saw at once that Mona, whatever else her characteristics, was a wife liberally absolving Templer from additional family ties. That fact, perhaps counting for little compared with deeper considerations, would at the same time seem a great advantage in his eyes. This desire to avoid new relations through marriage was connected with an innate unwillingness to identify himself too closely with any one social group. In that taste, oddly enough, he resembled Uncle Giles, each of them considering himself master of a more sweeping mobility of action by voluntary withdrawal from competition at any given social level of existence.

At the time of narration, I did not inwardly accept all Templer's highly coloured statements about his wife, but I was impressed by the apparent depths of his feeling for Mona. Even when telling the story of how his marriage had come about, he had completely abandoned any claim to have employed those high-handed methods he was accustomed to advocate for handling girls of her sort. I asked what time she was due at the Ritz.

'When she comes out of the cinema,' he said. 'She was

41

determined to see *Mädchen in Uniform*. I couldn't face it. After all, one meets quite enough lesbians in real life without going to the pictures to see them.'

'But it isn't a film about lesbians.'

'Oh, isn't it?' said Templer. 'Mona thought it was. She'll be disappointed if you're right. However, I'm sure you're wrong. Jimmy Brent told me about it. He usually knows what's what in matters of that kind. My sister Jean is with Mona. Did you ever meet her? I can't remember. They may be a little late, but I've booked a table. We can have a drink or two while we wait.'

Jean's name recalled the last time I had seen her at that luncheon party at Stourwater where I had been taken by the Walpole-Wilsons. I had not thought of her for ages, though some small residue of inner dissatisfaction, that survives all emotional expenditure come to nothing, now returned.

'Jean's having a spot of trouble with that husband of hers,' said Templer. 'That is why she is staying with us for the moment. She married Bob Duport, you know. He is rather a handful.'

'So I should imagine.'

'You don't know him.'

'We met when you drove us all into the ditch in your famous second-hand Vauxhall.'

'My God,' said Templer, laughing. 'That was a shambles, wasn't it? Fancy your remembering that. It must be nearly ten years ago now. The row those bloody girls made. Old Bob was in poor form that day, I remember. He thought he'd picked up a nail after a binge he'd been on a night or two before. Completely false alarm, of course.'

'As Le Bas once said: "I can't accept ill health as a valid excuse for ill manners."'

'Bob's not much your sort, but he's not a bad chap when

you get to know him. I was surprised you'd ever heard of him. I've had worse brothers-in-law, although, God knows, that's not saying much. But Bob *is* difficult. Bad enough running after every girl he meets, but when he goes and loses nearly all his money on top of that, an awkward situation is immediately created.'

'Are they living apart?'

'Not officially. Jean is looking for a small flat in town for herself and the kid.'

'What sex?'

'Polly, aged three.'

'And Duport?'

'Gone abroad, leaving a trail of girl-friends and bad debts behind him. He is trying to put through some big stuff on the metal market. I think the two of them will make it up in due course. I used to think she was mad about him, but you can never tell with women.'

The news that Polly was to be born was the last I had heard of her mother. Little as I could imagine how Jean had brought herself to marry Duport—far less be 'mad about him'—I had by then learnt that such often inexplicable things must simply be accepted as matters of fact. His sister's matrimonial troubles evidently impressed Templer as vexatious, though in the circumstances probably unavoidable; certainly not a subject for prolonged discussion.

'Talking of divorces and such things,' he said. 'Do you ever see Charles Stringham now?'

There had been little or no scandal connected with the break-up of Stringham's marriage. He and Peggy Stepney had parted company without apparent reason, just as their reason for marrying had been outwardly hard to understand. They had bought a house somewhere north of the Park, but neither ever seemed to have lived there for more

43

than a few weeks at a time, certainly seldom together. The house itself, decorated by the approved decorator of that moment, was well spoken of, but I had never been there. The marriage had simply collapsed, so people said, from inanition. I never heard it suggested that Peggy had taken a lover. Stringham, it was true, was seen about with all kinds of women, though nothing specific was alleged against him either. Soon after the decree had been made absolute, Peggy married a cousin, rather older than herself, and went to live in Yorkshire, where her husband possessed a large house, noted in books of authentically recorded ghost stories for being rather badly haunted.

'That former wife of his—The Lady Peggy—was a good-looking piece,' said Templer. 'But, as you know, such grand life is not for me. I prefer simpler pleasures——

' "Oh, give me a man to whom naught comes amiss,
    One horse or another, that country or this. . . ." '

'You know you've always hated hunting and hunting people. Anyway, whose sentiments were those?'

'Ah,' he said, 'chaps like you think I'm not properly educated, in spite of the efforts of Le Bas and others, and that I don't know about beautiful poetry. You find you're wrong. I know all sorts of little snatches. As a matter of fact I was thinking of women, really, rather than horses, and taking 'em as you find 'em. Not being too choosy about it as Charles has always been. Of course they are easier to take than to find, in my experience—though of course it is not gentlemanly to boast of such things. Anyway, as you know, I have given up all that now.'

At school I could remember Templer claiming that he had never read a book for pleasure in his life; and, although an occasional Edgar Wallace was certainly to be seen in his hand during the period of his last few terms, the quotation was surprising. That was a side of him not entirely unexpected, but usually kept hidden. Incidentally, it was a conversational trick acquired—perhaps consciously copied—from Stringham.

'You remember the imitations Charles used to do of Widmerpool?' he said. 'I expect he is much too grand to remember Widmerpool now.'

'I saw Widmerpool not so long ago. He is with Donners-Brebner.'

'But not much longer,' said Templer. 'Widmerpool is joining the Acceptance World.'

'What on earth is that?'

'Well, actually he is going to become a bill-broker,' said Templer, laughing. 'I should have made myself clearer to one not involved in the nefarious ways of the City.'

'What will he do?'

'Make a lot of heavy weather. He'll have to finish his lunch by two o'clock and spend the rest of the day wasting the time of the banks.'

'But what is the Acceptance World?'

'If you have goods you want to sell to a firm in Bolivia, you probably do not touch your money in the ordinary way until the stuff arrives there. Certain houses, therefore, are prepared to 'accept' the debt. They will advance you the money on the strength of your reputation. It is all right when the going is good, but sooner or later you are tempted to plunge. Then there is an alteration in the value of the Bolivian exchange, or a revolution, or perhaps the firm just goes bust—and you find yourself stung. That is, if you guess wrong.'

'I see. But why is he leaving Donners-Brebner? He always told me he was such a success there and that Sir Magnus liked him so much.'

'Widmerpool was doing all right in Donners-Brebner—in fact rather well, as you say,' said Templer. 'But he used to bore the pants off everyone in the combine by his intriguing. In the end he got on the nerves of Donners himself. Did you ever come across a fellow called Truscott? Widmerpool took against him, and worked away until he had got him out. Then Donners regretted it, after Truscott had been sacked, and decided Widmerpool was getting too big for his boots. He must go too. The long and the short of it is that Widmerpool is joining this firm of bill-brokers—on the understanding that a good deal of the Donners-Brebner custom follows him there.'

I had never before heard Templer speak of Widmerpool in this matter-of-fact way. At school he had disliked him, or, at best, treated him as a harmless figure of fun. Now, however, Widmerpool had clearly crystallised in Templer's mind as an ordinary City acquaintance, to be thought of no longer as a subject for laughter, but as a normal vehicle for the transaction of business; perhaps even one particularly useful in that respect on account of former associations.

'I was trying to get Widmerpool to lend a hand with old Bob,' said Templer.

'What would he do?'

'Bob has evolved some scheme for collecting scrap metal from some place in the Balkans and shipping it home. At least that is the simplest way of explaining what he intends. Widmerpool has said he will try to arrange for Bob to have the agency for Donners-Brebner.'

I was more interested in hearing of this development in Widmerpool's career than in examining its probable effect on Duport, whose business worries were no concern of mine. However, my attention was at that moment distracted from such matters by the sudden appearance in the palm court of a short, decidedly unconventional figure who

46

now came haltingly up the steps. This person wore a black leather overcoat. His arrival in the Ritz—in those days—was a remarkable event.

Pausing, with a slight gesture of exhaustion that seemed to imply arduous travel over many miles of arid desert or snowy waste (according to whether the climate within or without the hotel was accepted as prevailing), he looked about the room; gazing as if in amazement at the fountain, the nymph, the palms in their pots of Chinese design: then turning his eyes to the chandeliers and the glass of the roof. His bearing was at once furtive, resentful, sagacious, and full of a kind of confidence in his own powers. He seemed to be surveying the tables as if searching for someone, at the same time unable to believe his eyes, while he did so, at the luxuriance of the oasis in which he found himself. He carried no hat, but retained the belted leather overcoat upon which a few drops of moisture could be seen glistening as he advanced farther into the room, an indication that snow or sleet had begun to fall outside. This black leather garment gave a somewhat official air to his appearance, obscurely suggesting a Wellsian man of the future, hierarchic in rank. Signs of damp could also be seen in patches on his sparse fair hair, a thatch failing to roof in completely the dry, yellowish skin of his scalp.

This young man, although already hard to think of as really young on account of the maturity of his expression, was J. G. Quiggin. I had been reflecting on him only a short time earlier in connexion with Mark Members; for the pair of them—Members and Quiggin—were, for some reason, always associated together in the mind. This was not only because I myself had happened to meet both of them during my first term at the university. Other people, too, were accustomed to link their names together, as if they were a business firm, or, more authentically, a couple whose appearance together in public inevitably invoked the thought of a certain sort of literary life. Besides that, a kind of love-hate indissolubly connected them.

Whether or not the birth of this relationship had in fact taken place at that tea party in Sillery's rooms in college, where we had all met as freshmen, was not easy to say. There at any rate I had first seen Quiggin in his grubby starched collar and subfusc suit. On that occasion Sillery had rather maliciously suggested the acquaintance of Members and Quiggin dated from an earlier incarnation; in fact boyhood together—like Isbister and St. John Clarke—in some Midland town. So far as I knew, that assertion had neither been proved nor disproved. Some swore Quiggin and Members were neighbours at home; others that the story was a pure invention, produced in malice, and based on the fact that Sillery had found the two names in the same provincial telephone directory. Sillery certainly devoted a good deal of his time to the study of such works of reference as telephone books and county directories, from which he managed to extract a modicum of information useful to himself. At the same time there were those who firmly believed Members and Quiggin to be related; even first cousins. The question was largely irrelevant; although the acutely combative nature of their friendship, if it could be so called, certainly possessed all that intense, almost vindictive rivalry of kinship.

Quiggin had quietly disappeared from the university without taking a degree. Now, like Members, he had already made some name for himself, though at a somewhat different literary level. He was a professional reviewer of notable ability, much disliked by some of the older critics for the roughness with which he occasionally handled accepted reputations. One of the smaller publishing houses employed him as 'literary adviser'; a firm of which his friend Howard Craggs (formerly of the Vox Populi Press, now extinct, though partly reincorporated as Boggis & Stone) had recently become a director. A book by Quiggin had been advertised to appear in the spring, but as a rule his works never seemed, at the last moment, to satisfy their author's high standard of self-criticism. Up to then his manuscripts had always been reported as 'burnt', or at best held back for drastic revision.

Quiggin, certainly to himself and his associates, represented a more go-ahead school of thought to that of Members and his circle. Although not himself a poet, he was a great adherent of the new trends of poetry then developing, which deprecated 'Art for Art's sake', a doctrine in a general way propagated by Members. However, Members, too, was moving with the times, his latest volume of verse showing a concern with psychoanalysis; but, although 'modern' in the eyes of a writer of an older generation like St. John Clarke, Members—so Quiggin had once remarked—'drooped too heavily over the past, a crutch with which we younger writers must learn to dispense'. Members, for his part, had been heard complaining that he himself was in sympathy with 'all liberal and progressive movements', but 'J.G. had advanced into a state of mind too political to be understood by civilised people'. In spite of such differences, and reported statements of both of them that they 'rarely saw each other now', they were not uncommonly to be found together, arguing or sulking on the banquettes of the Café Royal.

When Quiggin caught sight of me in the Ritz he immediately made for our table. As he moved across the white marble floor his figure seemed thicker than formerly. From being the spare, hungry personage I had known as an undergraduate he had become solid, almost stout. It was possible that Members, perhaps maliciously, perhaps as a matter of convenience to himself, had arranged for Quiggin to pick him up for dinner at an hour when our business together would be at an end. Supposing this had been planned, I was preparing to explain that Members had not turned up, when all at once Quiggin himself began to speak in his small, hard, grating North Country voice; employing a tone very definitely intended to sweep aside any question of wasting time upon the idle formalities of introduction, or indeed anything else that might postpone, even momentarily, some matter that was his duty to proclaim without delay.

'I could not get away earlier,' he began, peremptorily. 'St. J. is rather seriously ill. It happened quite suddenly. Not only that, but a difficult situation has arisen. I should like to discuss things with you.'

This introductory speech was even less expected than Quiggin's own arrival, although the tense, angry seriousness with which he had invested these words was not uncommon in his way of talking. Once I had thought this abrupt, aggressive manner came from a kind of shyness; but later that theory had to be abandoned when it became clear that Quiggin's personality expressed itself naturally in this form. I was surprised to hear him refer to St. John Clarke as 'St. J.', a designation appropriated to himself by Mark Members, and rarely used by others; in fact a nickname almost patented by Members as an outward sign of his own intimacy with his friend and employer.

I could not imagine why Quiggin, on that particular night, should suddenly wish that we should dine *tête-à-tête*. In the past we had occasionally spent an evening together after meeting at some party, always by accident rather than design. We were on quite good terms, but there was no subject involving St. John Clarke likely to require urgent discussion between us. At the university, where he had

50

seemed a lonely, out-of-the-way figure, I had felt an odd interest in Quiggin; but our acquaintance there, such as it was, he now treated almost as a matter to live down. Perhaps that was natural as he came to invest more and more of his personality in his own literary status. At that moment, for example, his manner of speaking implied that any of his friends should be prepared to make sacrifices for an exceptional occasion like this one: a time when opportunity to be alone with him and talk seriously was freely offered.

'Did you come to meet Mark?' I asked. 'He hasn't turned up. It is not very likely he will appear now.'

Quiggin, refusing an invitation to sit down, stood upright by the table, still enveloped in his black, shiny livery. He had unfastened the large buttons of the overcoat, which now flapped open like Bonaparte's, revealing a dark grey jumper that covered all but the knot of a red tie. The shirt was also dark grey. His face wore the set, mask-like expression of an importunate beggar tormenting a pair of tourists seated on the perimeter of a café's *terrasse*. I felt suddenly determined to be no longer a victim of other people's disregard for their social obligations. I introduced Templer out of hand—an operation Quiggin had somehow prevented until that moment—explaining at the same time that I was that evening already irrevocably booked for a meal.

Quiggin showed annoyance at this downright refusal to be dislodged, simultaneously indicating his own awareness that Members had been unable to keep this appointment. It then occurred to me that Members had persuaded Quiggin to make the excuses for his own absence in person. Such an arrangement was unlikely, and would in any case not explain why Quiggin should expect me to dine with him. However, Quiggin shook his head at this suggestion, and gave a laugh—rather in Uncle Giles's manner—expressing scorn rather than amusement. Templer watched us with interest.

'As a matter of fact St. J. has a new secretary,' said Quiggin slowly, through closed lips. 'That is why Mark did not come this evening.'

'What, has Mark been sacked?'

Quiggin was evidently not prepared to reply directly to so uncompromising an enquiry. He laughed a little, though rather more leniently than before.

'Honourably retired, perhaps one might say.'

'On a pension?'

'You are very inquisitive, Nicholas.'

'You have aroused my interest. You should be flattered.'

'Life with St. J. never really gave Mark time for his own work.'

'He always produced a fair amount.'

'Too much, from one point of view,' said Quiggin, savagely; adding in a less severe tone: 'Mark, as you know, always insists on taking on so many things. He could not always give St. J. the attention a man of his standing quite reasonably demands. Of course, the two of them will continue to see each other. I think, in fact, Mark is going to look in once in a way to keep the library in order. After all, they are close friends, first and foremost, quite apart from whether or not Mark is St. J.'s secretary. As you probably know, there have been various difficulties from time to time. Minor ones, of course. Still, one thing leads to another. Mark can be rather querulous when he does not get his own way.'

'Who is taking Mark's place?'

'It is not exactly a question of one person taking another's place. Merely coping with the practical side of the job more —well—conscientiously.'

Quiggin bared his teeth, as if to excuse this descent on his own part to a certain smugness of standpoint.

'Yourself?'

'At first just as an experiment on both sides.'

I saw at once that in this change, if truly reported, all kind of implications were inherent. Stories had circulated in the past of jobs for which Quiggin and Members had been in competition, most of them comparatively unimportant employments in the journalistic field. This was rather larger game; because, apart from other considerations, there was the question of who was to be St. John Clarke's heir. He was apparently alone in the world. It was not a vast fortune, perhaps, but a tidy sum. A devoted secretary might stand in a favourable position for at least a handsome bequest. Although I had never heard hints that Quiggin was anxious to replace Members in the novelist's household, such an ambition was by no means unthinkable. In fact the change was likely to have been brought about by long intrigue rather than sudden caprice. The news was surprising, though of a kind to startle by its essential appropriateness rather than from any sense of incongruity.

Although I did not know St. John Clarke, I could not help feeling a certain pity for him, smitten down among his first editions, press cuttings, dinner invitations, and signed photographs of eminent contemporaries, a sick man of letters, fought over by Members and Quiggin.

'That was why I wanted to have a talk about St. J.'s affairs,' said Quiggin, continuing to speak in his more conciliatory tone. 'There have been certain changes lately in his point of view. You probably knew that. I think you are interested in getting this introduction. I see no reason why he should not write it. But I am of the opinion that he will probably wish to approach Isbister's painting from a rather different angle. The pictures, after all, offer a unique example of

53

what a capitalist society produces where art is concerned.' However, I see we shall have to discuss that another time.'

He stared hard at Templer as chief impediment to his plans for the evening. It was at that point that 'the girls' arrived; owing to this conversation, entering the room unobserved by me until they were standing beside us. I was immediately aware that I had seen Templer's wife before. Then I remembered that he had warned me I should recognise the stylised, conventionally smiling countenance, set in blonde curls, that had formerly appeared so often, on the walls of buses and underground trains, advocating a well-known brand of toothpaste. She must have been nearly six foot in height: in spite of a rather coarse complexion, a beautiful girl by any standards.

'It was *too* wonderful,' she said, breathlessly.

She spoke to Templer, but turned almost at once in the direction of Quiggin and myself. At the sight of her, Quiggin went rather red in the face and muttered inaudible phrases conveying that they already knew one another. She replied civilly to these, though evidently without any certainty as to where that supposed meeting had taken place. She was obviously longing to talk about the film, but Quiggin was not prepared for the matter of their earlier encounter to be left vague.

'It was years ago at a party over an antique shop,' he insisted, 'given by an old queen who died soon after. Mark Members introduced us.'

'Oh, yes,' she said, indifferently, 'I haven't seen Mark for ages.'

'Deacon, he was called.'

'I believe I remember.'

'Off Charlotte Street.'

'There were a lot of parties round there,' she agreed. Then I knew that something other than the toothpaste advertisements had caused Mona's face to seem so familiar. I, too, had seen her at Mr. Deacon's birthday party. Since then she had applied peroxide to her naturally dark hair. When Templer had spoken of his wife's former profession I had not connected her with 'Mona', the artist's model of whom Barnby, and others, used sometimes to speak. Barnby had not mentioned her for a long time.

In due course I found that Mona had abandoned that 'artist's' world for commercial employments that were more lucrative. The people she met in these less pretentious circles were also no doubt on the whole more sympathetic to her, although she would never have admitted that. Certainly the impact of her earlier career as a model for painters and sculptors was never erased from her own mind. With the extraordinary adaptability of women, she had managed to alter considerably the lines of her figure, formerly a striking synthesis of projections and concavities that certainly seemed to demand immediate expression in bronze or stone. Now her body had been disciplined into a fashionable, comparatively commonplace mould. She smiled in a friendly way at Quiggin, but made no effort to help him out in his efforts to suggest that they really already knew each other.

Quiggin himself continued to stand for a time resentfully beside us, giving the impression not so much that he wished to join the Templer party, as that he hoped for an invitation to do so, which would at once be curtly refused; though whether, had the chance arisen, he would in fact have withheld his company was, of course, speculative. Mona threw him another smile, her regular rows of teeth neatly displayed between pink lips parted in a cupid's bow: an ensemble invoking more than ever her career on the hoardings. For some reason this glance confirmed Quiggin's

55

intention to depart. After a final word with me to the effect that he would ring up early the following week and arrange a meeting, he nodded in an offended manner to the world in general, and tramped away across the room and down the steps. He held himself tautly upright, as if determined to avoid for ever in future such haunts of luxury and those who frequent them.

Just as he was making this move, Lady Ardglass, followed by her spruce, grey-haired admirers, at heel like a brace of well-groomed, well-bred, obedient sporting dogs, passed us on the way out. A natural blonde, Bijou Ardglass possessed a fleeting facial resemblance to Mona. She was said to have been a mannequin before her marriage. My attention had been caught momentarily by Quiggin's words, but, even while he was speaking, I was aware of this resemblance as Lady Ardglass approached; although her smooth hair and mink made a strong contrast with Mona's camel-hair coat and rather wild appearance. All the same there could be no doubt that the two of them possessed something in common. As the Ardglass cortège came level with us, I saw exchanged between the two of them one of those glances so characteristic of a woman catching sight of another woman who reminds her of herself: glances in which deep hatred and also a kind of passionate love seem to mingle voluptuously together for an instant of time.

Templer, at the same moment, shot out an all-embracing look, which seemed in an equally brief space to absorb Bijou Ardglass in her entirety. He appeared to do this more from force of habit than because she greatly interested him. It was a memorandum for some future date, should the need ever arise, recording qualities and defects, charms and blemishes, certainties and potentialities, both moral and physical. Jean saw Lady Ardglass too. Just as Quiggin was making his final remark to me, I was conscious that

56

she touched her brother's arm and muttered something to him that sounded like 'Bob's girl': words at which Templer raised his eyebrows.

I did not fully take in Jean's appearance until that moment. She was wearing a red dress with a black coat, and some kind of a scarf, folded over like a stock, emphasised the long, graceful curve of her neck. Mona's strident personality occupied the centre of the stage, and, besides, I felt for some reason a desire to postpone our meeting. Now, as she spoke to her brother, her face assumed an expression at once mocking and resigned, which had a sweetness about it that reminded me of the days when I had thought myself in love with her. I could still feel the tension her presence always brought, but without any of that hopeless romantic longing, so characteristic of love's very early encounters: perhaps always imperfectly recaptured in the more realistic love-making of later life. Now, I experienced a kind of resentment at the reserve which enclosed her. It suggested a form of self-love, not altogether attractive. Yet the look of irony and amusement that had come into her face when she whispered the phrase about 'Bob's girl' seemed to add something unexpected and charming to her still mysterious personality.

She was taller than I remembered, and carried herself well. Her face, like her brother's, had become a shade fuller, a change that had coarsened his appearance, while in her the sharp, almost animal look I remembered was now softened. She had not entirely lost her air of being a school-girl; though certainly, it had to be admitted, a very smartly dressed school-girl. I thought to myself, not without complacence, that I was able to appreciate her without in any way losing my head, as I might once have done. There was still a curious fascination about her grey-blue eyes, slanting a little, as it were caught tightly between soft, lazy lids and

57

dark, luxurious lashes. Once she had reminded me of Rubens's *Chapeau de Paille*. Now for some reason—though there was not much physical likeness between them—I thought of the woman smoking the hookah in Delacroix's *Femmes d'Alger dans leur appartement*. Perhaps there was something of the odalisque about Jean, too. She looked pale and rather tired. Any girl might excusably have appeared pale beside Mona, whose naturally high colouring had been increased by her own hand, almost as if for the stage or a cabaret performance.

'Do you remember where we last met?' she said, when Quiggin was gone.

'At Stourwater.'

'What a party.'

'Was it awful?'

'Some of it wasn't very nice. Terrible rows between Baby and our host.'

'But I thought they never had rows in public.'

'They didn't. That was what was so awful. Sir Magnus tremendously bland all the time and Baby absolutely bursting with bad temper.'

'Do you ever hear from Baby Wentworth now?'

'I had a card at Christmas. She is cloudlessly happy with her Italian.'

'What is his profession?'

'I don't think I know you well enough to tell you. Perhaps after dinner.'

This, I remembered, was the way things had been at Stourwater: brisk conversation that led in the end to acres of silence. I made up my mind that this time I would not feel put out by her behaviour, whatever form it took.

'Let's have some food,' said Templer, 'I'm famished. So must you girls be, after your intellectual film.'

Afterwards, I could never recall much about that dinner

in the Grill, except that the meal conveyed an atmosphere of powerful forces at work beneath the conversation. The sight of her husband's mistress had no doubt been disturbing to Jean, who as usual spoke little. It soon became clear that the Templers' mutual relationship was not an easy one. Different couples approach with varied technique the matrimonial vehicle's infinitely complicated machinery. In the case of the Templers, their method made it hard to believe that they were really married at all. Clearly each of them was accustomed to a more temporary arrangement. Their conduct was normal enough, but they remained two entirely separate individuals, giving no indication of a life in common. This was certainly not because Templer showed any lack of interest in his wife. On the contrary, he seemed extravagantly, almost obsessively fond of her, although he teased her from time to time. In the past he had sometimes spoken of his love affairs to me, but I had never before seen him, as it were, in action. I wondered whether he habitually showed this same tremendous outward enthusiasm when pursuing more casual inclinations; or whether Mona had touched off some hitherto unkindled spark.

How far Mona herself reciprocated these feelings was less easy to guess. Possibly she was already rather bored with being a wife, and her surfeit in this respect might explain her husband's conciliatory attitude. She spoke and acted in a manner so affected and absurd that there was something appealing about the artificiality of her gestures and conversation. She was like some savage creature, anxious to keep up appearances before members of a more highly civilised species, although at the same time keenly aware of her own superiority in cunning. There was something hard and untamed about her, probably the force that had attracted Templer and others. She seemed on good terms with Jean, who may have found her sister-in-law's crude, violent presence emphasised to advantage her own quieter, though still undisclosed nature.

Quiggin had made an impression upon Mona, because, almost immediately after we sat down to dinner, she began to make enquiries about him. Possibly, on thinking it over, she felt that his obvious interest in her had deserved greater notice. In answer to her questions, I explained that he was J. G. Quiggin, the literary critic. She at once asserted that she was familiar with his reviews in one of the 'weeklies', mentioning, as it happened, a periodical for which, so far as I knew, he had never written.

'He was a splendid fellow in his old leather overcoat,' said Templer. 'Did you notice his shirt, too? I expect you know lots of people like that, Nick. To think I was rather worried at not having struggled into a dinner-jacket tonight, and he just breezed in wearing the flannel trousers he had been sleeping in for a fortnight, and not caring a damn. I admire that.'

'I couldn't remember a thing about meeting him before,' said Mona. 'I expect I must have been a bit tight that night, otherwise I should have known his name. He said Mark Members introduced us. Have you heard of him? He is a well-known poet.'

She said this with an ineffable silliness that was irresistible.

'I was going to meet him here, as a matter of fact, but he never turned up.'

'Oh, *were* you?'

She was astonished at this; and impressed. I wondered what on earth Members had told her about himself to have won such respect in her eyes. Afterwards, I found that it was his status as 'a poet', rather than his private personality, that made him of such interest to her.

'I never knew Mark well,' she said, rather apologetic at having suggested such ambitious claims.

60

'He and Quiggin are usually very thick together.'

'I didn't realise Nick was waiting for an old friend of yours, sweetie,' said Templer. 'Is he one of those fascinating people you sometimes tell me about, who wear beards and sandals and have such curious sexual habits?'

Mona began to protest, but Jean interrupted her by saying: 'He's not a bad poet, is he?'

'I think rather good,' I said, feeling a sudden unaccountable desire to encourage in her an interest in poetry. 'He is St. John Clarke's secretary—or, at least, he was.'

I remembered then that, if Quiggin was to be believed, the situation between Members and St. John Clarke was a delicate one.

'I used to like St. John Clarke's novels,' said Jean. 'Now I think they are rather awful. Mona adores them.'

'Oh, but they are *too* wonderful.'

Mona began to detail some of St. John Clarke's plots, a formidable undertaking at the best of times. This expression of Jean's views—that Members was a goodish poet and St. John Clarke a bad novelist—seemed to me to indicate an impressive foothold in literary criticism. I felt now that I wanted to discuss all kind of things with her, but hardly knew where to begin on account of the barrier she seemed to have set up between herself and the rest of the world. I suspected that she might merely be trying to veer away conversation from a period of Mona's life that would carry too many painful implications for Templer as a husband. It could be design, rather than literary interest. However, Mona herself was unwilling to be deflected from the subject.

'Do you run round with all those people?' she went on. 'I used to myself. Then—oh, I don't know—I lost touch with them. Of course Peter doesn't much care for that sort of person, do you, sweetie?'

'Rubbish,' said Templer. 'I've just said how much I liked Mr. J. G. Quiggin. In fact I wish I could meet him again, and find out the name of his tailor.'

Mona frowned at this refusal to take her remark seriously. She turned to me and said: 'You know, you are not much like most of Peter's usual friends yourself.'

That particular matter was all too complicated to explain, even if amenable to explanation, which I was inclined to doubt. I knew, of course, what she meant. Probably there was something to be said for accepting that opinion. The fact that I was not specially like the general run of Templer's friends had certainly been emphasised by the appearance of Quiggin. I was rather displeased that the Templers had seen Quiggin. To deal collectively with them on their own plane would have been preferable to that to which Quiggin had somehow steered us all.

'What was the flick like?' Templer enquired.

'Marvellous,' said Mona. 'The sweetest—no, really—but *the* sweetest little girl you ever saw.'

'She was awfully good,' said Jean.

'But what happened?'

'Well, this little girl—who was called Manuela—was sent to a very posh German school.'

'*Posh?*' said Templer. 'Sweetie, what an awful word. Please never use it in my presence again.'

Rather to my surprise, Mona accepted this rebuke meekly: even blushing slightly.

'Well, Manuela went to this school, and fell *passionately* in love with one of the mistresses.'

'What did I tell you?' said Templer. 'Nick insisted the film wasn't about lesbians. You see he just poses as a man of the world, and hasn't really the smallest idea what is going on round him.'

'It isn't a bit what *you* mean,' said Mona, now bursting

with indignation. 'It was a really beautiful story. Manuela tried to *kill* herself. I cried and cried and cried.'

'It really was good,' said Jean to me. 'Have you seen it?'

'Yes. I liked it.'

'He's lying,' said Templer. 'If he had seen the film, he would have known it was about lesbians. Look here, Nick, why not come home with us for the week-end? We can run you back to your flat and get a toothbrush. I should like you to see our house, uncomfortable as staying there will be.'

'Yes, *do* come, darling,' said Mona, drawing out the words with her absurd articulation. 'You will find everything quite mad, I'm afraid.'

She had by then drunk rather a lot of champagne.

'You must come,' said Jean, speaking in her matter-of-fact tone, almost as if she were giving an order. 'There are all sorts of things I want to talk about.'

'Of course he'll come,' said Templer. 'But we might have the smallest spot of armagnac first.'

Afterwards, that dinner in the Grill seemed to partake of the nature of a ritual feast, a rite from which the four of us emerged to take up new positions in the formal dance with which human life is concerned. At the time, its charm seemed to reside in a difference from the usual run of things. Certainly the chief attraction of the projected visit would be absence of all previous plan. But, in a sense, nothing in life is planned—or everything is—because in the dance every step is ultimately the corollary of the step before; the consequence of being the kind of person one chances to be.

While we were at dinner heavy snow was descending outside. This downfall had ceased by the time my things were collected, though a few flakes were still blowing about in the clear winter air when we set out at last for the

Templers' house. The wind had suddenly dropped. The night was very cold.

'Had to sell the Buick,' Templer said. 'I'm afraid you won't find much room at the back of this miserable vehicle.'

Mona, now comatose after the wine at dinner, rolled herself up in a rug and took the seat in front. Almost immediately she went to sleep. Jean and I sat at the back of the car. We passed through Hammersmith, and the neighbourhood of Chiswick: then out on to the Great West Road. For a time I made desultory conversation. At last she scarcely answered, and I gave it up. Templer, smoking a cigar in the front, also seemed disinclined to talk now that he was at the wheel. We drove along at a good rate.

On either side of the highway, grotesque buildings, which in daytime resembled the temples of some shoddy, utterly unsympathetic Atlantis, now assumed the appearance of an Arctic city's frontier forts. Veiled in snow, these hideous monuments of a lost world bordered a broad river of black, foaming slush, across the surface of which the car skimmed and jolted with a harsh crackling sound, as if the liquid beneath were scalding hot.

Although not always simultaneous in taking effect, nor necessarily at all equal in voltage, the process of love is rarely unilateral. When the moment comes, a secret attachment is often returned with interest. Some know this by instinct; others learn in a hard school.

The exact spot must have been a few hundred yards beyond the point where the electrically illuminated young lady in a bathing dress dives eternally through the petrol-tainted air; night and day, winter and summer, never reaching the water of the pool to which she endlessly glides. Like some image of arrested development, she returns for ever, voluntarily, to the springboard from which she started her leap. A few seconds after I had seen this bathing belle

64

journeying, as usual, imperturbably through the frozen air, I took Jean in my arms.

Her response, so sudden and passionate, seemed surprising only a minute or two later. All at once everything was changed. Her body felt at the same time hard and yielding, giving a kind of glow as if live current issued from it. I used to wonder afterwards whether, in the last resort, of all the time we spent together, however ecstatic, those first moments on the Great West Road were not the best.

To what extent the sudden movement that brought us together was attributable to sentiment felt years before; to behaviour that was almost an obligation within the Templer orbit; or, finally, to some specific impetus of the car as it covered an unusually bad surface of road, was later impossible to determine with certainty. All I knew was that I had not thought it all out beforehand. This may seem extraordinary in the light of what had gone before; but the behaviour of human beings is, undeniably, extraordinary. The incredible ease with which this evolution took place was almost as if the two of us had previously agreed to embrace at that particular point on the road. The timing had been impeccable.

We had bowled along much farther through the winter night, under cold, glittering stars, when Templer turned the car off the main road. Passing through byways lined with beech trees, we came at last to a narrow lane where snow still lay thick on the ground. At the end of this, the car entered a drive, virginally white. In the clear moonlight the grotesquely gabled house ahead of us, set among firs, seemed almost a replica of that mansion by the sea formerly inhabited by Templer's father. Although smaller in size, the likeness of general outline was uncanny. I almost expected to hear the crash of wintry waves beneath a neighbouring cliff. The trees about the garden were powdered with white. Now and then a muffled thud re-sounded as snow fell through the branches on to the thickly coated ground. Otherwise, all was deathly silent.

Templer drew up with a jerk in front of the door, the wheels churning up the snow. He climbed quickly from his seat, and went round to the back of the car, to unload from the boot some eatables and wine they had brought from London. At the same moment Mona came out of her sleep or coma. With the rug still wrapped round her, she jumped out of her side of the car, and ran across the Sisley landscape to the front door, which someone had opened from within. As she ran she gave a series of little shrieks of agony at the cold. Her footprints left deep marks on the face of the drive, where the snow lay soft and tender, like the clean, clean sheets of a measureless bed.

'Where shall I find you?'

'Next to you on the left.'

'How soon?'

'Give it half an hour.'

'I'll be there.'

'Don't be too long.'

She laughed softly when she said that, disengaging herself from the rug that covered both of us.

The interior of the house was equally reminiscent of the Templers' former home. Isbister's huge portrait of Mr. Templer still hung in the hall, a reminder of everyday life and unsolved business problems. Such things seemed far removed from this mysterious, snowy world of unreality, where all miracles could occur. There were the same golf clubs and shooting-sticks and tennis racquets; the same barometer, marking the weather on a revolving chart; the same post-box for letters; even the same panelling in light wood that made the place seem like the interior of a vast, extravagant cabinet for cigars.

'What we need,' said Templer, 'is a drink. And then I think we shall all be ready for bed.'

For a second I wondered whether he were aware that something was afoot; but, when he turned to help Mona with the bottles and glasses, I felt sure from their faces that neither had given a thought to any such thing.

3.

EARLY in the morning, snow was still drifting from a
darkened sky across the diamond lattices of the window-
panes; floating drearily down upon the white lawns and
grey muddy paths of a garden flanked by pines and fir
trees. Through these coniferous plantations, which arose
above thick laurel bushes, appeared at no great distance
glimpses of two or three other houses similar in style
to the one in which I found myself; the same red brick
and gables, the same walls covered with ivy or virginia
creeper.

This was, no doubt, a settlement of prosperous business
men; a reservation, like those created for indigenous inhabitants, or wild animal life, in some region invaded by
alien elements: a kind of refuge for beings unfitted to battle
with modern conditions, where they might live their own
lives, undisturbed and unexploited by an aggressive outer
world. In these confines the species might be saved from
extinction. I felt miles away from everything, lying there in
that bedroom: almost as if I were abroad. The weather was
still exceedingly cold. I thought over a conversation I had
once had with Barnby.

'Has any writer ever told the truth about women?' he
had asked.

One of Barnby's affectations was that he had read little
or nothing, although, as a matter of fact, he knew rather
thoroughly a small, curiously miscellaneous collection of
books.

'Few in this country have tried.'

'No one would believe it if they did.'

'Possibly. Nor about men either, if it comes to that.'

'I intend no cheap cynicism,' Barnby said. 'It is merely that in print the truth is not credible for those who have not thought deeply of the matter.'

'That is true of almost everything.'

'To some extent. But painting, for example—where women are concerned—is quite different from writing. In painting you can state everything there is to be said on the subject. In other words, the thing is treated purely æsthetically, almost scientifically. Writers always seem to defer to the wishes of the women themselves.'

'So do painters. What about Reynolds or Boucher?'

'Of course, of course,' said Barnby, whose capacity for disregarding points made against him would have supplied the foundation for a dazzling career at the Bar. 'But in writing—perhaps, as you say, chiefly writing in this country —there is no equivalent, say, of Renoir's painting. Renoir did not think that all women's flesh was *literally* a material like pink satin. He used that colour and texture as a convention to express in a simple manner certain pictorial ideas of his own about women. In fact he did so in order to get on with the job in other aspects of his picture. I never find anything like that in a novel.'

'You find plenty of women with flesh like that sitting in the Ritz.'

'Maybe. And I can paint them. But can you write about them?'

'No real tradition of how women behave exists in English writing. In France there is at least a good rough and ready convention, perhaps not always correct—riddled with every form of romanticism—but at least a pattern to which a writer can work. A French novelist may conform with the

69

convention, or depart from it. His readers know, more or less, which he is doing. Here, every female character has to be treated empirically.'

'Well, after all, so does every woman,' said Barnby, another of whose dialectical habits was suddenly to switch round and argue against himself. 'One of the troubles, I think, is that there are too many novelists like St. John Clarke.'

'But novelists of the first rank have not always been attracted to women physically.'

'If of the first rank,' said Barnby, 'they may rise above it. If anything less, abnormal novelists are, I believe, largely responsible for some of the extraordinary ideas that get disseminated about women and their behaviour.'

Barnby's sententious tone had already indicated to me that he was himself entangled in some new adventure. Those utterances, which Mr. Deacon used to call 'Barnby's generalisations about women', were almost always a prelude to a story involving some woman individually. So it had turned out on that occasion.

'When you first make a hit with someone,' he had continued, 'you think everything is going all right with the girl, just because it is all right with you. But when you are more used to things, you are always on your guard—prepared for trouble of one sort or another.'

'Who is it this time?'

'A young woman I met on a train.'

'How promiscuous.'

'She inspired a certain confidence.'

'And things are going wrong?'

'On the contrary, going rather well. That is what makes me suspicious.'

'Have you painted her?'

Barnby rummaged among the brushes, tubes of paint,

newspapers, envelopes and bottles that littered the table; coming at last to a large portfolio from which he took a pencil drawing. The picture was of a girl's head. She looked about twenty. The features, suggested rather than outlined, made her seem uncertain of herself, perhaps on the defensive. Her hair was untidy. There was an air of self-conscious rebellion. Something about the portrait struck me as familiar.

'What is her name?'

'I don't know.'

'Why not?'

'She won't tell me.'

'How very secretive.'

'That's what I think.'

'How often has she been here?'

'Two or three times.'

I examined the drawing again.

'I've met her.'

'Who is she?'

'I'm trying to remember.'

'Have a good think,' said Barnby, sighing. 'I like to clear these matters up.'

But for the moment I was unable to recall the girl's name. I had the impression our acquaintance had been slight, and was of a year or two earlier. There had been something absurd, or laughable, in the background of the occasion when we had met.

'It would be only polite to reveal her identity by now,' Barnby said, returning the drawing to the portfolio and making a grimace.

'How did it start?'

'I was coming back from a week-end with the Manaschs'. She arrived in the compartment about an hour before we reached London. We began to talk about films. For some reason we got on to the French Revolution. She said she was on the side of the People.'

'Dark eyes and reddish hair?'

'The latter unbrushed.'

'Christian name, Anne?'

'There was certainly an "A" on her handkerchief. That was a clue I forgot to tell you.'

'Generally untidy?'

'Decidedly. As to baths, I shouldn't think she overdid them.'

'I think I can place her.'

'Don't keep me in suspense.'

'Lady Anne Stepney.'

'A friend of yours?'

'I sat next to her once at dinner years ago. She made the same remark about the French Revolution.'

'Did she, indeed,' said Barnby, perhaps a shade piqued at this apparently correct guess. 'Did you follow up those liberal convictions at the time?'

'On the contrary. I doubt if she would even remember my name. Her sister married Charles Stringham, whom I've sometimes talked of. They are getting a divorce, so I saw in the paper.'

'Oh, yes,' said Barnby. 'I read about it too. Stringham was the Great Industrialist's secretary at one moment, wasn't he? I met him with Baby and liked him. He has that very decorative mother, Mrs. Foxe, whom really I wouldn't——'

He became silent; then returned to the subject of the girl.

'Her parents are called Bridgnorth?'

'That's it.'

'One starts these things,' Barnby said, 'and then the question arises: how is one to continue them? Before you know where you are, you are thoroughly entangled. That is what we all have to remember.'

'We do, indeed.'

Lying in bed in the Templers' house, feeling more than a little unwilling to rise into a chilly world, I thought of these words of Barnby's. There could be no doubt that I was now, as he had said, 'thoroughly entangled'.

Everyone came down late to breakfast that morning. Mona was in a decidedly bad temper. Her irritation was perhaps due to an inner awareness that a love affair was in the air, the precise location of which she was unable to identify; for I was fairly certain that neither of the Templers guessed anything was 'on' between Jean and myself. They seemed, indeed, fully occupied by the discord of their own relationship. As it happened, I found no opportunity to be alone with Jean. She seemed almost deliberately to arrange that we should always be chaperoned by one of the other two. She would once more have appeared as calm, distant, unknown to me, as when first seen, had she not twice smiled submissively, almost shyly, when our eyes met.

Mona's sulkiness cast a gloom over the house. Although obviously lazy and easy-going in her manner of life, she possessed also an energy and egotism that put considerable force behind this display of moodiness. Templer made more than one effort to cheer her up, from time to time becoming annoyed himself at his lack of success; when conciliation would suddenly turn to teasing. However, his continued attempts to fall in with his wife's whims led in due course to an unexpected development in the composition of the party.

We were sitting in a large room of nebulous character, where most of the life of the household was carried on, reading the Sunday papers, talking, and playing the gramophone. The previous night's encounter with Quiggin had enflamed Mona's memories of her career as an artist's model. She began to talk of the 'times' she had had in various studios, and to question me about Mark Members; perhaps regretting that she had allowed this link with her past to be severed so entirely. Professionally, she had never come across such figures as Augustus John, or Epstein, trafficking chiefly with a few of the lesser academic painters; though she had known a few young men, like Members and Barnby, who frequented more 'advanced' circles. She had never even sat for Isbister, so she told me. All the same, that period of her life was now sufficiently far away to be clouded with romance; at least when compared in her own mind with her married circumstances.

When I agreed that both Members and Quiggin were by then, in their different ways, quite well-known 'young writers', she became more than ever enthusiastic about them, insisting that she must meet Quiggin again. In fact conversation seemed to have been deliberately steered by her into these channels with that end in view. Templer, lying in an armchair with his legs stretched out in front of him, listened indifferently to her talk while he idly turned the pages of the *News of the World*. His wife's experiences among 'artists' probably cropped up fairly often as a subject: a regular, almost legitimate method of exciting a little domestic jealousy when life at home seemed flat. Her repeated questions at last caused me to explain the change of secretary made by St. John Clarke.

'But this is all *too* thrilling,' she said. 'I told you St. John Clarke was my favourite author. Can't we get Mr. Quiggin to lunch and ask him what really *has* happened?'

'Well——'

'Look, Pete,' she exclaimed noisily. '*Do* let's ask J. G.

74

Quiggin to lunch today. He could get a train. Nick would ring him up—you will, won't you, darling?'

Templer threw the *News of the World* on to the carpet, and, turning towards me, raised his eyebrows and nodded his head slowly up and down to indicate the fantastic lengths to which caprice could be carried by a woman.

'But would Mr. Quiggin want to come?' he asked, imitating Mona's declamatory tone. 'Wouldn't he want to finish writing one of his brilliant articles?'

'We could try.'

'By all means, if you like. Half-past eleven on the day of the luncheon invitation is considered a bit late in the best circles, but fortunately we do not move in the best circles. I suppose there will be enough to eat. You remember Jimmy is bringing a girl friend?'

'Jimmy doesn't matter.'

'I agree.'

'What do you think, Nick?' she asked. 'Would Quiggin come?'

One of the charms of staying with the Templers had seemed the promise of brief escape from that routine of the literary world so relentlessly implied by the mere thought of Quiggin. It was the world in which I was thoroughly at home, and certainly did not wish to change for another, only for once to enjoy a week-end away from it. However, to prevent the Templers from asking Quiggin to lunch if they so desired was scarcely justifiable to any-one concerned. Besides, I was myself curious to hear further details regarding St. John Clarke; although I should have preferred by then to have heard Members's side of the story. Apart from all that—indeed quite overriding such con-siderations—were my own violent feelings about Jean which had to be reduced inwardly to some manageable order.

'Who is "Jimmy"?' I asked.

'Surely you remember Jimmy Stripling when you stayed with us years ago?' said Templer. 'My brother-in-law. At least he was until Babs divorced him. Somehow I've never been able to get him out of my life. Babs can demand her freedom and go her own way. For me there is no legal redress. Jimmy hangs round my neck like a millstone. I can't even get an annulment.'

'Didn't he go in for motor racing?'

'That's the chap.'

'Who disliked Sunny Farebrother so much?'

'Hated his guts. Well, Jimmy is coming to lunch today and bringing some sort of a piece with him—he asked if he could. Not too young, I gather, so your eyes need not brighten up. I can't remember her name. I could not refuse for old times' sake, though he is a terrible bore is poor old Jimmy these days. He had a spill at Brooklands a year or two ago. Being shot out of his car arse-first seems to have affected his brain in some way—though you wouldn't think there was much there to affect.'

'What does he do?'

'An underwriter at Lloyd's. It is not his business capacity so much as his private life that has seized up. He still rakes in a certain amount of dough. But he has taken up astrology and theosophy and numerology and God knows what else. Could your friend Quiggin stand that? Probably love it, wouldn't he? The more the merrier so far as I'm concerned.'

'Quiggin would eat it up.'

'*Do* ring him, then,' said Mona.

'Shall I?'

'Go ahead,' said Templer. 'The telephone is next door.'

There was no reply from Quiggin's Bloomsbury flat, so I rang St. John Clarke's number; on the principle that if a thing is worth doing, it is worth doing well. The bell buzzed for some seconds, and then Quiggin's voice sounded, gratingly, at the other end of the line. As I had supposed, he was already engaged on his new duties. At first he was very suspicious of my seeking him out at that place. These suspicions were not allayed when I explained about the invitation to lunch with the Templers.

'But *today*?' he said, irritably. 'Lunch today? Why, it's nearly lunch-time already.'

I repeated to him Mona's apologies for the undoubted lateness of the invitation.

'But I don't know them,' said Quiggin. 'Are they very rich?'

He still sounded cross, although a certain interest was aroused in him. I referred again to his earlier meeting with Mona.

'So she remembered me at Deacon's party after all?' he asked, rather more hopefully this time.

'She has talked of nothing but that evening.'

'I don't think I ought to leave St. J.'

'Is he bad?'

'Better, as a matter of fact. But there ought to be someone responsible here.'

'Couldn't you get Mark?' I asked, to tease him.

'St. J. does not want to see Mark just at the moment,' said Quiggin, in his flattest voice, ignoring any jocular implications the question might have possessed. 'But I suppose there is really no reason why the maid should not look after him perfectly well if I went out for a few hours.'

This sounded like weakening.

'You could catch the train if you started now.'

He was silent for a moment, evidently anxious to accept, but at the same time trying to find some excuse for making himself so easily available.

'Mona reads your articles.'

77

'She does?'

'Always quoting them.'

'Intelligently?'

'Come and judge for yourself.'

'Should I like their house?'

'You'll have the time of your life.'

'I think I will,' he said. 'Of course I shall be met at the station?'

'Of course.'

'All right, then.'

He replaced the receiver with a bang, as if closing an acrimonious interchange. I returned to the drawing-room. Templer was sprawling on the sofa, apparently not much interested whether Quiggin turned up or not.

'He's coming.'

'Is he *really*?' said Mona, shrilly. 'How *wonderful*.'

'Mona gets a bit bored with my friends,' said Templer. 'I must say I don't blame her. Now you can sample something of another kind at lunch, sweetie.'

'Well, we never see anybody *interesting,* sweetie,' said Mona, putting on a stage pout. 'He'll at least remind me of the days when I *used* to meet intelligent people.'

'Intelligent people?' said Templer. 'Come, come, darling, you aren't being very polite to Nick. He regards himself as tremendously intelligent.'

'Then we are providing some intelligent company for him,' said Mona. 'Your ex-brother-in-law isn't likely to come out with anything very sparkling in the way of conversation—unless he has changed a lot since we went with him to Wimbledon.'

'What do you expect at Wimbledon?' said Templer. 'To sit in the centre court listening to a flow of epigrams about foot-faults and forehand drives? Still, I see what you mean.'

I remembered Jimmy Stripling chiefly on account of

various practical jokes in which he had been concerned when, as a boy, I had stayed with the Templers. In this horseplay he had usually had the worst of it. He remained in my memory as a big, gruff, bad-tempered fellow, full of guilty feelings about having taken no part in the war. I had not much cared for him. I wondered how he would get on with Quiggin, who could be crushing to people he disliked. However, one of the traits possessed by Quiggin in common with his new employer was a willingness to go almost anywhere where a free meal was on offer; and this realistic approach to social life implied, inevitably, if not toleration of other people, at least a certain rough and ready technique for dealing with all sorts. I could not imagine why Mona was so anxious to see Quiggin again. At that time I failed entirely to grasp the extent to which in her eyes Quiggin represented high romance.

'What happened to Babs when she parted from Jimmy Stripling?'

'Married a lord,' said Templer. 'The family is going up in the world. But I expect she still thinks about Jimmy. After all, you couldn't easily forget a man with breath like his.'

Some interruption changed the subject before I was able to ask the name of Babs's third husband. Mona went to tell the servants that there would be an additional guest. Templer followed her to look for more cigarettes. For a moment Jean and I were left alone together. I slipped my hand under her arm. She pressed down upon it, giving me a sense of being infinitely near to her; an assurance that all would be well. There is always a real and an imaginary person you are in love with; sometimes you love one best, sometimes the other. At that moment it was the real one I loved. We had scarcely time to separate and begin a formal conversation when Mona returned to the room.

79

There the four of us remained until the sound came of a car churning up snow before the front door. This was Quiggin's arrival. Being, in a way, so largely responsible for his presence at the Templers' house, I was rather relieved to observe, when he entered the room, that he had cleaned himself up a bit since the previous evening. Now he was wearing a suit of cruelly blue cloth and a green knitted tie. From the start it was evident that he intended to make himself agreeable. His sharp little eyes darted round the walls, taking in the character of his hosts and their house.

'I see you have an Isbister in the hall,' he said, dryly.

The harsh inflexion of his voice made it possible to accept this comment as a compliment, or, alternatively, a shared joke. Templer at once took the words in the latter sense.

'Couldn't get rid of it,' he said. 'I suppose you don't know anybody who would make an offer? An upset price, of course. Now's the moment.'

'I'll look about,' said Quiggin. 'Isbister was a typical artist-business man produced by a decaying society, don't you think? As a matter of fact Nicholas and I have got to have a talk about Isbister in the near future.'

He grinned at me. I hoped he was not going to raise the whole question of St. John Clarke's introduction there and then. His tone might have meant anything or nothing, so far as his offer of help was concerned. Perhaps he really intended to suggest that he would try to sell the picture for Templer; and get a rake-off. His eyes continued to stray over the very indifferent nineteenth-century seascapes that covered the walls; hung together in patches as if put up hurriedly when the place was first occupied. No doubt that was exactly what had happened to them. In the Templers' house by the sea they had hung in the dining-room. Before the Isbister could be discussed further, the two other guests arrived.

The first through the door was a tall, rather overpower-

ing lady, followed closely by Jimmy Stripling himself, looking much older than I had remembered him. The smooth-
ness of the woman's movements, as she advanced towards
Mona, almost suggested that Stripling was propelling her
in front of him like an automaton on castors. I knew at
once that I had seen her before, but could not at first recall
the occasion: one so different, as it turned out, from that of
the moment.

'How are you, Jimmy?' said Templer.

Stripling took the woman by the arm.

'This is Mrs. Erdleigh,' he said, in a rather strangled
voice. 'I have told you so much about her, you know, and
here she is.'

Mrs. Erdleigh shook hands graciously all round, much as
if she were a visiting royalty. When she came to me, she
took my hand in hers and smiled indulgently.

'You see I was right,' she said. 'You did not believe me,
did you? It is just a year.'

Once more, suffocating waves of musk-like scent were distilled by her presence. By then, as a matter of fact, a month
or two must have passed beyond the year that she had foretold would precede our next meeting. All the same, it was a
respectable piece of prognostication. I thought it wiser to
leave Uncle Giles unmentioned. If she wished to speak of
him, she could always raise the subject herself. I reflected,
at the same time, how often this exterior aspect of Uncle
Giles's personality must have remained 'unmentioned'
throughout his life; especially where his relations were concerned.

However, Mrs. Erdleigh gave the impression of knowing
very well what was advisable to 'mention' and what in-
advisable. She looked well; younger, if anything, than
when I had seen her at the Ufford, and smartly dressed in
a style that suggested less than before her inexorably

apocalyptic role in life. In fact, her clothes of that former occasion seemed now, in contrast, garments of a semi-professional kind; vestments, as it were, appropriate to the ritual of her vocation. With Stripling under her control—as he certainly was—she could no doubt allow herself frivolously to enjoy the fashion of the moment.

Stripling himself, on the other hand, had changed noticeably for the worse in the ten years or more gone since our former meeting. His bulk still gave the impression that he was taking up more than his fair share of the room, but the body, although big, seemed at the same time shrivelled. His hair, still parted in the middle, was grey and grizzled. Although at that time still perhaps under forty, he looked prematurely old. There was an odd, disconnected stare in his eyes, which started from his head when he spoke at all emphatically. He appeared to be thoroughly under the thumb of Mrs. Erdleigh, whose manner, kindly though firm, implied supervision of a person not wholly responsible for his own actions. Later, it was noticeable how fixedly he watched her, while in conversation he inclined to refer even the most minor matters to her arbitration. In spite of his cowed air, he was far more friendly than when we had met before, an occasion he assured me he remembered perfectly.

'We had a lot of fun that summer with my old pal, Sunny Farebrother, didn't we?' he said in a melancholy voice.

He spoke as if appealing for agreement that the days when fun could be had with Sunny Farebrother, or indeed with anyone else, were now long past.

'Do you remember how we were going to put a po in his hat-box or something?' he went on. 'How we all laughed. Good old Sunny. I never seem to see the old boy now, though I hear he's making quite a bit of money.

It's just the same with so many folks one used to know. They pass by on the other side or join the Great Majority.'

His face had lighted up when, upon entering the room, he had seen Jean, and he had taken both her hands in his and kissed her enthusiastically. She did not seem to regard this act as anything out of the way, nor even specially repugnant to her. I felt a twinge of annoyance at that kiss. I should have liked no one else to kiss her for at least twenty-four hours. However, I reminded myself that such familiarity was reasonable enough in an ex-brother-in-law; in fact, if it came to that, reasonable enough in any old friend; though for that reason no more tolerable to myself. Stripling also held Jean's arm for a few seconds, but, perhaps aware of Mrs. Erdleigh's eye upon him, removed his hand abruptly. Fumbling in his pocket, he produced a long gold cigarette-case and began to fill it from a packet of Players. Although physically dilapidated, he still gave the impression of being rich. The fact that his tweeds were crumpled and the cuffs of his shirt greasy somehow added to this impression of wealth. If there had been any doubt about Stripling's money, his satisfactory financial position could have been estimated from Quiggin's manner towards him, a test like litmus paper where affluence was concerned. Quiggin was evidently anxious—as I was myself—to learn more of this strange couple.

'How's the world, Jimmy?' said Templer, clapping his former brother-in-law on the back, and catching my eye as he handed him an unusually stiff drink.

'Well,' said Stripling, speaking slowly, as if Templer's enquiry deserved very serious consideration before an answer was made, 'well, I don't think the *World* will get much better as long as it clings to material values.'

At this Quiggin laughed in a rather more aggressive manner than he had adopted hitherto. He was evidently trying to decide whether it would be better to be ingratiating to Stripling or to attack him; either method could be advantageous from its respective point of view.

'I think material values are just what want reassessing,' Quiggin said. 'Nor do I see how we can avoid clinging to them, since they are the only values that truly exist. However, they might be linked with a little social justice for a change.'

Stripling disregarded this remark, chiefly, I think, because his mind was engrossed with preoccupations so utterly different that he had not the slightest idea what Quiggin was talking about. Templer's eyes began to brighten as he realised that elements were present that promised an enjoyable clash of opinions. Luncheon was announced. We passed into the dining-room. As I sat down at the table I saw Mrs. Erdleigh's forefinger touch Mona's hand.

'As soon as I set eyes on you, my dear,' she said, gently, 'I knew that you belonged to the Solstice of Summer. When *is* your birthday?'

As usual, her misty gaze seemed to envelop completely whomsoever she addressed. There could be no doubt that her personality had immediately delighted Mona, who had by then already lost all her earlier sulkiness. Indeed, as the meal proceeded, Mrs. Erdleigh showed herself to be just what Mona had required. She provided limitlessly a kind of conversational balm at once maternal and sacerdotal. The two of them settled down to a detailed discussion across the table of horoscopes and their true relation to peculiarities of character. I was for some reason reminded of Sillery dealing with some farouche undergraduate whom he wished especially to enclose within his net. Even Mona's so recently excited interest in Quiggin was forgotten in this torrent of astrological self-examination, systematically controlled, in spite of its urgency of expression, by such a sympathetic informant. Mona seemed now entirely absorbed in Mrs. Erdleigh, whose manner, vigorous, calm, mystical, certainly dominated the luncheon table.

The meal passed off, therefore, with more success than might have been expected from such oddly assorted company. I reflected, not for the first time, how mistaken it is to suppose there exists some 'ordinary' world into which it is possible at will to wander. All human beings, driven as they are at different speeds by the same Furies, are at close range equally extraordinary. This party's singular composition was undoubtedly enhanced by the common-place nature of its surroundings. At the same time it was evident that the Templers themselves saw nothing in the least out-of-the-way about the guests collected round their table for Sunday luncheon; except possibly the fact that both Quiggin and I were professionally connected with books.

If Quiggin disapproved—and he did undoubtedly dis-approve—of the turn taken by Mona's and Mrs. Erdleigh's talk, he made at first no effort to indicate his dissatisfaction. He was in possession of no clue to the fact that he had been arbitrarily deposed from the position of most honoured guest in the house that day. In any case, as a person who himself acted rarely if ever from frivolous or disinterested motives, he would have found it hard, perhaps impossible, to understand the sheer irresponsibility of his invitation. To have been asked simply and solely on account of Mona's whim, if he believed that to be the reason, must have been in itself undeniably flattering to his vanity; but, as Mr. Deacon used sadly to remark, 'those who enjoy the delights of caprice must also accustom themselves to bear caprice's lash'. Even if Quiggin were aware of this harsh law's operation, he had no means of appreciating the ruthless manner in which it had been put into execution that afternoon. Mona's wish to see him had been emphasised by me when I had spoken with him on the telephone. If she continued to ignore him, Quiggin would logically assume that for one reason or another either Templer, or I myself, must have desired his presence. He would suspect some ulterior motive as soon as he began to feel sceptical as to Mona's interest in him being the cause of his invitation. As the meal progressed, this lack of attention on her part undoubtedly renewed earlier suspicions. By the time we were drinking coffee he was already showing signs of becoming less amenable.

I think this quite fortuitous situation brought about by the presence of Mrs. Erdleigh was not without effect on Quiggin's future behaviour towards Mona herself. If Mrs. Erdleigh had not been at the table he would undoubtedly have received the full force of his hostess's admiration. This would naturally have flattered him, but his shrewdness would probably also have assessed her deference as something fairly superficial. As matters turned out, apparent disregard for him keenly renewed his own former interest in her. Perhaps Quiggin thought she was deliberately hiding her true feelings at luncheon. Perhaps he was right in thinking that. With a woman it is impossible to say.

In the early stages of the meal Quiggin had been perfectly agreeable, talking to Jean of changes taking place in contemporary poetry, and of the personalities involved in these much advertised literary experiments. He explained that he considered the work of Mark Members commendable, if more than a trifle old-fashioned.

'Mark has developed smoothly from beginnings legitimately influenced by Browning, paused perhaps too long in byways frequented by the Symbolists, and reached in his own good time a categorically individual style and

86

phraseology. Unfortunately his *œuvre* is at present lacking in any real sense of social significance.'

He glanced at Mona after saying this, perhaps hoping that a former friend of Gypsy Jones might notice the political implications of his words. However he failed to catch her attention, and turned almost immediately to lighter matters, evidently surprising even Templer by sagacious remarks regarding restaurant prices in the South of France, and an unexpected familiarity with the *Barrio chino* quarter in Barcelona. However, in spite of this conversational versatility, I was aware that Quiggin was inwardly turning sour. This could be seen from time to time in his face, especially in the glances of dislike he was beginning to cast in the direction of Stripling. He had probably decided that, rich though Stripling might be, he was not worth cultivating.

Stripling, for his part, did not talk much; when he spoke chiefly addressing himself to Jean. He had shown—perhaps not surprisingly—no interest whatever in Quiggin's admirably lucid exposition of the New School's poetic diction, in which Communist convictions were expressed in unexpected metre and rhyme. On the other hand Stripling did sometimes rouse himself in an attempt to break into the stream of astrological chatter that bubbled between Mrs. Erdleigh and Mona. His mind seemed to wander perpetually through the mystic territories of clairvoyance, a world of the spirit no doubt incarnate to him in Mrs. Erdleigh herself. Although this appearance of permanent preoccupation, coupled with his peculiar, jerky manner, conveyed the impression that he might not be quite sane, Templer seemed to attach more importance to Stripling's City gossip than his father had ever done. Mr. Templer, I remembered, had been very curt with his son-in-law when financial matters were in question.

All the while I felt horribly bored with the whole lot of them, longing to be alone once more with Jean, and yet also in some odd manner almost dreading the moment when that time should come; one of those mixed sensations so characteristic of intense emotional excitement. There is always an element of unreality, perhaps even of slight absurdity, about someone you love. It seemed to me that she was sitting in an awkward, almost melodramatic manner, half-turned towards Quiggin, while she crumbled her bread with fingers long and subtly shaped. I seemed to be looking at a picture of her, yet felt that I could easily lose control of my senses, and take her, then and there, in my arms.

'But in these days you can't believe in such things as astrology,' said Quiggin. 'Why, even apart from other considerations, the very astronomical discoveries made since the time of the ancients have negatived what was once thought about the stars.'

We had returned to the drawing-room. Already it was obvious that the afternoon must be spent indoors. The leaden, sunless sky, from which sleet was now falling with a clatter on to the frozen snow of the lawn, created in the house an atmosphere at once gloomy and sinister: a climate in itself hinting of necromancy. The electric light had to be turned on, just as if we were sitting in the lounge of the Ufford. The heavy claret drunk at luncheon prompted a desire to lie at full length on the sofa, or at least to sit well back and stretch out the legs and yawn. For a second —soft and exciting and withdrawn immediately—I felt Jean's hand next to mine on the cushion. Quiggin lurked in the corners of the room, pretending to continue his examination of the pictures, his silence scarcely concealing the restlessness that had overtaken him. From time to time he shot out a remark, more or less barbed. He must by then

88

have tumbled to the implications of his own status at the party. Nettled at Mrs. Erdleigh's capture of Mona, he was probably planning how best to express his irritation openly.

'Oh, but I *do*,' said Mona, drawling out the words. 'I think those occult things are almost always right. They are in my case, I *know*.'

'Yes, yes,' said Quiggin, brushing aside this affirmation with a tolerant grin, as the mere fancy of a pretty girl, and at the same time addressing himself more directly to Stripling, at whom his first attack had certainly been aimed, 'but *you* can't believe all that—a hard-headed business man like yourself?'

'That's just it,' said Stripling, ignoring, in fact probably not noticing, the sneering, disagreeable tone of Quiggin's voice. 'It's just the fact that I *am* occupied all day long with material things that makes me realise they are not the whole of life.'

However, his eyes began to start from his head, so that he was perhaps becoming aware that Quiggin was deliberately teasing him. No doubt he was used to encountering a certain amount of dissent from his views, though opposition was probably not voiced as usual in so direct and dialectical a manner as this. Quiggin continued to smile derisively.

'You certainly find in me no champion of the City's methods,' he said. 'But at least what you call "material things" represent reality.'

'Hardly at all.'

'Oh, come.'

'Money is a delusion.'

'Not if you haven't got any.'

'That is just when you realise most money's unreality.'

'Why not get rid of yours, then?'

89

'I might any day.'

'Let me know when you decide to.'

'You must understand the thread that runs through life,' said Stripling, now speaking rather wildly, and looking stranger than ever. 'It does not matter that there may be impurities and errors in one man's method of seeking the Way. What matters is that he *is* seeking it—and knows there is a Way to be found.'

'Commencement—Opposition—Equilibrium,' said Mrs. Erdleigh in her softest voice, as if to offer Stripling some well-earned moral support. 'You can't get away from it— Thesis—Antithesis—Synthesis.'

'That's just what I mean,' said Stripling, as if her words brought him instant relief. 'Brahma—Vishnu—Siva.'

'It all sounded quite Hegelian until you brought in the Indian gods,' said Quiggin angrily.

He would no doubt have continued to argue had not a new element been introduced at this moment by Jean: an object that became immediately the focus of attention.

While this discussion had been in progress she had slipped from the room. I had been wondering how I could myself quietly escape from the others and look for her, when she returned carrying in her hand what first appeared to be a small wooden palette for oil paints. Two castors, or wheels, were attached to this heart-shaped board, the far end of which was transfixed with a lead pencil. I recalled the occasion when Sunny Farebrother had ruined so many of Stripling's starched collars in a patent device in which he had a business interest, and I wondered whether this was something of a similar kind. However, Mrs. Erdleigh immediately recognised the significance of the toy and began to laugh a little reprovingly.

'Planchette?' she said. 'You know, I really rather dis- approve. I do not think Good Influences make themselves known through Planchette as a rule. And the things it writes cause such a lot of bad feeling sometimes.'

'It really belongs to Baby,' said Jean. 'She heard of it somewhere and made Sir Magnus Donners get her one. She brought it round to us once when she was feeling depressed about some young man of hers. We couldn't make it work. She forgot to take it away and I have been carrying it round—meaning to give it back to her—ever since.'

Stripling's eyes lit up and began once more to dilate.

'Shall we do it?' he asked, in a voice that shook slightly. 'Do let's.'

'Well,' said Mrs. Erdleigh, speaking kindly, as if to a child who has proposed a game inevitably associated with the breakage of china, 'I *know* trouble will come of it if we do.'

'But for once,' begged Stripling. 'Don't you think for once, Myra? It's such a rotten afternoon.'

'Then don't complain afterwards that I did not warn you.'

Although I had often heard of Planchette, I had never, as it happened, seen the board in operation; and I felt some curiosity myself to discover whether its writings would indeed set down some of the surprising disclosures occasionally described by persons in the habit of playing with it. The very name was new to both the Templers. Stripling explained that the machine was placed above a piece of blank paper, upon which the pencil wrote words, when two or three persons lightly rested their fingers upon the wooden surface: castors and pencil point moving without deliberate agency. Stripling was obviously delighted to be allowed for once to indulge in this forbidden practice, in spite of Mrs. Erdleigh's tempered disparagement. Whether her disapproval was really deep-seated, or due merely to a conviction that the game was unwise in that particular company, could only be guessed.

Quiggin was plainly annoyed; even rather insulted, at this step taken towards an actual physical attempt to invoke occult forces.

'I thought such things had been forgotten since the court of Napoleon III,' he said. 'You don't really believe it will write anything, do you?'

'You may be surprised by the knowledge it displays of your own life, old chap,' said Stripling, with an effort to recover the breeziness of earlier days.

'Obviously—when someone is rigging it.'

'It's hardly possible to rig it, old chap. You try and write something, just using the board by yourself. You'll find it damned difficult.'

Quiggin gave an annoyed laugh. Some sheets of foolscap, blue and ruled with red lines for keeping accounts, were found in a drawer. One of these large sheets of paper was set out upon a table. The experiment began with Mona, Stripling and Mrs. Erdleigh as executants, the last of whom, having once registered her protest, showed no un-graciousness in her manner of joining the proceedings, if they were fated to take place. Templer obviously felt com-plete scepticism regarding the whole matter, which he could not be induced to take seriously even to the extent of agreeing to participate. Quiggin, too, refused to join in, though he showed an almost feverish interest in what was going forward.

Naturally, Quiggin was delighted when, after a trial of several minutes, no results whatever were achieved. Then the rest of us, in various combinations of persons, attempted to work the board. All these efforts were unsuccessful. Sometimes the pencil shot violently across the surface of the paper, covering sheet after sheet, as a new surface was substituted, with dashes and scribbles. More often, it would not move at all.

'You none of you seem to be getting very far,' said Templer.

'It may be waste of time,' said Mrs. Erdleigh. 'Planchette can be very capricious. Perhaps there is an unsympathetic presence in the room.'

'I should not be at all surprised,' said Quiggin, speaking with elaborately satirical emphasis.

He stood with his heels on the fender, his hands in his pockets—rather in the position Le Bas used to adopt when giving a lecture on wiping your boots before coming into the house—very well pleased with the course things were taking.

'I think you are horrid,' said Mona.

She made a face at him; in itself a sign of a certain renewed interest.

'I don't think you ought to believe in such things,' said Quiggin, nasally.

"But I *do*.'

She smiled encouragingly. She had probably begun to feel that occult phenomena, at least by its absence, was proving itself a bore; and that perhaps she might find more fun in returning to her original project of exploring Quiggin's own possibilities. However, this exchange between them was immediately followed by sudden development among the group resting their fingers on the board. Jean and Mona had been trying their luck with Stripling as third partner. Jean now rose from the table, and, dropping one of those glances at once affectionate and enquiring that raised such a storm within me, she said: 'You have a go.'

I took the chair and placed my fingers lightly where hers had been. Previously, when I had formed a trio with Mrs.

Erdleigh and Mona—who had insisted on being party to every session—nothing of note had happened. Now, almost at once, Planchette began to move in a slow, regular motion.

At first, from the 'feel' of the movement, I thought Stripling must be manipulating the board deliberately. A glassy look had come into his eye and his loose, rather brutal mouth sagged open. Then the regular, up-and-down rhythm came abruptly to an end. The pencil, as if impatient of all of us, shot off the paper on to the polished wood of the table. A sentence had been written. It was inverted from where Stripling was sitting. In fact the only person who could reasonably be accused of having written the words was myself. The script was long and sloping, Victorian in character. Mrs. Erdleigh took a step forward and read it aloud:

'Karl is not pleased.'

There was great excitement at this. Everyone crowded round our chairs.

'You must ask who "Karl" is,' said Mrs. Erdleigh, smiling.

She was the only one who remained quite unmoved by this sudden manifestation. Such things no longer surprised her. Quiggin, on the other hand, moved quickly round to my side of the table. He seemed divided between a wish to accuse me of having written these words as a hoax, and at the same time an unwillingness to make the admission, obviously necessary in the circumstances, that any such deception must have required quite exceptional manipulative agility. In the end he said nothing, but stood there frowning hard at me.

'Is it Karl speaking?' asked Stripling, in a respectful, indeed reverential voice.

We replaced our hands on the board.

'Who else,' wrote Planchette.

'Shall we continue?'

'*Antwortet er immer.*'

'Is that German?' said Stripling.

'What does it mean, Pete?' Mona called out shrilly.

Templer looked a little surprised at this.

'Isn't it: "He always answers"?' he said. 'My German is strictly commercial—not intended for communication with the Next World.'

'Have you a message? Please write in English if you do not mind.'

Stripling's voice again trembled a little when he said this. '*Nothing to the Left.*'

This was decidedly enigmatic.

'Does he mean we should move the coffee tray?' Mona almost shouted, now thoroughly excited. 'He doesn't say whose left. Perhaps we should clear the whole table.'

Quiggin took a step nearer.

'Which of you is faking this?' he said roughly. 'I believe it is you, Nick.'

He was grinning hard, but I could see that he was extremely irritated. I pointed out that I could not claim to write neat Victorian calligraphy sideways, and also upside-down, at considerable speed: especially when unable to see the paper written upon.

'You must know "Nothing to the Left" is a quotation,' Quiggin insisted.

'Who said it?'

'You got a degree in history, didn't you?'

'I must have missed out that bit.'

'Robespierre, of course,' said Quiggin, with great contempt. 'He was speaking politically. Does no one in this country take politics seriously?'

I could not understand why he had become quite so angry.

'Let's get on with it,' said Templer, now at last beginning

to show some interest. 'Perhaps he'll make himself clearer
if pressed.'

'This is *too* exciting,' said Mona.

She clasped her hands together. We tried again.

'*Wives in common.*'

This was an uncomfortable remark. It was impossible
to guess what the instrument might write next. However,
everyone was far too engrossed to notice whether the
comment had brought embarrassment to any individual
present.

'Look here——' began Quiggin.

Before he could complete the sentence, the board began
once more to race beneath our fingers.

'*Force is the midwife.*'

'I hope he isn't going to get too obstetric,' said Templer.

Quiggin turned once more towards me. He was definitely
in a rage.

'You must know where these phrases come from,' he
said. 'You can't be as ignorant as that.'

'Search me.'

'You are trying to be funny.'

'Never less.'

'Marx, of course, Marx,' said Quiggin testily, but perhaps
wavering in his belief that I was responsible for faking the
writing. '*Das Kapital*. . . . The Communist Manifesto.'

'So it's Karl Marx, is it?' asked Mona.

The name was evidently vaguely familiar to her, no
doubt from her earlier days when she had known Gypsy
Jones; had perhaps even taken part in such activities as selling *War Never Pays!*

'Don't be ridiculous,' said Quiggin, by implication including Mona in this reproof, probably more violently than
he intended. 'It was quite obvious that one of you was
rigging the thing. I admit I can't at present tell which of

you it was. I suspect it was Nick, as he is the only one who knows I am a practising Marxist—and he persuaded me to come here.'

'I didn't know anything of the sort—and I've already told you I can't write upside-down.'

'Steady on,' said Templer. 'You can't accuse a fellow guest of cheating at Planchette. Duels have been fought for less. This will turn into another Tranby Croft case unless we moderate our tone.'

Quiggin made a despairing gesture at such frivolity of manner.

'I can't believe no one present knows the quotation, "Force is the midwife of every old society pregnant with a new one," ' he said. 'You will be telling me next you never heard the words, "The Workers have no country." '

'I believe Karl Marx has been "through" before,' said Stripling, slowly and with great solemnity. 'Wasn't he a revolutionary writer?'

'He was,' said Quiggin, with heavy irony. 'He *was* a revolutionary writer.'

'*Do* let's try again,' said Mona.

This time the writing changed to a small, niggling hand, rather like that of Uncle Giles.

'*He is sick.*'

'Who is sick?'

'*You know well.*'

'Where is he?'

'*In his room.*'

'Where is his room?'

'*The House of Books.*'

The writing was getting smaller and smaller. I felt as if I were taking part in one of those scenes from *Alice in Wonderland* in which the characters change their size.

'What can it mean now?' asked Mona.

'*You have a duty.*'

Quiggin's temper seemed to have moved from annoyance, mixed with contempt, to a kind of general uneasiness.

'I suppose it isn't talking about St. John Clarke,' I suggested.

Quiggin's reaction to this remark was unexpectedly violent. His sallow skin went white, and, instead of speaking with his usual asperity, he said in a quiet, worried voice: 'I was beginning to wonder just the same thing. I don't know that I really ought to have left him. Look here, can I ring up the flat—just to make sure that everything is all right?'

'Of course,' said Templer.

'This way?'

We tried again. Before Quiggin had reached the door, the board had moved and stopped. This time the result was disappointing. Planchette had written a single word, mono-syllabic and indecent. Mona blushed.

'That sometimes happens,' said Mrs. Erdleigh, calmly.

She spoke as if it were as commonplace to see such things written on blue ruled accounting paper as on the door or wall of an alley. Neatly detaching that half of the sheet, she tore it into small pieces and threw them into the waste-paper basket.

'Only too often,' said Stripling with a sigh.

He had evidently accepted the fact that his enjoyment for that afternoon was at an end. Mona giggled.

'We will stop now,' said Mrs. Erdleigh, speaking with the voice of authority. 'It is really no use continuing when a Bad Influence once breaks through.'

'I'm surprised he knew such a word,' said Templer.

We sat for a time in silence. Quiggin's action in going to the telephone possessed the force of one of those utterly unexpected conversions, upon which a notorious drunkard swears never again to touch alcohol, or a declared pacifist enlists in the army. It was scarcely credible that Planchette should have sent him bustling out of the room to enquire after St. John Clarke's health, even allowing for the importance to himself of the novelist as a livelihood.

'We shall have to be departing soon, *mon cher*,' said Mrs. Erdleigh, showing Stripling the face of her watch.

'Have some tea,' said Templer. 'It will be appearing at any moment.'

'No, we shall certainly have to be getting along, Pete,' said Stripling, as if conscious that, having been indulged over Planchette, he must now behave himself specially well. 'It has been a wonderful afternoon. Quite like the old days. Wish old Sunny could have been here. Most interesting too.'

He had evidently not taken in Quiggin's reason for hurrying to the telephone, nor had any idea of the surprising effect that Planchette's last few sentences had had on such a professional sceptic. Perhaps he would have been pleased to know that Quiggin had acquired at least enough belief to be thrown into a nervous state by those cryptic remarks. More probably, he would not have been greatly interested. For Stripling, this had been a perfectly normal manner of passing his spare time. He would never be able to conceive how far removed were such activities from Quiggin's daily life and manner of approaching the world. In Stripling, profound belief had taken the place of any sort of halting imagination he might once have claimed.

Quiggin now reappeared. He was even more disturbed than before.

'I am afraid I must go home immediately,' he said, in some agitation. 'Do you know when there is a train? And can I be taken to the station? It is really rather urgent.'

'Is he dying?' asked Mona, in an agonised voice.

She was breathless with excitement at the apparent confirmation of a message from what Mrs. Erdleigh called 'the Other Side'. She took Quiggin's arm, as if to soothe him. He did not answer at once, apparently undecided at what should be made public. Then he addressed himself to me.

'The telephone was answered by Mark,' he said, through his teeth.

For Quiggin to discover Members reinstated in St. John Clarke's flat within a few hours of his own departure was naturally a serious matter.

'And *is* St. John Clarke worse?'

'I couldn't find out for certain,' said Quiggin, almost wretchedly, 'but I think he must be for Mark to be allowed back. I suppose St. J. wanted something done in a hurry, and told the maid to ring up Mark as I wasn't there. I must go at once.'

He turned towards the Templers.

'I am afraid there is no train for an hour,' Templer said, 'but Jimmy is on his way to London, aren't you, Jimmy? He will give you a lift.'

'Of course, old chap, of course.'

'Of course he can. So you can go with dear old Jimmy and arrive in London in no time. He drives like hell.'

'No longer,' said Mrs. Erdleigh, with a smile. 'He drives with care.'

I am sure that the last thing Quiggin wanted at that moment was to be handed over to Stripling and Mrs. Erdleigh, but there was no alternative if he wanted to get to London with the least possible delay. A curious feature of the afternoon had been the manner in which all direct contact between himself and Mrs. Erdleigh had somehow been avoided. Each no doubt realised to the full that the other possessed nothing to offer: that any exchange of energy would have been waste of time.

In Quiggin's mind, the question of St. John Clarke's

worsened state of health, as such, had now plainly given place to the more immediate threat of Members re-entering the novelist's household on a permanent footing. His fear that the two developments might be simultaneous was, I feel sure, not necessarily based upon entirely cynical premises. In a weakened state, St. John Clarke might easily begin to regret his earlier suspension of Members as a secretary. Sick persons often vacillate. Quiggin's anxiety was understandable. No doubt he regarded himself, politically and morally, as a more suitable secretary than Members. It was, therefore, reasonable that he should wish to return as soon as possible to the field of operations.

Recognising at once that he must inevitably accompany the two of them, Quiggin accepted Stripling's offer of conveyance. He did this with a bad grace, but at the same time insistently, to show there must be no delay now the matter had been decided. This sudden disintegration of the party was displeasing to Mona, who probably felt now that she had wasted her opportunity of having Quiggin in the house; just as on the previous day she had wasted her meeting with him in the Ritz. She seemed, at any rate, overwhelmed with vague, haunting regrets for the manner in which things had turned out; all that unreasoning bitterness and mortification to which women are so subject. For a time she begged them to stay, but it was no good.

'But *promise* you will ring up.'

She took Quiggin's hand. He seemed surprised, perhaps even rather touched at the warmth with which she spoke. He replied with more feeling than was usual in his manner that he would certainly communicate with her.

'I will let you know how St. J. is.'

'Oh, *do*.'

'Without fail.'

'Don't forget.'

Mrs. Erdleigh, in her travelling clothes, had reverted to my first impression of her at the Ufford as priestess of some esoteric cult. Wrapped about with scarves, veils and stoles, she took my hand.

'Have you met *her* yet?' she enquired in a low voice.

'Yes.'

'Just as I told you?'

'Yes.'

Mrs. Erdleigh smiled to herself. They piled into the car, Quiggin glowering in the back, hatless, but with a fairly thick overcoat. Stripling drove off briskly, sending the crisp snow in a shower from the wheels. The car disappeared into the gloomy shadows of the conifers.

We returned to the drawing-room. Templer threw himself into an armchair.

'What a party,' he said. 'Poor old Jimmy really has landed something this time. I wouldn't be surprised if he didn't have to marry that woman. She's like Rider Haggard's *She—She who must be obeyed.*'

'I thought she was wonderful,' said Mona.

'So does Jimmy,' said Templer. 'You know, I can see a look of Babs. Something in the way she carries herself.'

I, too, had noticed an odd, remote resemblance in Mrs. Erdleigh to his elder sister. However, Mona disagreed strongly, and they began to argue.

'It was extraordinary all that stuff about Marx coming up,' said Templer. 'I suppose it was swilling about in old Quiggin's head and somehow got released.'

'Of course, you can never believe anything you can't explain quite simply,' said Mona.

'Why should I?' said Templer.

Tea merged into drinks. Mona's temper grew worse. I began to feel distinctly tired. Jean had brought out some work, and was sewing. Templer yawned in his chair. I wondered why he and his wife did not get on better. It was extraordinary that he seemed to please so many girls, and yet not her.

'It was a pretty stiff afternoon,' he said.

'I enjoyed it,' said Mona. 'It was a change.'

'It certainly was.'

They began to discuss Planchette again; ending inevitably in argument. Mona stood up.

'Let's go out tonight.'

'Where to?'

'We could dine at Skindles.'

'We've done that exactly a thousand and twenty-seven times. I've counted.'

'Then the Ace of Spades.'

'You know how I feel about the Ace of Spades after what happened to me there.'

'But I like it.'

'Anyway, wouldn't it be nicer to eat in tonight? Unless Nick and Jean are mad to make a night of it.'

I had no wish to go out to dinner; Jean was non-committal. The Templers continued to argue. Suddenly Mona burst into tears.

'You never want to do *anything* I want,' she said. 'If I can't go out. I shall go to bed. They can send up something on a tray. As a matter of fact I haven't been feeling well all day.'

She turned from him, and almost ran from the room.

'Oh, hell,' said Templer. 'I suppose I shall have to see about this. Help yourselves to another drink when you're ready.'

He followed his wife through the door. Jean and I were alone. She gave me her hand, smiling, but resisting a closer embrace.

'Tonight?'

'No.'

'Why not?'

'Not a good idea.'

'I see.'

'Sorry.'

'When?'

'Any time.'

'Will you come to my flat?'

'Of course.'

'When?'

'I've told you. Any time you like.'

'Tuesday?'

'No, not Tuesday.'

'Wednesday, then?'

'I can't manage Wednesday either.'

'But you said any time.'

'Any time but Tuesday or Wednesday.'

I tried to remember what plans were already made, and which could be changed. Thursday was a tangle of engagements, hardly possible to rearrange at short notice without infinite difficulties arising. Matters must be settled quickly, because Templer might return to the room at any moment.

'Friday?'

She looked doubtful. I thought she was going to insist on Thursday. Perhaps the idea of doing so had crossed her mind. A measure of capriciousness is, after all, natural in women; perhaps fulfils some physiological need for both sexes. A woman who loves you likes to torment you from time to time; if not actually hurt you. If her first intention had been to make further difficulties, she abandoned the idea, but at the same time she did not speak. She seemed to have no sense of the urgency of making some arrangement quickly—so that we should not lose touch with each other, and be reduced to the delay of writing letters. I suffered some agitation. This conversation was failing entirely to express my own feelings. Perhaps it seemed equally unreal to her. If so, she was unwilling, perhaps unable, to alleviate the strain. Probably women enjoy such moments, which undoubtedly convey by intensity and uncertainty a heightened awareness of their power. In spite of apparent coldness of manner her eyes were full of tears. As if we had already decided upon some definite and injudicious arrangement, she suddenly changed her approach.

'You must be discreet,' she said.

'All right.'

'But really discreet.'

'I promise.'

'You will?'

'Yes.'

While talking, we had somehow come close together in a manner that made practical discussion difficult. I felt tired, and rather angry, and very much in love with her; on the edge of one of those outbursts of irritation so easily excited by love.

'I'll come to your flat on Friday,' she said abruptly.

4.

WHEN, in early spring, pale sunlight was flickering behind the mist above Piccadilly, the Isbister Memorial Exhibition opened on the upper floor of one of the galleries there. I was attending the private view, partly for business reasons, partly from a certain weakness for bad pictures, especially bad portraits. Such a taste is hard to justify. Perhaps the inclination is no more than a morbid curiosity to see how far the painter will give himself away. Pictures, apart from their æsthetic interest, can achieve the mysterious fascination of those enigmatic scrawls on walls, the expression of Heaven knows what psychological urge on the part of the executant; for example, the for ever anonymous drawing of Widmerpool in the *cabinet* at La Grenadière.

In Isbister's work there was something of that inner madness. The deliberate naïveté with which he accepted his business men, ecclesiastics and mayors, depicted by him with all the crudeness of his accustomed application of paint to canvas, conveyed an oddly sinister effect. Perhaps it would be more accurate to say that Isbister set out to paint what he supposed to be the fashionable view of such people at any given moment. Thus, in his early days, a general, or the chairman of some big concern, would be represented in the respectively appropriate terms of Victorian romantic success; the former, hero of the battlefield: the latter, the industrious apprentice who has achieved his worthy ambition. But as military authority and commercial achievement became increasingly subject to political and economic denigration, Isbister, keeping up with the times, introduced a certain amount of what he judged to be satirical comment. Emphasis would be laid on the general's red face and medals, or the industrialist's huge desk and cigar. There would be a suggestion that all was not well with such people about. Probably Isbister was right from a financial point of view to make this change, because certainly his sitters seemed to grow no fewer. Perhaps they too felt a compulsive need for representation in contemporary idiom, even though a tawdry one. It was a kind of insurance against the attacks of people like Quiggin: a form of public apology and penance. The result was certainly curious. Indeed, often, even when there hung near-by something far worthier of regard, I found myself stealing a glance at an Isbister, dominating, by its aggressive treatment, the other pictures hanging about.

If things had turned out as they should, *The Art of Horace Isbister* would have been on sale at the table near the door, over which a young woman with a pointed nose and black fringe presided. As things were, it was doubtful whether that volume would ever appear. The first person I saw in the gallery was Sir Gavin Walpole-Wilson, who stood in the centre of the room, disregarding the pictures, but watching the crowd over the top of huge horn-rimmed spectacles, which he had pushed well forward on his nose. His shaggy homespun overcoat was swinging open, stuffed with long envelopes and periodicals which protruded from the pockets. He looked no older; perhaps a shade less sane. We had not met since the days when I used to dine with the Walpole-Wilsons for 'debutante dances'; a period now infinitely remote. Rather to my surprise he appeared to recognise me immediately, though it was unlikely that he knew my name. I enquired after Eleanor.

'Spends all her time in the country now,' said Sir Gavin. 'As you may remember, Eleanor was never really happy away from Hinton.'

He spoke rather sadly. I knew he was confessing his own and his wife's defeat. His daughter had won the long conflict with her parents. I wondered if Eleanor still wore her hair in a bun at the back and trained dogs with a whistle. It was unlikely that she would have changed much.

'I expect she finds plenty to do,' I offered.

'Her breeding keeps her quiet,' said Sir Gavin.

He spoke almost with distaste. However, perceiving that I felt uncertain as to the precise meaning of this explanation of Eleanor's existing state, he added curtly:

'Labradors.'

'Like Sultan?'

'After Sultan died she took to breeding them. And then she sees quite a lot of her friend, Norah Tolland.'

By common consent we abandoned the subject of Eleanor. Taking my arm, he led me across the floor of the gallery, until we stood in front of a three-quarter-length picture of a grey-moustached man in the uniform of the diplomatic corps; looking, if the truth be known, not unlike Sir Gavin himself.

'Isn't it terrible?'

'Awful.'

'It's Saltonstall,' said Sir Gavin, his voice suggesting that some just retribution had taken place. 'Saltonstall who always posed as *a Man of Taste*.'

'Isbister has made him look more like a Christmas Tree of Taste.'

'You see, my father-in-law's portrait is a different matter,' said Sir Gavin, as if unable to withdraw his eyes from this likeness of his former colleague. 'There is no parallel at all. My father-in-law was painted by Isbister, it is true. Isbister was what he liked. He possessed a large collection of thoroughly bad pictures which we had some difficulty in disposing of at his death. He bought them simply and solely because he liked the subjects. He knew about shipping and finance—not about painting. But he did not pose as a Man of Taste. Far from it.'

'Deacon's *Boyhood of Cyrus* in the hall at Eaton Square is from his collection, isn't it?'

I could not help mentioning this picture that had once meant so much to me; and to name the dead is always a kind of tribute to them: one I felt Mr. Deacon deserved.

'I believe so,' said Sir Gavin. 'It sounds his style. But Saltonstall, on the other hand, with his *vers de société*, and all his talk about Foujita and Pruna and goodness knows who else—but when it comes to his own portrait, it's Isbister. Let's see how they have hung my father-in-law.'

We passed on to Lord Aberavon's portrait, removed from its usual place in the dining-room at Hinton Hoo, now flanked by Sir Horrocks Rusby, K.C., and Cardinal Whelan. Lady Walpole-Wilson's father had been painted in peer's robes over the uniform of a deputy-lieutenant, different tones of scarlet contrasted against a crimson velvet curtain: a pictorial experiment that could not be considered successful. Through french windows behind Lord Aberavon stretched a broad landscape—possibly the vale of Glamorgan—in which something had also gone seriously wrong with the colour values. Even Isbister himself, in his own lifetime, must have been aware of deficiency.

I glanced at the cardinal next door, notable as the only picture I had ever heard Widmerpool spontaneously praise. Here, too, the reds had been handled with some savagery. Sir Gavin shook his head and moved on to examine two of Isbister's genre pictures. 'Clergyman eating an apple' and 'The Old Humorists'. I found myself beside Clapham, a director of the firm that published St. John Clarke's books. He was talking to Smethyck, a museum official I had known slightly at the university.

'When is your book on Isbister appearing?' Clapham asked at once. 'You announced it some time ago. This would have been the moment—with the St. John Clarke introduction.'

Clapham had spoken accusingly, his voice implying the fretfulness of all publishers that one of their authors should betray them with a colleague, however lightly.

'I went to see St. John Clarke the other day,' Clapham continued. 'I was glad to find him making a good recovery after his illness. Found him reading one of the young Communist poets. We had an interesting talk.'

'Does anybody read St. John Clarke himself now?' asked Smethyck, languidly.

Like many of his profession, Smethyck was rather proud of his looks, which he had been carefully re-examining in the dark, mirror-like surface of Sir Horrocks Rusby, framed for some unaccountable reason under glass. Clapham was up in arms at once at such superciliousness.

'Of course people read St. John Clarke,' he said, snappishly. 'Though perhaps not in your ultra-sophisticated circles, where everything ordinary people understand is sneered at.'

'Personally, I don't hold any views about St. John Clarke,' said Smethyck, without looking round. 'I've never read any of them. All I wanted to know was whether people bought his books.'

He continued to ponder the cut of his suit in this adventitious looking-glass, deciding at last that his hair needed smoothing down on one side.

'I don't mind admitting to you both,' said Clapham, moving a step or two closer and speaking rather thickly, 'that when I finished *Fields of Amaranth* there were tears in my eyes.'

Smethyck made no reply to this; nor could I myself think of a suitable rejoinder.

'That was some years ago,' said Clapham.

This qualification left open the alternative of whether St. John Clarke still retained the power of exciting such strong feeling in a publisher, or whether Clapham himself had grown more capable of controlling his emotions.

'Why, there's Sillery,' said Smethyck, who seemed thoroughly bored by the subject of St. John Clarke. 'I believe he was to be painted by Isbister, if he had recovered. Let's go and talk to him.'

We left Clapham, still muttering about the extent of St. John Clarke's sales, and the beauty and delicacy of his early style. I had not seen Sillery since Mrs. Andriadis's party, three or four years before, though I had heard by chance that he had recently returned from America, where he had held some temporary academical post, or been on a lecture tour. His white hair and dark, Nietzschean moustache remained unchanged, but his clothes looked older than ever. He was carrying an unrolled umbrella in one hand; in the other a large black homburg, thick in grease. He began to grin widely as soon as he saw us.

'Hullo, Sillers,' said Smethyck, who had been one of Sillery's favourites among the undergraduates who constituted his *salon*. 'I did not know you were interested in art.'

'Not interested in art?' said Sillery, enjoying this accusation a great deal. 'What an idea. Still, I am, as it happens, here for semi-professional reasons, as you might say. I expect you are too, Michael. There is some nonsense about the College wanting a pitcher o' me ole mug. Can't think why they should need such a thing, but there it is. 'Course

Isbister can't do it 'cos 'e's tucked 'is toes in now, but I thought I'd just come an' take a look at the sorta thing that's expected.'

'And what do you think, Sillers?'

'Just as well he's passed away, perhaps,' sniggered Sillery, suddenly abandoning his character-acting. 'In any case I always think an artist is rather an embarrassment to his own work. But what Ninetyish things I am beginning to say. It must come from talking to so many Americans.'

'But you can't want to be painted by anyone even remotely like Isbister,' said Smethyck. 'Surely you can get a painter who is a little more modern than that. What about this man Barnby, for example?'

'Ah, we are very conservative about art at the older universities,' said Sillery, grinning delightedly. 'Wouldn't say myself that I want an Isbister exactly, though I heard the Warden comparing him with Antonio Moro the other night. 'Fraid the Warden doesn't know much about the graphic arts, though. But then *I* don't want the wretched picture painted at all. What do members of the College want to look at my old phiz for, I should like to know?'

We assured him that his portrait would be welcomed by all at the university.

'I don't know about Brightman,' said Sillery, showing his teeth for a second. 'I don't at all know about Brightman. I don't think Brightman would want a picture of me. But what have you been doing with yourself, Nicholas? Writing more books, I expect. I am afraid I haven't read the first one yet. Do you ever see Charles Stringham now?'

'Not for ages.'

'A pity about that divorce,' said Sillery. 'You young men will get married. It is so often a mistake. I hear he is drinking just a tiny bit too much nowadays. It was a mistake to leave Donners-Brebner, too.'

'I expect you've heard about J. G. Quiggin taking Mark Members's place with St. John Clarke?'

'Hilarious that, wasn't it?' agreed Sillery. 'That sort of thing always happens when two clever boys come from the same place. They can't help competing. Poor Mark seems quite upset about it. Can't think why. After all, there are plenty of other glittering prizes for those with stout hearts and sharp swords, just as Lord Birkenhead remarked. I shall be seeing Quiggin this afternoon, as it happens—a little political affair—Quiggin lives a very *mouvementé* life these days, it seems.'

Sillery chuckled to himself. There was evidently some secret he did not intend to reveal. In any case he had by then prolonged the conversation sufficiently for his own satisfaction.

'Saw you chatting to Gavin Walpole-Wilson,' he said. 'Ought to go and have a word with him myself about these continuous hostilities between Bolivia and Paraguay. Been going on too long. Want to get in touch with his sister about it. Get one of her organisations to work. Time for liberal-minded people to step in. Can't have them cutting each other's throats in this way. Got to be quick, or I shall be late for Quiggin.'

He shambled off. Smethyck smiled at me and shook his head, at the same time indicating that he had seen enough for one afternoon.

I strolled on round the gallery. I had noted in the catalogue a picture called 'The Countess of Ardglass with Faithful Girl' and, when I arrived before it, I found Lady Ardglass herself inspecting the portrait. She was leaning on the arm of one of the trim grey-haired men who had accompanied her in the Ritz: or perhaps another example of their category, so like as to be indistinguishable. Isbister had painted her in an open shirt and riding breeches, standing beside the mare, her arm slipped through the reins: with much attention to the high polish of the brown boots.

'Pity Jumbo could never raise the money for it,' Bijou Ardglass was saying. 'Why don't you make an offer, Jack, and give it me for my birthday? You'd probably get it dirt cheap.'

'I'm much too broke,' said the grey-haired man.

'You always say that. If you'd given me the car you promised me I should at least have saved the nine shillings I've already spent on taxis this morning.'

Jean never spoke of her husband, and I knew no details of the episode with Lady Ardglass that had finally separated them. At the same time, now that I saw Bijou, I could not help feeling that she and I were somehow connected by what had happened. I wondered what Duport had in common with me that linked us through Jean. Men who are close friends tend to like different female types; perhaps the contrary process also operated, and the fact that he had seemed so unsympathetic when we had met years before was due to some innate sense of rivalry. I was to see Jean that afternoon. She had borrowed a friend's flat for a week or so, while she looked about for somewhere more permanent to live. This had made things easier. Emotional crises always promote the urgent need for executive action, so that the times when we most hope to be free from the practical administration of life are always those when the need to cope with a concrete world is more than ever necessary.

Owing to domestic arrangements connected with getting a nurse for her child, she would not be at home until late in the afternoon. I wasted some time at the Isbister show, before walking across the park to the place where she was living. I had expected to see Quiggin at the gallery, but

Sillery's remarks indicated that he would not be there. The last time I had met him, soon after the Templer week-end, it had turned out that, in spite of the temporary reappearance of Members at St. John Clarke's sick bed, Quiggin was still firmly established in his new position. He now seemed scarcely aware that there had ever been a time when he had not acted as the novelist's secretary, referring to his employer's foibles with a weary though tolerant familiarity, as if he had done the job for years. He had quickly brushed aside enquiry regarding his journey to London with Mrs. Erdleigh and Jimmy Stripling.

'What a couple,' he commented.

I had to admit they were extraordinary enough. Quiggin had resumed his account of St. John Clarke, his state of health and his eccentricities, the last of which were represented by his new secretary in a decidedly different light from that in which they had been displayed by Members. St. John Clarke's every action was now expressed in Marxist terms, as if some political Circe had overnight turned the novelist into an entirely Left Wing animal. No doubt Quiggin judged it necessary to handle his new situation firmly on account of the widespread gossip regarding St. John Clarke's change of secretary; for in circles frequented by Members and Quiggin ceaseless argument had taken place as to which of them had 'behaved badly'.

Thinking it best from my firm's point of view to open diplomatic relations, as it were, with the new government, I had asked if there was any hope of our receiving the Isbister introduction in the near future. Quiggin's answer to this had been to make an affirmative gesture with his hands. I had seen Members employ the same movement, perhaps derived by both of them from St. John Clarke himself.

'That was exactly what I wanted to discuss when I came

to the Ritz,' Quiggin had said. 'But you insisted on going out with your wealthy friends.'

'You must admit that I arranged for you to meet my wealthy friends, as you call them, at the first opportunity—within twenty-four hours, as a matter of fact.'

Quiggin smiled and inclined his head, as if assenting to my claim that some amends had been attempted.

'As I have tried to explain,' he said, 'St. J.'s views have changed a good deal lately. Indeed, he has entirely come round to my own opinion—that the present situation cannot last much longer. *We will not tolerate it.* All thinking men are agreed about that. St. J. *wants* to do the introduction when his health gets a bit better—and he has time to spare from his political interests—but he has decided to write the Isbister foreword from a Marxist point of view.'

'You ought to have obtained some first-hand information for him when Marx came through on Planchette.'

Quiggin frowned at this levity.

'What rot that was,' he said. 'I suppose Mark and his psychoanalyst friends would explain it by one of their dissertations on the subconscious. Perhaps in that particular respect they would be right. No doubt they would add a lot of irrelevant stuff about Surrealism. But to return to Isbister's pictures, I think they would not make a bad subject treated in that particular manner.'

'You could preach a whole Marxist sermon on the portrait of Peter Templer's father alone.'

'You could, indeed,' said Quiggin, who seemed not absolutely sure that the matter in hand was being negotiated with sufficient seriousness. 'But what a charming person Mrs. Templer is. She has changed a lot since her days as a model, or mannequin, or whatever she was. It is a great pity she never seems to see any intelligent people now. I can't think how she can stand that stockbroker husband of hers. How rich is he?'

'He took a bit of a knock in the slump.'

'How do they get on together?'

'All right, so far as I know.'

'St. J. always says there is "nothing sadder than a happy marriage".'

'Is that why he doesn't risk it himself?'

'I should think Mona will go off with somebody,' said Quiggin, decisively.

I considered this comment impertinent, though there was certainly no reason why Quiggin and Templer should be expected to like one another. Perhaps Quiggin's instinct was correct, I thought, however unwilling I might be to agree openly with him. There could be no doubt that the Templers' marriage was not going very well. At the same time, I did not intend to discuss them with Quiggin, to whom, in any case, there seemed no point in explaining Templer's merits. Quiggin would not appreciate these even if they were brought to his notice; while, if it suited him, he would always be ready to reverse his opinion about Templer or anyone else.

By then I had become sceptical of seeing the Isbister introduction, Marxist or otherwise. In itself, this latest suggestion did not strike me as specially surprising. Taking into account the fact that St. John Clarke had made the plunge into 'modernism', the project seemed neither more nor less extraordinary than tackling Isbister's pictures from the point of view of Psychoanalysis, Surrealism, Roman Catholicism, Social Credit, or any other specialised approach. In fact some such doctrinal method of attack was then becoming very much the mode; taking the place of the highly coloured critical flights of an earlier generation that still persisted in some quarters, or the severely technical criticism of the æsthetic puritans who had ruled the roost since the war.*

The foreword would now, no doubt, speak of Isbister 'laughing up his sleeve' at the rich men and public notabilities he had painted; though Members, who, with St. John Clarke, had once visited Isbister's studio in St. John's Wood for some kind of a reception held there, had declared that nothing could have exceeded the painter's obsequiousness to his richer patrons. Members was not always reliable in such matters, but it was certainly true that Isbister's portraits seemed to combine as a rule an effort to flatter his client with apparent attempts to make some comment to be easily understood by the public. Perhaps it was this inward struggle that imparted to his pictures that peculiar fascination to which I have already referred. However, so far as my firm was concerned, the goal was merely to get the introduction written and the book published.

'What is Mark doing now?' I asked.

Quiggin looked surprised at the question; as if everyone must know by now that Members was doing very well for himself.

'With Boggis & Stone—you know they used to be the Vox Populi Press—we got him the job.'

'Who were "we"?'

'St. J. and myself. St. J. arranged most of it through Howard Craggs. As you know, Craggs used to be the managing director of the Vox Populi.'

'But I thought Mark wasn't much interested in politics. Aren't all Boggis & Stone's books about Lenin and Trotsky and Litvinov and the Days of October and all that?'

Quiggin agreed, with an air of rather forced gaiety.

'Well, haven't most of us been living in a fool's paradise far too long now?' he said, speaking as if to make an appeal to my better side. 'Isn't it time that Mark—and others too—took some notice of what is happening in the world?'

'Does he get a living wage at Boggis & Stone's?'

'With his journalism he can make do. A small firm like that can't afford to pay a very munificent salary, it's true. He still gets a retainer from St. J. for sorting out the books once a month.'

I did not imagine this last arrangement was very popular with Quiggin from the way he spoke of it.

'As a matter of fact,' he said, 'I persuaded St. J. to arrange for Mark to have some sort of a footing in a more politically alive world before he got rid of him. That is where the future lies for all of us.'

'Did Gypsy Jones transfer from the Vox Populi to Boggis & Stone?'

Quiggin laughed now with real amusement.

'Oh, no,' he said. 'I forgot you knew her. She left quite a time before the amalgamation took place. She has something better to do now.'

He paused and moistened his lips; adding rather mysteriously:

'They say Gypsy is well looked on by the Party.'

This remark did not convey much to me in those days. I was more interested to see how carefully Quiggin's plans must have been laid to have prepared a place for Members even before he had been ejected from his job. That certainly showed forethought.

'Are you writing another book?' said Quiggin.

'Trying to—and you?'

'I liked your first,' said Quiggin.

He conveyed by these words a note of warning that, in spite of his modified approval, things must not go too far where books were concerned.

'Personally, I am not too keen to rush into print,' he said.

'I am still collecting material for my survey, *Unburnt Boats.*'

I did not meet Members to hear his side of the story until much later, in fact on that same afternoon of the Isbister Memorial Exhibition. I ran into him on my way through Hyde Park, not far from the Achilles Statue. (As it happened, it was close to the spot where I had come on Barbara Goring and Eleanor Walpole-Wilson, the day we had visited the Albert Memorial together.)

The weather had turned colder again, and the park was dank, with a kind of sea mist veiling the trees. Members looked shabbier than was usual for him: shabby and rather worried. In our undergraduate days he had been a tall, willowy, gesticulating figure, freckled and beady-eyed; hurrying through the lanes and byways of the university, abstractedly alone, like the Scholar-Gypsy, or straggling along the shopfronts of the town in the company of acquaintances, seemingly chosen for their peculiar resemblance to himself. Now he had grown into a terse, emaciated, rather determined young man, with a neat profile and chilly manner: a person people were beginning to know by name. In fact the critics, as a whole, had spoken so highly of his latest volume of verse—the one through which an undercurrent of psychoanalytical phraseology had intermittently run—that even Quiggin (usually as sparing of praise as Uncle Giles himself) had, in one of his more unbending moments at a sherry party, gone so far as to admit publicly:

'Mark has arrived.'

As St. John Clarke's secretary, Members had been competent to deal at a moment's notice with most worldly problems. For example, he could cut short the beery protests of some broken-down crony of the novelist's past, arrived unexpectedly on the doorstep—or, to be more precise, on

120

the landing of the block of flats where St. John Clarke lived—with a view to borrowing 'a fiver' on the strength of 'the old days'. Any such former boon companion, if strong-willed, might have got away with 'half a sovereign' (as St. John Clarke always called that sum) had he gained entry to the novelist himself. With Members as a buffer, he soon found himself escorted to the lift, having to plan, as he descended, both then and for the future, economic attack elsewhere.

Alternatively, the matter to be regulated might be the behaviour of some great lady, aware that St. John Clarke was a person of a certain limited eminence, but at the same time ignorant of his credentials to celebrity. Again, Members could put right a situation that had gone amiss. Lady Huntercombe must have been guilty of some such social dissonance at her own table (before a secretary had come into existence to adjust such matters by a subsequent word) because Members was fond of quoting a *mot* of his master's to the effect that dinner at the Huntercombes' possessed 'only two dramatic features—the wine was a farce and the food a tragedy'.

In fact to get rid of a secretary who performed his often difficult functions so effectively was a rash step on the part of a man who liked to be steered painlessly through the shoals and shallows of social life. Indeed, looking back after-wards, the dismissal of Members might almost be regarded as a landmark in the general disintegration of society in its traditional form. It was an act of individual folly on the part of St. John Clarke; a piece of recklessness that well illustrates the mixture of self-assurance and *ennui* which together contributed so much to form the state of mind of people like St. John Clarke at that time. Of course I did not recognise its broader aspects then. The duel between Members and Quiggin seemed merely an entertaining conflict to watch, rather than the significant crumbling of social foundations.

On that dank afternoon in the park Members had abandoned some of his accustomed coldness of manner. He seemed glad to talk to someone—probably to anyone—about his recent ejection. He began on the subject at once, drawing his tightly-waisted overcoat more closely round him, while he contracted his sharp, beady brown eyes. Separation from St. John Clarke, and association with the firm of Boggis & Stone, had for some reason renewed his former resemblance to an ingeniously constructed marionette or rag doll.

'There had been a slight sense of strain for some months between St. J. and myself,' he said. 'An absolutely trivial matter about taking a girl out to dinner. Perhaps rather foolishly, I had told St. J. I was going to a lecture on the Little Entente. Howard Craggs—whom I am now working with—happened to be introducing the lecturer, and so of course within twenty-four hours he had managed to mention to St. J. the fact that I had not been present. It was awkward, naturally, but I did not think St. J. really minded.

'But why did you want to know about the Little Entente?'

'St. J. had begun to be rather keen on what he called "the European Situation",' said Members, brushing aside my surprise as almost impertinent. 'I always liked to humour his whims.'

'But I thought his great thing was the Ivory Tower?'

'Of course, I found out later that Quiggin had put him up to "the European Situation",' admitted Members, grudgingly. 'But after all, an artist has certain responsibilities. I expect you are a supporter of the League yourself, my dear Nicholas.'

He smiled as he uttered the last part of the sentence, though speaking as if he intended to administer a slight, if well deserved, rebuke. In doing this he involuntarily adopted a more personal rendering of Quiggin's own nasal intonation, which rendered quite unnecessary the explanation that the idea had been Quiggin's. Probably the very words he used were Quiggin's, too.

'But politics were just what you used to complain of in Quiggin.'

'Perhaps Quiggin was right in that respect, if in no other,' said Members, giving his tinny, bitter laugh.

'And then?'

'It turned out that St. J.'s feelings *were* rather hurt.'

Members paused, as if he did not know how best to set about explaining the situation further. He shook his head once or twice in his old, abstracted Scholar-Gypsy manner. Then he began, as it were, at a new place in his narrative.

'As you probably know,' he continued, 'I can say without boasting that I have done a good deal to change—why should I not say it?—to improve St. J.'s attitude towards intellectual matters. Do you know, when I first came to him he thought Matisse was a *plage*—no, I mean it.'

He made no attempt to relax his features, nor join in audible amusement at such a state of affairs. Instead, he continued to record St. John Clarke's shortcomings.

'That much quoted remark of his: "Gorki is a Russian d'Annunzio"—he got it from me. I happened to say at tea one day that I thought if d'Annunzio had been born in Nijni Novgorod he would have had much the same career as Gorki. All St. J. did was to turn the words round and use them as his own.'

'But you still see him from time to time?'

Members shied away his rather distinguished profile like a high-bred but displeased horse.

'Yes—and no,' he conceded. 'It's rather awkward. I don't

123

know how much Quiggin told you, nor if he spoke the truth.'

'He said you came in occasionally to look after the books.'

'Only once in a way. I've got to earn a living somehow. Besides, I am attached to St. J.—even after the way he has behaved. I need not tell you that he does not like parting with money. I scarcely get enough for my work on the books to cover my bus fares. It is a strain having to avoid that *âme de boue,* too, whenever I visit the flat. He is usually about somewhere, spying on everyone who crosses the threshold.'

'And what about St. John Clarke's conversion to Marxism?'

'When I first persuaded St. J. to look at the world in a contemporary manner,' said Members slowly, adopting the tone of one determined not to be hurried in his story by those whose interest in it was actuated only by vulgar curiosity—'When I first persuaded him to that, I took an early opportunity to show him Quiggin. After all, Quiggin was supposed to be my friend—and, whatever one may think of his behaviour as a friend, he has—or had—some talent.'

Members waited for my agreement before continuing, as if the thought of displacement by a talentless Quiggin would add additional horror to his own position. I concurred that Quiggin's talent was only too apparent.

'From the very beginning I feared the risk of things going wrong on account of St. J.'s squeamishness about people's personal appearance. For example, I insisted that Quiggin should put on a clean shirt when he came to see St. J. I told him to attend to his nails. I even gave him an orange stick with which to do so.'

'And these preparations were successful?'

'They met once or twice. Quiggin was even asked to the

flat. They got on better than I had expected. I admit that. All the same, I never felt that the meetings were really *enjoyable*. I was sorry about that, because I thought Quiggin's ideas would be useful to St. J. I do not always agree with Quiggin's approach to such things as the arts, for example, but he is keenly aware of present-day tendencies. However, I decided in the end to explain to Quiggin that I feared St. J. was not very much taken with him.'

'Did Quiggin accept that?'

'He did,' said Members, again speaking with bitterness. 'He accepted it without a murmur. That, in itself, should have put me on my guard. I know now that almost as soon as I introduced them, they began to see each other when I was not present.'

Members checked himself at this point, perhaps feeling that to push his indictment to such lengths bordered on absurdity.

'Of course, there was no particular reason why they should not meet,' he allowed. 'It was just odd—and rather unfriendly—that neither of them should have mentioned their meetings to me. St. J. always loves new people. "Unmade friends are like unmade beds," he has often said. "They should be attended to early in the morning."'

Members drew a deep breath that was almost a sigh. There was a pause.

'But I thought you said he was so squeamish about people?'

'Not when he has once decided they are going to be successful.'

'That's what he thinks about Quiggin?'

Members nodded.

'Then I noticed St. J. was beginning to describe everything as "bourgeois",' he said. 'Wearing a hat was "bourgeois", eat-

ing pudding with a fork was "bourgeois", the Ritz was "bourgeois", Lady Huntercombe was "bourgeois"—he meant
"bourgeoise", of course, but French is not one of St. J.'s
long suits. Then one morning at breakfast he said Cézanne
was "bourgeois". At first I thought he meant that only
middle-class people put too much emphasis on such things—
that a true aristocrat could afford to ignore them. It was a
favourite theme of St. J.'s that "natural aristocrats" were the
only true ones. He regarded himself as a "natural aristocrat". At the same time he felt that a "natural aristocrat"
had a right to mix with the ordinary kind, and latterly he
had spent more and more of his time in rather grand circles
—and in fact had come almost to hate people who were not
rather smart, or at least very rich. For example, I remember
him describing—well, I won't say whom, but he is a novelist
who sells very well and you can probably guess the name—
as "the kind of man who knows about as much about *place-
ment* as to send the wife of a younger son of a marquess
in to dinner before the daughter of an earl married to a
commoner". He thought a lot about such things. That was
why I had been at first afraid of introducing him to
Quiggin. And then—when we began discussing Cézanne—
it turned out that he had been using the word "bourgeois"
all the time in the Marxist sense. I didn't know he had
even heard of Marx, much less was at all familiar with his
theories.'

'I seem to remember an article he wrote describing himself as a "Gladstonian Liberal"—in fact a Liberal of the
most old-fashioned kind.'

'You do, you do,' said Members, almost passionately. 'I
wrote it for him, as a matter of fact. You couldn't have
expressed it better. *A Liberal of the most old-fashioned
kind*. Local Option—Proportional Representation—Welsh
Disestablishment—the whole bag of tricks. That was just

about as far as he got. But now everything is "bourgeois"—
Liberalism, I have no doubt, most of all. As a matter of fact,
his politics were the only liberal thing about him.'

'And it began as soon as he met Quiggin?'

'I first noticed the change when he persuaded me to
join in what he called "collective action on the part of
writers and artists"—going to meetings to protest against
Manchuria and so on. I agreed, first of all, simply to humour
him. It was just as well I did, as a matter of fact, because
it led indirectly to another job when he turned his back on
me. You know, what St. J. really wants is a son. He wants
to be a father without having a wife.'

'I thought everyone always tried to avoid that.'

'In the Freudian sense,' said Members, impatiently, 'his
nature requires a father-son relationship. Unfortunately,
the situation becomes a little too life-like, and one is faced
with a kind of artificially constructed Œdipus situation.'

'Can't you re-convert him from Marxism to psychoanalysis?'

Members looked at me fixedly.

'St. J. has always pooh-poohed the subconscious,' he said.

We were about to move off in our respective directions
when my attention was caught by a disturbance coming
from the road running within the railings of the park. It
was a sound, harsh and grating, though at the same time
shrill and suggesting complaint. These were human voices
raised in protest. Turning, I saw through the mist that
increasingly enveloped the park a column of persons entering beneath the arch. They trudged behind a mounted
policeman, who led their procession about twenty yards
ahead. Evidently a political 'demonstration' of some sort
was on its way to the north side where such meetings were
held. From time to time these persons raised a throaty
cheer, or an individual voice from amongst them bawled

out some form of exhortation. A strident shout, similar to that which had at first drawn my attention, now sounded again. We moved towards the road to obtain a better view.

The front rank consisted of two men in cloth caps, one with a beard, the other wearing dark glasses, who carried between them a banner upon which was inscribed the purpose and location of the gathering. Behind these came some half a dozen personages, marching almost doggedly out of step, as if to deprecate even such a minor element of militarism. At the same time there was a vaguely official air about them. Among these, I thought I recognised the face and figure of a female Member of Parliament whose photograph occasionally appeared in the papers. Next to this woman tramped Sillery. He had exchanged his black soft hat of earlier afternoon for a cloth cap similar to that worn by the bearers of the banner: his walrus moustache and thick strands of white hair blew furiously in the wind. From time to time he clawed at the arm of a gloomy-looking man next to him who walked with a limp. He was grinning all the while to himself, and seemed to be hugely enjoying his role in the procession.

In the throng that straggled several yards behind these mort important figures I identified two young men who used to frequent Mr. Deacon's antique shop; one of whom, indeed, was believed to have accompanied Mr. Deacon himself on one of his holidays in Cornwall. I thought, immediately, that Mr. Deacon's other associate, Gypsy Jones, might also be of the party, but could see no sign of her. Probably, as Quiggin had suggested, she belonged by then to a more distinguished grade of her own hierarchy than that represented by this heterogeneous collection, nearly all apparently 'intellectuals' of one kind or another.

However, although interested to see Sillery in such

circumstances, there was another far more striking aspect of the procession which a second later riveted my eyes. Members must have taken in this particular spectacle at the same instant as myself, because I heard him beside me give a gasp of irritation.

Three persons immediately followed the group of notables with whom Sillery marched. At first, moving closely together through the mist, this trio seemed like a single grotesque three-headed animal, forming the figure-head of an ornamental car on the roundabout of a fair. As they jolted along, however, their separate entities became revealed, manifesting themselves as a figure in a wheeled chair, jointly pushed by a man and a woman. At first I could not believe my eyes, perhaps even wished to disbelieve them, because I allowed my attention to be distracted for a moment by Sillery's voice shouting in high, almost jocular tones: 'Abolish the Means Test!' He had uttered this cry just as he came level with the place where Members and I stood; but he was too occupied with his own concerns to notice us there, although the park was almost empty.

Then I looked again at the three other people, thinking I might find myself mistaken in what I had at first supposed. On the contrary, the earlier impression was correct. The figure in the wheeled chair was St. John Clarke. He was being propelled along the road, in unison, by Quiggin and Mona Templer.

'My God!' said Members, quite quietly.

'Did you see Sillery?'

I asked this because I could think of no suitable comment regarding the more interesting group. Members took no notice of the question.

'I never thought they would go through with it,' he said.

Neither St. John Clarke, nor Quiggin, wore hats. The novelist's white hair, unenclosed in a cap such as Sillery wore, was lifted high, like an elderly Struwwelpeter's, in the stiff breeze that was beginning to blow through the branches. Quiggin was dressed in the black leather overcoat he had worn in the Ritz, a red woollen muffler riding up round his neck, his skull cropped like a convicts'. No doubt intentionally, he had managed to make himself look like a character from one of the novels of Dostoievski. Mona, too, was hatless, with dishevelled curls: her face very white above a high-necked polo jumper covered by a tweed overcoat of smart cut. She was looking remarkably pretty, and, like Sillery, seemed to be enjoying herself. On the other hand, the features of the two men with her expressed only inexorable sternness. Every few minutes, when the time came for a general shout to be raised, St. John Clarke would brandish in his hand a rolled-up copy of one of the 'weeklies', as he yelled the appropriate slogan in a high, excited voice.

'It's an absolute scandal,' said Members breathlessly. 'I heard rumours that something of the sort was on foot. The strain may easily kill St. J. He ought not to be up—much less taking part in an open-air meeting before the warmer weather comes.'

I was myself less surprised at the sight of Quiggin and St. John Clarke in such circumstances than to find Mona teamed up with the pair of them. For Quiggin, this kind of thing had become, after all, almost a matter of routine. It was 'the little political affair' Sillery had mentioned at the private view. St. John Clarke's collaboration in such an outing was equally predictable—apart from the state of his health—after what Members and Quiggin had both said about him. From his acceptance of Quiggin's domination he would henceforward join that group of authors, dons, and clergymen increasingly to be found at that period on political platforms of a 'Leftish' sort. To march in some public 'demonstration' was an almost unavoidable condition of his new commitments. As it happened he was fortunate enough on this, his first appearance, to find himself in a conveyance. In the wheeled chair, with his long white locks, he made an effective figure, no doubt popular with the organisers and legitimately gratifying to himself.

It was Mona's presence that was at first inexplicable to me. She could hardly have come up for the day to take part in all this. Perhaps the Templers were again in London for the week-end, and she had chosen to walk in the procession as an unusual experience; while Peter had gone off to amuse himself elsewhere. Then all at once the thing came to me in a flash, as such things do, requiring no further explanation. Mona had left Templer. She was now living with Quiggin. For some reason this was absolutely clear. Their relationship was made unmistakable by the manner in which they moved together side by side.

'Where are they going?' I asked.

'To meet some Hunger-Marchers arriving from the Midlands,' said Members, as if it were a foolish, irrelevant question. 'They are camping in the park, aren't they?'

'This crowd?'

'No, the Hunger-Marchers, of course.'

'Why is Mona there?'

'Who is Mona?'

'The girl walking with Quiggin and helping to push St. John Clarke. She was a model, you remember. I once saw you with her at a party years ago.'

'Oh, yes, it was her, wasn't it?' he said, indifferently.

Mona's name seemed to mean nothing to him.

'But why is she helping to push the chair?'

'Probably because Quiggin is too bloody lazy to do all the work himself,' he said.

Evidently he was ignorant of Mona's subsequent career since the days when he had known her. The fact that she was helping to trundle St. John Clarke through the mists of Hyde Park was natural enough for the sort of girl she had been. In the eyes of Members she was just another 'arty' woman roped in by Quiggin to assist Left Wing activities. His own thoughts were entirely engrossed by St. John Clarke and Quiggin. I could not help being impressed by the extent to which the loss of his post as secretary had upset him. His feelings had undoubtedly been lacerated. He watched them pass by, his mouth clenched.

The procession wound up the road towards Marble Arch. Two policemen on foot brought up the rear, round whom, whistling shrilly, circled some boys on bicycles, apparently unconnected with the marchers. The intermittent shouting grew gradually fainter, until the column disappeared from sight into the still foggy upper reaches of the park.

Members looked round at me.

'Can you beat it?' he said.

'I thought St. John Clarke disliked girls near him?'

'I don't expect he cares any longer,' said Members, in a voice of despair. 'Quiggin will make him put up with anything by now.'

On this note we parted company. As I continued my way through the park I was conscious of having witnessed a spectacle that was distinctly strange. Jean had already told me more than once that the Templers were getting on badly. These troubles had begun, so it appeared, a few months after their marriage, Mona complaining of the dullness of life away from London. She was for ever making scenes, usually about nothing at all. Afterwards there would be tears and reconciliations; and some sort of a 'treat' would be arranged for her by Peter. Then the cycle would once more take its course. Jean liked Mona, but thought her 'impossible' as a wife.

'What is the real trouble?' I had asked.

'I don't think she likes men.'

'Ah.'

'But I don't think she likes women either. Just keen on herself.'

'How will it end?'

'They may settle down. If Peter doesn't lose interest. He is used to having his own way. He has been unexpectedly good so far.'

She was fond of Peter, though free from that obsessive interest that often entangles brother and sister. They were not alike in appearance, though her hair, too, grew down like his in a 'widow's peak' on her forehead. There was also something about the set of her neck that recalled her brother. That was all.

'They might have a lot of children.'

'They might.'

'Would that be a good thing?'

'Certainly.'

I was surprised that she was so decisive, because in those days children were rather out of fashion. It always seemed strange to me, and rather unreal, that so much of her own time should be occupied with Polly.

'You know, I believe Mona has taken quite a fancy for your friend J. G. Quiggin,' she had said, laughing.

'Not possible.'

'I'm not so sure.'

'Has he appeared at the house again?'

'No—but she keeps talking about him.'

'Perhaps I ought never to have introduced him into the household.'

'Perhaps not,' she had replied, quite seriously.

At the time, the suggestion had seemed laughable. To regard Quiggin as a competitor with Templer for a woman —far less his own wife—was ludicrous even to consider.

'But she took scarcely any notice of him.'

'Well, I thought *you* were rather wet the first time you came to the house. But I've made up for it later, haven't I?'

'I adored you from the start.'

'I'm sure you didn't.'

'Certainly at Stourwater.'

'Oh, at Stourwater I was very impressed too.'

'And I with you.'

'Then why didn't you write or ring up or something? *Why didn't you?*'

'I did—you were away.'

'You ought to have gone on trying.'

'I wasn't sure you weren't rather lesbian.'

'How ridiculous. Pretty rude of you, too.'

'I had a lot to put up with.'

'Nonsense.'

'But I had.'

'How absurd you are.'

When the colour came quickly into her face, the change used to fill me with excitement. Even when she sat in silence, scarcely answering if addressed, such moods seemed a necessary part of her: something not to be utterly regretted. Her forehead, high and white, gave a withdrawn look, like a great lady in a medieval triptych or carving; only her lips, and the elegantly long lashes under slanting eyes, gave a hint of latent sensuality. But descriptions of a woman's outward appearance can hardly do more than echo the terms of a fashion paper. Their nature can be caught only in a refractive beam, as with light passing through water: the rays of character focused through the person with whom they are intimately associated. Perhaps, therefore, I alone was responsible for what she seemed to me. To another man—Duport, for example—she no doubt appeared —indeed, actually was—a different woman.

'But why, when we first met, did you never talk about books and things?' I had asked her.

'I didn't think you'd understand.'

'How hopeless of you.'

'Now I see it was,' she had said, quite humbly.

She shared with her brother the conviction that she 'belonged' in no particular world. The other guests she had found collected round Sir Magnus Donners at Stourwater had been on the whole unsympathetic.

'I only went because I was a friend of Baby's,' she had said; 'I don't really like people of that sort.'

'But surely there were people of all sorts there?'

'Perhaps I don't much like people anyway. I am probably too lazy. They always want to sleep with one, or something.'

'But that is like me.'

'I know. It's intolerable.'

We laughed, but I had felt the chill of sudden jealousy; the fear that her remark had been made deliberately to tease.

'Of course Baby loves it all,' she went on. 'The men hum round her like bees. She is so funny with them.'

'What did she and Sir Magnus do?'

'Not even I know. Whatever it was, Bijou Ardglass refused to take him on.'

'She was offered the job?'

'So I was told. She preferred to go off with Bob.'

'Why did that stop?'

'Bob could no longer support her in the style to which she was accustomed—or rather the style to which she was unaccustomed, as Jumbo Ardglass never had much money.'

It was impossible, as ever, to tell from her tone what she felt about Duport. I wondered whether she would leave him and marry me. I had not asked her, and had no clear idea what the answer would be. Certainly, if she did, like Lady Ardglass, she would not be supported in the style to which she had been accustomed. Neither, for that matter, would Mona, if she had indeed gone off with Quiggin, for I felt sure that the final domestic upheaval at the Templers' had now taken place. Jean had been right. Something about the way Quiggin and Mona walked beside one another connected them inexorably together. 'Women can be immensely obtuse about all kinds of things,' Barnby was fond of saying, 'but where the emotions are concerned their opinion is always worthy of consideration.'

The mist was lifting now, and gleams of sunlight were once more coming through the clouds above the waters of the Serpentine. Not unwillingly dismissing the financial side of marriage from my mind, as I walked on through the melancholy park, I thought of love, which, from the very beginning perpetually changes its shape: sometimes in the ascendant, sometimes in decline. At present we sailed in comparatively calm seas because we lived from meeting to meeting, possessing no plan for the future. Her abandonment remained; the abandonment that had so much surprised me at that first embrace, as the car skimmed the muddy surfaces of the Great West Road.

But in love, like everything else—more than anything else—there must be bad as well as good; and by silence or some trivial remark she could inflict unexpected pain. Away from her, all activities seemed waste of time, yet sometimes just before seeing her I was aware of an odd sense of antagonism that had taken the place of the longing that had been in my heart for days before. This sense of being out of key with her sometimes survived the first minutes of our meeting. Then, all at once, tension would be relaxed; always, so it seemed to me, by some mysterious force emanating from her: intangible, invisible, yet at the same time part of a whole principle of behaviour: a deliberate act of the will by which she exercised power. At times it was almost as if she intended me to feel that unexpected accident, rather than a carefully arranged plan, had brought us together on some given occasion; or at least that I must always be prepared for such a mood. Perhaps these are inward irritations always produced by love: the acutely sensitive nerves of intimacy: the haunting fear that all may not go well.

Still thinking of such things, I rang the bell of the ground-floor flat. It was in an old-fashioned red-brick block of buildings, situated somewhere beyond Rutland Gate, concealed among obscure turnings that seemed to lead nowhere. For some time there was no answer to the ring. I waited, peering through the frosted glass of the front door, feeling every second an eternity. Then the door opened a few inches and Jean looked out. I saw her face only for a moment. She was laughing.

'Come in,' she said quickly. 'It's cold.'

As I entered the hall, closing the door behind me, she ran back along the passage. I saw that she wore nothing but a pair of slippers.

'There is a fire in here,' she called from the sitting-room.

I hung my hat on the grotesque piece of furniture, designed for that use, that stood by the door. Then I followed her down the passage and into the room. The furniture and decoration of the flat were of an appalling banality.

'Why are you wearing no clothes?'

'Are you shocked?'

'What do you think?'

'I think you are.'

'Surprised, rather than shocked.'

'To make up for the formality of our last meeting.'

137

'Aren't I showing my appreciation?'

'Yes, but you must not be so conventional.'

'But if it had been the postman?'

'I could have seen through the glass.'

'He, too, perhaps.'

'I had a dressing-gown handy.'

'It was a kind thought, anyway.'

'You like it?'

'Very much.'

'Tell me something nice.'

'This style suits you.'

'Not too *outré*?'

'On the contrary.'

'Is this how you like me?'

'Just like this.'

There is, after all, no pleasure like that given by a woman who really wants to see you. Here, at last, was some real escape from the world. The calculated anonymity of the surroundings somehow increased the sense of being alone with her. There was no sound except her sharp intake of breath. Yet love, for all the escape it offers, is closely linked with everyday things, even with the affairs of others. I knew Jean would burn with curiosity when I told her of the procession in the park. At the same time, because passion in its transcendence cannot be shared with any other element, I could not speak of what had happened until the time had come to decide where to dine.

She was pulling on her stockings when I told her. She gave a little cry, indicating disbelief.

'After all, you were the first to suggest something was "on" between them.'

'But she would be insane to leave Peter.'

We discussed this. The act of marching in a political demonstration did not, in itself, strike her as particularly unexpected in Mona. She said that Mona always longed to take part in anything that drew attention to herself. Jean was unwilling to believe that pushing St. John Clarke's chair was the outward sign of a decisive step in joining Quiggin.

'She must have done it because Peter is away. It is exactly the kind of thing that would appeal to her. Besides, it would annoy him just the right amount. A little, but not too much.'

'Where is Peter?'

'Spending the week-end with business friends. Mona thought them too boring to visit.'

'Perhaps she was just having a day out, then. Even so, it confirms your view that Quiggin made a hit with her.'

She pulled on the other stocking.

'True, they had a splitting row just before Peter left home,' she said. 'You know, I almost believe you are right.'

'Put a call through.'

'Just to see what the form is?'

'Why not?'

'Shall I?'

She was undecided.

'I think I will,' she said at last.

Still only partly dressed, she took up the telephone and lay on the sofa. At the other end of the line the bell rang for some little time before there was an answer. Then a voice spoke from the Templers' house. Jean made some trivial enquiry. A short conversation followed. I saw from her face that my guess had been somewhere near the mark. She hung up the receiver.

'Mona left the house yesterday, saying she did not know when she would be back. She took a fair amount of luggage and left no address. I think the Burdens believe something is up. Mrs. Burden told me Peter had rung up about something he had forgotten. She told him Mona had left unexpectedly.

'She may be taking a few days off.'

'I don't think so,' said Jean.

Barnby used to say: 'All women are stimulated by the news that any wife has left any husband.' Certainly I was aware that the emotional atmosphere in the room had changed. Perhaps I should have waited longer before telling her my story. Yet to postpone the information further was scarcely possible without appearing deliberately secretive. I have often pondered on the conversation that followed, without coming to any definite conclusion as to why things took the course they did.

We had gone on to talk of the week-end when Quiggin had been first invited to the Templers' house. I had remarked something to the effect that if Mona had really left for good, the subject would have been apt for one of Mrs. Erdleigh's prophecies. In saying this I had added some more or less derogatory remark about Jimmy Stripling. Suddenly I was aware that Jean was displeased with my words. Her face took on a look of vexation. I supposed that some out-of-the-way loyalty had for some reason made her take exception to the idea of laughing at her sister's ex-husband. I could not imagine why this should be, since Stripling was usually regarded in the Templer household as an object of almost perpetual derision.

'I know he isn't *intelligent*,' she said.

'Intelligence isn't everything,' I said, trying to pass the matter off lightly. 'Look at the people in the Cabinet.'

'You said the other day that you found it awfully difficult to get on with people who were not intelligent.'

'I only meant where writing was concerned.'

'It didn't sound like that.'

A woman's power of imitation and adaptation make her

capable of confronting you with your own arguments after even the briefest acquaintance: how much more so if a state of intimacy exists. I saw that we were about to find ourselves in deep water. She pursed her lips and looked away. I thought she was going to cry. I could not imagine what had gone wrong and began to feel that terrible sense of exhaustion that descends, when, without cause or warning, an unavoidable, meaningless quarrel develops with someone you love. Now there seemed no way out. To lavish excessive praise on Jimmy Stripling's intellectual attainments would not be accepted, might even sound satirical; on the other hand, to remain silent would seem to confirm my undoubtedly low opinion of his capabilities in that direction. There was also, of course, the more general implication of her remark, the suggestion of protest against a state of mind in which intellectual qualities were automatically put first. Dissent from this principle was, after all, reasonable enough, though not exactly an equitable weapon in Jean's hands; for she, as much as any-one—so it seemed to me as her lover—was dependent, in the last resort, on people who were 'intelligent' in the sense in which she used the word.

Perhaps it was foolish to pursue the point of what was to all appearances only an irritable remark. But the circumstances were of a kind when irritating remarks are particularly to be avoided. Otherwise, it would have been easier to find an excuse.

Often enough, women love the arts and those who practice them; but they possess also a kind of jealousy of those activities. They like wit, but hate analysis. They are always prepared to fall back upon traditional rather than intellectual defensive positions. We never talked of Duport, as I have already recorded, and I scarcely knew, even then, why she had married him; but married they were. Accordingly, it seemed to me possible that what she had said possessed reference, in some oblique manner, to her husband; in the sense that adverse criticism of this kind cast a reflection upon him, and consequently upon herself. I had said nothing of Duport (who, as I was to discover years later, had a deep respect for 'intelligence'), but the possibility was something to be taken into account.

I was quite wrong in this surmise, and, even then, did not realise the seriousness of the situation; certainly was wholly unprepared for what happened next. A moment later, for no apparent reason, she told me she had had a love affair with Jimmy Stripling.

'When?'

'After Babs left him,' she said.

She went white, as if she might be about to faint. I was myself overcome with a horrible feeling of nausea, as if one had suddenly woken from sleep and found oneself chained to a corpse. A desire to separate myself physically from her and the place we were in was linked with an overwhelming sensation that, more than ever, I wanted her for myself. To think of her as wife of Bob Duport was bad enough, but that she should also have been mistress of Jimmy Stripling was barely endurable. Yet it was hard to know how to frame a complaint regarding that matter even to myself. She had not been 'unfaithful' to me. This odious thing had happened at a time when I myself had no claim whatsoever over her. I tried to tranquillise myself by considering whether a liaison with some man, otherwise possible to like or admire, would have been preferable. In the face of such an alternative, I decided Stripling was on the whole better as he was: with all the nightmarish fantasies implicit in the situation. The mystery remained why she should choose that particular moment to reveal this experience of hers, making of it a kind of defiance.

When you are in love with someone, their life, past, present and future, becomes in a curious way part of your life; and yet, at the same time, since two separate human entities in fact remain, you merely carry your own prejudices into another person's imagined existence; not even into their 'real' existence, because only they themselves can estimate what their 'real' existence has been. Indeed, the situation might be compared with that to be experienced in due course in the army where an officer is responsible for the conduct of troops stationed at a post too distant from him for the exercise of any effective control.

Not only was it painful enough to think of Jean giving herself to another man; the pain was intensified by supposing—what was, of course, not possible—that Stripling must appear to her in the same terms that he appeared to me. Yet clearly she had, once, at least, looked at Stripling with quite different eyes, or such a situation could never have arisen. Therefore, seeing Stripling as a man for whom it was evidently possible to feel at the very least a passing *tendresse*—perhaps even love—this incident, unforgettably horrible as it seemed to me at the time, would more rationally be regarded as a mere error of judgment. In love, however, there is no rationality. Besides, that she had seen him with other eyes than mine made things worse. In such ways one is bound, inescapably, to the actions of others.

We finished dressing in silence. By that time it was fairly late. I felt at once hungry, and without any true desire for food.

'Where shall we go?'

'Anywhere you like.'

'But where would you like to go?'

'I don't care.'

'We could have a sandwich at Foppa's.'

'The club?'

'Yes.'

'All right.'

In the street she slipped her arm through mine. I looked, and saw that she was crying a little, but I was no nearer understanding her earlier motives. The only thing clear was that some sharp change had taken place in the kaleidoscope of our connected emotions. In the pattern left by this transmutation of coloured crystals an increased intimacy had possibly emerged. Perhaps that was something she had intended.

'I suppose I should not have told you.'

'It would have come out sooner or later.'

'But not just then.'

'Perhaps not.'

Still, in spite of it all, as we drove through dingy Soho streets, her head resting on my shoulder, I felt glad she still seemed to belong to me. Foppa's was open. That was a relief, for there was sometimes an intermediate period when the restaurant was closed down and the club had not yet come into active being. We climbed the narrow staircase, over which brooded a peculiarly Italian smell: minestrone: salad oil: stale tobacco: perhaps a faint reminder of the lotion Foppa used on his hair.

Barnby had first introduced me to Foppa's club a long time before. One of the merits of the place was that no one either of us knew ever went there. It was a single room over Foppa's Restaurant. In theory the club opened only after the restaurant had shut for the night, but in practice Foppa himself, sometimes feeling understandably bored with his customers, would retire upstairs to read the paper, or practise billiard strokes. On such occasions he was glad of company at an earlier hour than was customary. Alternatively, he would sometimes go off with his friends to another haunt of theirs, leaving a notice on the door, written in indelible pencil, saying that Foppa's Club was temporarily closed for cleaning.

There was a narrow window at the far end of this small, smoky apartment; a bar in one corner, and a table for the game of Russian billiards in the other. The walls were white and bare, the vermouth bottles above the little bar shining out in bright stripes of colour that seemed to form a kind of spectrum in red, white and green. These patriotic colours linked the aperitifs and liqueurs with the portrait of Victor Emmanuel II which hung over the mantelpiece. Surrounded by a wreath of laurel, the King of Sardinia and United Italy wore a wasp-waisted military frock-coat swagged with coils of yellow aiguillette. The bold treatment of his costume by the artist almost suggested a Bakst design for one of the early Russian ballets.

If Foppa himself had grown his moustache to the same enormous length, and added an imperial to his chin, he would have looked remarkably like the *re galantuomo*; with just that same air of royal amusement that anyone could possibly take seriously—even for a moment—the preposterous world in which we are fated to have our being. Hanging over the elaborately gilded frame of this coloured print was the beautiful Miss Foppa's black fez-like cap, which she possessed by virtue of belonging to some local, parochial branch of the Fascist Party; though her father was believed to be at best only a lukewarm supporter of Mussolini's régime. Foppa had lived in London for many years. He had even served as a cook during the war with a British light infantry regiment; but he had never taken out papers of naturalisation.

'Look at me,' he used to say, when the subject arose, 'I am not an Englishman. You see.'

The truth of that assertion was undeniable. Foppa was

not an Englishman. He did not usually express political opinions in the presence of his customers, but he had once, quite exceptionally, indicated to me a newspaper photograph of the Duce declaiming from the balcony of the Palazzo Venezia. That was as near as he had ever gone to stating his view. It was sufficient. Merely by varying in no way his habitual expression of tolerant amusement, Foppa had managed to convey his total lack of anything that could possibly be accepted as Fascist enthusiasm. All the same, I think he had no objection to his daughter's association with that or any other party which might be in power at the moment.

Foppa was decidedly short, always exquisitely dressed in a neat blue, or brown, suit, his tiny feet encased in excruciatingly tight shoes of light tan shade. The shoes were sharply pointed and polished to form dazzling highlights. In summer he varied his footgear by sporting white brogues picked out in snakeskin. He was a great gambler, and sometimes spent his week-ends taking part in trotting races somewhere not far from London, perhaps at Greenford in Middlesex. Hanging behind the bar was a framed photograph of himself competing in one of these trotting events, armed with a long whip, wearing a jockey cap, his small person almost hidden between the tail of his horse and the giant wheels of the sulky. The snapshot recalled a design of Degas or Guys. That was the world, æsthetically speaking, to which Foppa belonged. He was a man of great good nature and independence, who could not curb his taste for gambling for high stakes; a passion that brought him finally, I believe, into difficulties.

Jean and I had already been to the club several times, because she liked playing Russian billiards, a game at which she was extremely proficient. Sixpence in the slot of the table brought to the surface the white balls and the red.

After a quarter of an hour the balls no longer reappeared for play, vanishing one by one, while scores were doubled. Foppa approved of Jean. Her skill at billiards was a perpetual surprise and delight to him.

'He probably tells all his friends I'm his mistress,' she used to say.

She may have been right in supposing that; though I suspect, if he told any such stories, that Foppa would probably have boasted of some enormous lady, at least twice his own size, conceived in the manner of Jordaens. His turn of humour always suggested something of that sort.

I thought the club might be a good place to recover some sort of composure. The room was never very full, though sometimes there would be a party of three or four playing cards gravely at one of the tables in the corner. On that particular evening Foppa himself was engrossed in a two-handed game, perhaps piquet. Sitting opposite him, his back to the room, was a man of whom nothing could be seen but a brown check suit and a smoothly brushed head, greying and a trifle bald at the crown. Foppa rose at once, poured out Chianti for us, and shouted down the service hatch for sandwiches to be cut. Although the cook was believed to be a Cypriot, the traditional phrase for attracting his attention was always formulated in French.

'Là bas!' Foppa would intone liturgically, as he leant forward into the abyss that reached down towards the kitchen, 'Là bas!'

Perhaps Miss Foppa herself attended to the provision of food in the evenings. If so, she never appeared in the club. Her quiet, melancholy beauty would have ornamented the place. I had, indeed, never seen any woman but Jean in that room. No doubt the clientèle would have objected to the presence there of any lady not entirely removed from their own daily life.

Two Soho Italians were standing by the bar. One, a tall, sallow, mournful character, resembling a former ambassador fallen on evil days, smoked a short, stinking cigar. The other, a nondescript ruffian, smaller in size than his companion, though also with a certain air of authority, displayed a suggestion of side-whisker under his faun velour hat. He was picking his teeth pensively with one of the toothpicks supplied in tissue paper at the bar. Both were probably neighbouring head-waiters. The two of them watched Jean slide the cue gently between finger and thumb before making her first shot. The ambassadorial one removed the cigar from his mouth and, turning his head a fraction, remarked sententiously through almost closed lips:

'Bella posizione.'

'E in gamba,' agreed the other. 'Una fuori classe davvero.'

The evening was happier now, though still something might easily go wrong. There was no certainty. People are differently equipped for withstanding emotional discomfort. On the whole women can bear a good deal of that kind of strain without apparently undue inconvenience. The game was won by Jean.

'What about another one?'

We asked the Italians if they were waiting for the billiard table, but they did not want to play. We had just arranged the balls again, and set up the pin, when the door of the club opened and two people came into the room. One of them was Barnby. The girl with him was known to me, though it was a second before I remembered that she was Lady Anne Stepney. We had not met for three years or more. Barnby seemed surprised, perhaps not altogether pleased, to find someone he knew at Foppa's.

Although it had turned out that Anne Stepney was the girl he had met on the train after his week-end with the

Manaschs', he had ceased to speak of her freely in conversation. At the same time I knew he was still seeing her. This was on account of a casual word dropped by him. I had never before run across them together in public. Some weeks after his first mention of her, I had asked whether he had finally established her identity. Barnby had replied brusquely:

'Of course her name is Stepney.'

I sometimes wondered how the two of them were getting along; even whether they had plans for marriage. A year was a long time for Barnby to be occupied with one woman. Like most men of his temperament, he held, on the whole, rather strict views regarding other people's morals. For that reason alone he would probably not have approved had I told him about Jean. In any case he was not greatly interested in such things unless himself involved. He only knew that something of the sort was in progress, and he would have had no desire, could it have been avoided, to come upon us unexpectedly in this manner.

The only change in Anne Stepney (last seen at Stringham's wedding) was her adoption of a style of dress implicitly suggesting an art student; nothing outrageous: just a general assertion that she was in some way closely connected with painting or sculpture. I think Mona had struggled against such an appearance; in Anne Stepney, it had no doubt been painfully acquired. Clothes of that sort certainly suited her large dark eyes and reddish hair, seeming also appropriate to a general air of untidiness, not to say grubbiness, that always possessed her. She had by then, I knew, passed almost completely from the world in which she had been brought up; that in which her sister, Peggy, still moved, or, at least, in that portion of it frequented by young married women.

The Bridgnorths had taken their younger daughter's

behaviour philosophically. They had gone through all the normal processes of giving her a start in life, a ball for her 'coming out', and everything else to be reasonably expected of parents in the circumstances. In the end they had agreed that 'in these days' it was impossible to insist on the hopes or standards of their own generation. Anne had been allowed to go her own way, while Lady Bridgnorth had returned to her hospital committees and Lord Bridgnorth to his politics and racing. They had probably contented themselves with the thought that Peggy, having quietly divorced Stringham, had now settled down peacefully enough with her new husband in his haunted, Palladian Yorkshire home, which was said to have given St. John Clarke the background for a novel. Besides, their eldest son, Mountfichet, I had been told, was turning out well at the university, where he was a great favourite with Sillery.

When introductions took place, it seemed simpler to make no reference to the fact that we had met before. Anne Stepney stared round the room with severe approval. Indicating Foppa and his companion, she remarked:

'I always think people playing cards make such a good pattern.'

'Rather like a Chardin,' I suggested.

'Do you think so?' she replied, implying contradiction rather than agreement.

'The composition?'

'You know I am really only interested in Chardin's highlights,' she said.

Before we could pursue the intricacies of Chardin's technique further, Foppa rose to supply further drinks. He had already made a sign of apology at his delay in doing this, to be accounted for by the fact that his game was on the point of completion when Barnby arrived. He now noted the score on a piece of paper and came towards us.

He was followed this time to the bar by the man with whom he had been at cards. Foppa's companion could now be seen more clearly. His suit was better cut and general appearance more distinguished than was usual in the club. He had stood by the table for a moment, stretching himself and lighting a cigarette, while he regarded our group. A moment later, taking a step towards Anne Stepney, he said in a soft, purring, rather humorous voice, with something almost hypnotic about its tone:

'I heard your name when you were introduced. You must be Eddie Bridgnorth's daughter.'

Looking at him more closely as he said this, I was surprised that he had remained almost unobserved until that moment. He was no ordinary person. That was clear. Of medium height, even rather small when not compared with Foppa, he was slim, with that indefinably 'horsey' look that seems even to affect the texture of the skin. His age was hard to guess: probably he was in his forties. He was very trim in his clothes. They were old, neat, well preserved clothes, a little like those worn by Uncle Giles. This man gave the impression of having handled large sums of money in his time, although he did not convey any presumption of affluence at that particular moment. He was clean-shaven, and wore a hard collar and Brigade of Guards tie. I could not imagine what someone of that sort was doing at Foppa's. There was something about him of Buster Foxe, third husband of Stringham's mother: the same cool, tough, socially elegant personality, though far more genial than Buster's. He lacked, too, that carapace of professional egotism acquired in boyhood that envelops protectively even the most good-humoured naval officer. Perhaps the similarity to Buster was after all only the outer veneer acquired by all people of the same generation.

Anne Stepney replied rather stiffly to this enquiry, that

'Eddie Bridgnorth' was indeed her father. Having decided to throw in her lot so uncompromisingly with 'artists', she may have felt put out to find herself confronted in such a place by someone of this kind. Since he claimed acquaintance with Lord Bridgnorth, there was no knowing what information he might possess about herself; nor what he might report subsequently if he saw her father again. However, the man in the Guards tie seemed instinctively to understand what her feelings would be on learning that he knew her family.

'I am Dicky Umfraville,' he said. 'I don't expect you have ever heard of me, because I have been away from this country for so long. I used to see something of your father when he owned Yellow Jack. In fact I won a whole heap of money on that horse once. None of it left now, I regret to say.'

He smiled gently. By the confidence, and at the same time the modesty, of his manner he managed to impart an extraordinary sense of reassurance. Anne Stepney seemed hardly to know what to say in answer to this account of himself. I remembered hearing Sillery speak of Umfraville, when I was an undergraduate. Perhaps facetiously, he had told Stringham that Umfraville was a man to beware of. That had been apropos of Stringham's father, and life in Kenya. Stringham himself had met Umfraville in Kenya, and spoke of him as a well-known gentleman-rider. I also remembered Stringham complaining that Le Bas had once mistaken him for Umfraville, who had been at Le Bas's house at least fifteen years earlier. Now, in spite of the difference in age and appearance, I could see that Le Bas's error had been due to something more than the habitual vagueness of schoolmasters. The similarity between Stringham and Umfraville was of a moral rather than physical sort. The same dissatisfaction

152

with life and basic melancholy gave a resemblance, though Umfraville's features and expression were more formalised and, in some manner, coarser—perhaps they could even be called more brutal—than Stringham's.

There was something else about Umfraville that struck me, a characteristic I had noticed in other people of his age. He seemed still young, a person like oneself; and yet at the same time his appearance and manner proclaimed that he had had time to live at least a few years of his grown-up life before the outbreak of war in 1914. Once I had thought of those who had known the epoch of my own childhood as 'older people'. Then I had found there existed people like Umfraville who seemed somehow to span the gap. They partook of both eras, specially forming the tone of the post-war years; much more so, indeed, than the younger people. Most of them, like Umfraville, were melancholy; perhaps from the strain of living simultaneously in two different historical periods. That was his category, certainly. He continued now to address himself to Anne Stepney.

'Do you ever go to trotting races?'

'No.'

She looked very surprised at the question.

'I thought not,' he said, laughing at her astonishment. 'I became interested when I was in the States. The Yanks are very keen on trotting races. So are the French. In this country no one much ever seems to go. However, I met Foppa, here, down at Greenford the other day and we got on so well that we arranged to go to Caversham together. The next thing is I find myself playing piquet with him in his own joint.'

Foppa laughed at this account of the birth of their friendship, and rubbed his hands together.

'You had all the luck tonight, Mr. Umfraville,' he said. 'Next time I have my revenge.'

'Certainly, Foppa, certainly.'

However, in spite of the way the cards had fallen, Foppa seemed pleased to have Umfraville in the club. Later, I found that one of Umfraville's most fortunate gifts was a capacity to take money off people without causing offence.

A moment or two of general conversation followed in which it turned out that Jean had met Barnby on one of his visits to Stourwater. She knew, of course, about his former connection with Baby Wentworth, but when we had talked of this together, she had been uncertain whether or not they had ever stayed with Sir Magnus Donners at the same time. They began to discuss the week-end during which they had both been in the same large house-party. Anne Stepney, possibly to avoid a further immediate impact with Umfraville before deciding on how best to treat him, crossed the room to examine Victor Emmanuel's picture. Umfraville and I were, accordingly, left together. I asked if he remembered Stringham in Kenya.

'Charles Stringham?' he said. 'Yes, of course I knew him. Boffles Stringham's son. A very nice boy. But wasn't he married to *her* sister?'

He lowered his voice, and jerked his head in Anne's direction.

'They are divorced now.'

'Of course they are. I forgot. As a matter of fact I heard Charles was in rather a bad way. Drinking enough to float a battleship. Of course, Boffles likes his liquor hard, too. Have you known Charles long?'

'We were at the same house at school—Le Bas's.'

'Not possible.'

'Why not?'

'Because I was at Le Bas's too. Not for very long. I started at Corderey's. Then Corderey's house was taken over by Le Bas. I was asked to leave quite soon after that—

not actually sacked, as is sometimes maliciously stated by
my friends. I get invited to Old Boy dinners, for example.
Not that I ever go. Usually out of England. As a matter of
fact I might go this year. What about you?'

'I might. I haven't been myself for a year or two.'

'Do come. We'll make up a party and raise hell. Tear
Claridge's in half. That's where they hold it, isn't it?'

'Or the Ritz.'

'You must come.'

There was a suggestion of madness in the way he shot
out his sentences; not the kind of madness that was raving,
nor even, in the ordinary sense, dangerous; but a warning
that no proper mechanism existed for operating normal
controls. At the same time there was also something
impelling about his friendliness: this sudden decision that
we must attend the Old Boy dinner together. Even though
I knew fairly well—at least flattered myself I knew well—
the type of man he was, I could not help being pleased by
the invitation. Certainly, I made up my mind immediately
that I would go to the Le Bas dinner, upon which I was
far from decided before. In fact, it would be true to say
that Umfraville had completely won me over; no doubt by
the shock tactics against which Sillery had issued his
original warning. In such matters, though he might often
talk nonsense, Sillery possessed a strong foundation of
shrewdness. People who disregarded his admonitions sometimes lived to regret it.

'Do you often come here?' Umfraville asked.

'Once in a way—to play Russian billiards.'

'Tell me the name of that other charming girl.'

'Jean Duport.'

'Anything to do with the fellow who keeps company with
Bijou Ardglass?'

'Wife.'

'Dear me. How eccentric of him with something so nice at home. Anne, over there, is a dear little thing, too. Bit of a handful, I hear. Fancy her being grown up. Only seems the other day I read the announcement of her birth. Wouldn't mind taking her out to dinner one day, if I had the price of a dinner on me.'

'Do you live permanently in Kenya?'

'Did for a time. Got rather tired of it lately. Isn't what it was in the early days. But, you know, something seems to have gone badly wrong with this country too. It's quite different from when I was over here two or three years ago. Then there was a party every night—two or three, as a matter of fact. Now all that is changed. No parties, no gaiety, everyone talking in a dreadfully serious manner about economics or world disarmament or something of the sort. That was why I was glad to come here and take a hand with Foppa. No nonsense about economics or world disarmament with him. All the people I know have become so damned serious, what? Don't you find that yourself?'

'It's the slump.'

Umfraville's face had taken on a strained, worried expression while he was saying this, almost the countenance of a priest preaching a gospel of pleasure to a congregation now fallen away from the high standards of the past. There was a look of hopelessness in his eyes, as if he knew of the terrible odds against him, and the martyrdom that would be his final crown. At that moment he again reminded me, for some reason, of Buster Foxe. I had never heard Buster express such opinions, though in general they were at that time voiced commonly enough.

'Anyway, it's nice to find all of you here,' he said. 'Let's have another drink.'

Barnby and Anne Stepney now began to play billiards together. They seemed not on the best of terms, and had

156

perhaps had some sort of a quarrel earlier in the evening. If Mrs. Erdleigh had been able to examine the astrological potentialities of that day she would perhaps have warned groups of lovers that the aspects were ominous. Jean came across to the bar. She took my arm, as if she wished to emphasise to Umfraville that we were on the closest terms. This was in spite of the fact that she herself was always advocating discretion. All the same, I felt delighted and warmed by her touch. Umfraville smiled, almost paternally, as if he felt that here at least he could detect on our part some hope of a pursuit of pleasure. He showed no disposition to return to his game with Foppa, now chatting with the two Italians.

'Charles Stringham was mixed up with Milly Andriadis at one moment, wasn't he?' Umfraville asked.

'About three years ago—just before his marriage.'

'I think it was just starting when I was last in London. Don't expect that really did him any good. Milly has got a way of exhausting chaps, no matter who they are. Even her Crowned Heads. They can't stand it after a bit. I remember one friend of mine had to take a voyage round the world to recover. He got D.T.s in Hongkong. Thought he was being hunted by naked women riding on unicorns. What's happened to Milly now?'

'I only met her once—at a party Charles took me to.'

'Why don't we all go and see her?'

'I don't think any of us really know her.'

'But *I* couldn't know her better.'

'Where does she live?'

'Where's the telephone book?' said Umfraville. 'Though I don't expect she will be in England at this time of year.'

He moved away, lost in thought, and disappeared through the door. It occurred to me that he was pretty drunk, but at the same time I was not sure. Equally possible

157

was the supposition that this was his first drink of the evening. The mystery surrounded him that belongs especially to strong characters who have only pottered about in life. Jean slipped her hand in mine.

'Who is he?'

I tried to explain to her who Umfraville was.

'I am enjoying myself,' she said.

'Are you?'

I could not be quite sure whether I was enjoying myself or not. We watched the other two playing billiards. The game was evidently war to the knife. They were evenly matched. There could be no doubt now that there had been some sort of disagreement between them before their arrival at Foppa's. Perhaps all girls were in a difficult mood that night.

'I've often heard of Umfraville,' said Barnby, chalking his cue. 'Didn't he take two women to St. Moritz one year, and get fed up with them, and left them there to pay the hotel bill?'

'Who is he married to now?' Anne Stepney asked.

'Free as air at the moment, I believe,' said Barnby. 'He has had several wives—three at least. One of them poisoned herself. Another left him for a marquess—and almost immediately eloped again with a jockey. What happened to the third I can't remember. Your shot, my dear.'

Umfraville returned to the room. He watched the completion of the game in silence. It was won by Barnby. Then he spoke.

'I have a proposition to make,' he said. 'I got on to Milly Andriadis just now on the telephone and told her we were all coming round to see her.'

My first thought was that I could not make a habit of arriving with a gang of friends at Mrs. Andriadis's house as an uninvited guest; even at intervals of three or four

158

years. A moment later I saw the absurdity of such diffidence, because, apart from any other consideration, she would not have the faintest remembrance of ever having met me before. At the same time, I could not inwardly disregard the pattern of life which caused Dicky Umfraville not only to resemble Stringham, but also, by this vicarious invitation, to re-enact Stringham's past behaviour.

'What is this suggestion?' enquired Anne Stepney.

She spoke coldly, but I think Umfraville had already thoroughly aroused her interest. At any rate her eyes reflected that rather puzzled look that in women is sometimes the prelude to an inclination for the man on whom it is directed.

'Someone called Mrs. Andriadis,' said Umfraville. 'She has been giving parties since you were so high. Rather a famous lady. A very old friend of mine. I thought we might go round and see her. I rang her up just now and she can't wait to welcome us.'

'Oh, do let's go,' said Anne Stepney, suddenly abandoning her bored, listless tone. 'I've always longed to meet Mrs. Andriadis. Wasn't she some king's mistress—was it——'

'It was,' said Umfraville.

'I've heard so many stories of the wonderful parties she gives.'

Umfraville stepped forward and took her hand. 'Your ladyship wishes to come,' he said softly, as if playing the part of a courtier in some ludicrously mannered ceremonial. 'We go, then. Yours to command.'

He bent his head over the tips of her fingers. I could not see whether his lips actually touched them, but the burlesque was for some reason extraordinarily funny, so that we all laughed. Yet, although absurd, Umfraville's gesture had also a kind of grace which clearly pleased and flattered Anne Stepney. She even blushed a little. Although he laughed with the rest of us, I saw that Barnby was a trifle put out, as indeed most men would have been in the circumstances. He had certainly recognised Umfraville as a rival with a technique entirely different from his own. I looked across to Jean to see if she wanted to join the expedition. She nodded quickly and smiled. All at once things were going all right again between us.

'I've only met Mrs. Andriadis a couple of times,' said Barnby. 'But we got on very well on both occasions—in fact she bought a drawing. I suppose she won't mind such a large crowd?'

'Mind?' said Umfraville. 'My dear old boy, Milly will be tickled to death. Come along. We can all squeeze into one taxi. Foppa, we shall meet again. You shall have your revenge.'

Mrs. Andriadis was, of course, no longer living in the Duports' house in Hill Street, where Stringham had taken me to the party. That house had been sold by Duport at the time of his financial disaster. She was now installed, so it appeared, in a large block of flats recently erected in Park Lane. I was curious to see how her circumstances would strike me on re-examination. Her party had seemed, at the time, to reveal a new and fascinating form of life, which one might never experience again. Such a world now was not only far less remarkable than formerly, but also its special characteristics appeared scarcely necessary to seek in an active manner. Its elements had, indeed, grown up all round one like strange tropical vegetation: more luxuriant, it was true, in some directions rather than others: attractive here, repellent there, but along every track that could be followed almost equally dense and imprisoning.

'She really said she would like to see us?' I asked, as, tightly packed, we ascended in the lift.

Umfraville's reply was less assuring than might have been hoped.

'She said, "Oh, God, you again, Dicky. Somebody told me you died of drink in 1929." I said, "Milly, I'm coming straight round with a few friends to give you that kiss I forgot when we were in Havana together." She said, "Well, I hope you'll bring along that pony you owe me, too, which you forgot at the same time." So saying, she snapped the receiver down.'

'So she has no idea how many we are?'

'Milly knows I have lots of friends.'

'All the same——'

'Don't worry, old boy. Milly will eat you all up. Especially as you are a friend of Charles.'

I was, on the contrary, not at all sure that it would be wise to mention Stringham's name to Mrs. Andriadis.

'We had to sue her after she took our house,' said Jean.

'Yes, I expect so,' said Umfraville.

The circumstances of our arrival did not seem specially favourable in the light of these remarks. We were admitted to what was evidently a large flat by an elderly lady's-maid, who had the anxious, authoritative demeanour of a nanny, or nursery governess, long established in the family.

'Well, Ethel,' said Umfraville. 'How are you keeping? Quite a long time since we met.'

Her face brightened at once when she recognised him.

'And how are *you*, Mr. Umfraville? Haven't set eyes on you since the days in Cuba. You look very well indeed, sir. Where did you get your sunburn?'

'Not too bad, Ethel. What a time it was in Cuba. And how is Mrs. A.?'

'She's been a bit poorly, sir, on and off. Not quite her own old self. She has her ups and downs.'

'Which of us doesn't, Ethel? Will she be glad to see me?'

It seemed rather late in the day to make this enquiry. Ethel's reply was not immediate. Her face contracted a trifle as she concentrated her attention upon an entirely truthful answer to this delicate question.

'She was pleased when you rang up,' she said. 'Very pleased. Called me in and told me, just as she would have done in the old days. But then Mr. Guggenbühl telephoned just after you did, and after that I don't know that she was so keen. She's changeable, you know. Always was.'

'Mr. Guggenbühl is the latest, is he?'

Ethel laughed, with the easy good manners of a trusted servant whose tact is infinite. She made no attempt to indicate the identity of Mr. Guggenbühl.

'What's he like?' Umfraville asked, wheedling in his manner.

'He's a German gentleman, sir.'

'Old, young? Rich, poor?'

'He's quite young, sir. Shouldn't say he was specially wealthy.'

'One of that kind, is he?' said Umfraville. 'Everybody seems to have a German boy these days. I feel quite out of fashion not to have one in tow myself. Does he live here?'

'Stays sometimes.'

'Well, we won't remain long,' said Umfraville. 'I quite understand.'

We followed him through a door, opened by Ethel, which led into a luxurious rather than comfortable room. There was an impression of heavy damask curtains and fringed chair-covers. Furniture and decoration had evidently been designed in one piece, little or nothing having been added to the original scheme by the present owner. A few books and magazines lying on a low table in Chinese Chippendale seemed strangely out of place; even

162

more so, a model theatre, like a child's, which stood on a Louis XVI commode.

Mrs. Andriadis herself was lying in an armchair, her legs resting on a pouf. Her features had not changed at all from the time when I had last seen her. Her powder-grey hair remained beautifully trim; her dark eyebrows still arched over very bright brown eyes. She looked as pretty as before, and as full of energy. She wore no jewellery except a huge square cut diamond on one finger.

Her clothes, on the other hand, had undergone a strange alteration. Her small body was now enveloped in a black cloak, its velvet collar clipped together at the neck by a short chain of metal links. The garment suggested an Italian officer's uniform cloak, which it probably was. Beneath this military outer covering was a suit of grey flannel pyjamas, mean in design and much too big for her: in fact obviously intended for a man. One trouser leg was rucked up, showing her slim calf and ankle. She did not rise, but made a movement with her hand to show that she desired us all to find a place to sit.

'Well, Dicky,' she said, 'why the hell do you want to bring a crowd of people to see me at this time of night?'

She spoke dryly, though without bad temper, in that distinctly cockney drawl that I remembered.

'Milly, darling, they are all the most charming people imaginable. Let me tell you who they are.'

Mrs. Andriadis laughed.

'I know *him*,' she said, nodding in the direction of Barnby.

'Lady Anne Stepney,' said Umfraville. 'Do you remember when we went in her father's party to the St. Leger?'

'You'd better not say anything about *that*,' said Mrs. Andriadis. 'Eddie Bridgnorth has become a pillar of respectability. How is your sister, Anne? I'm not surprised she had to leave Charles Stringham. Such a charmer, but no woman could stay married to him for long.'

Anne Stepney looked rather taken aback at this peremptory approach.

'And Mrs. Duport,' said Umfraville.

'Was it your house I took in Hill Street?'

'Yes,' said Jean, 'it was.'

I wondered whether there would be an explosion at this disclosure. The trouble at the house had involved some question of a broken looking-glass and a burnt-out boiler. Perhaps there had been other items too. Certainly there had been a great deal of unpleasantness. However, in the un-expected manner of persons who live their lives at a furious rate, Mrs. Andriadis merely said in a subdued voice:

'You know, my dear, I want to apologise for all that happened in that wretched house. If I told you the whole story, you would agree that I was not altogether to blame. But it is all much too boring to go into now. At least you got your money. I hope it really paid for the damage.'

'We've got rid of the house now,' Jean said, laughing. 'I didn't ever like it much anyway.'

'And Mr. Jenkins,' Umfraville said. 'A friend of Charles's——'

She gave me a keen look.

'I believe I've seen you before, too,' she said.

I hoped she was not going to recall the scene Mr. Deacon had made at her party. However, she carried the matter no further.

'Ethel,' she shouted, 'bring some glasses. There is beer for those who can't drink whisky.'

She turned towards Umfraville.

'I'm quite glad to see you all,' she said; 'but you mustn't stay too long after Werner appears. He doesn't approve of people like you.'

164

'Your latest beau, Milly?'

'Werner Guggenbühl. Such a charming German boy. He will be terribly tired when he arrives. He has been walking in a procession all day.'

'To meet the Hunger-Marchers?' I asked.

It had suddenly struck me that in the extraordinary pattern life forms, this visit to Mrs. Andriadis was all part of the same diagram as that in which St. John Clarke, Quiggin and Mona had played their part that afternoon.

'I think so. Were you marching too?'

'No—but I knew some people who were.'

'What an extraordinary world we live in,' said Umfraville. 'All one's friends marching about in the park.'

'Rather sweet of Werner, don't you agree?' said Mrs. Andriadis. 'Considering this isn't his own country and all the awful things we did to Germany at the Versailles Treaty.'

Before she could say more about him, Guggenbühl himself arrived in the room. He was dark and not bad-looking in a very German style. His irritable expression recalled Quiggin's. He bowed slightly from the waist when introduced, but took no notice of any individual, not even Mrs. Andriadis herself, merely glancing round the room and then glaring straight ahead of him. There could be no doubt that he was the owner of the grey pyjamas. He reminded me of a friend of Mr. Deacon's called 'Willi': described by Mr. Deacon as having 'borne much of the heat of the day over against Verdun when nation rose against nation'. Guggenbühl was a bit younger than Willi, but in character they might easily have a good deal in common.

'What sort of a day did you have, Werner?' asked Mrs. Andriadis.

She used a coaxing voice, quite unlike the manner in which she had spoken up to that moment. The tone made me think of Templer trying to appease Mona. It was equally unavailing, for Guggenbühl made an angry gesture with his fist.

'What was it like, you ask,' he said. 'So it was like everything in this country. Social-Democratic antics. Of it let us not speak.'

He turned away in the direction of the model theatre. Taking no further notice of us, he began to manipulate the scenery, or play about in some other manner with the equipment at the back of the stage.

'Werner is writing a play,' explained Mrs. Andriadis, speaking now in a much more placatory manner. 'We sometimes run through the First Act in the evening. How is it going, Werner?'

'Oh, are you?' said Anne Stepney. 'I'm terribly interested in the Theatre. Do tell us what it is about.'

Guggenbühl turned his head at this.

'I think it would not interest you,' he said. 'We have done with old theatre of bourgeoisie and capitalists. Here is *Volksbühnen*—for actor that is worker like industrial worker—actor that is machine of machines.'

'Isn't it too thrilling?' said Mrs. Andriadis. 'You know the October Revolution was the real turning point in the history of the Theatre.'

'Oh, I'm sure it was,' said Anne Stepney. 'I've read a lot about the Moscow Art Theatre.'

Guggenbühl made a hissing sound with his lips, expressing considerable contempt.

'Moscow Art Theatre is just to tolerate,' he said, 'but what of biomechanics, of *Trümmer-Kunst*, has it? Then Shakespeare's *Ein Sommernachtstraum* or Toller's *Masse-Mensch* will you take? The modern ethico-social play I think you do not like. Hauptmann, Kaiser, plays to Rosa Luxemburg and Karl Liebknecht, yes. The new corporate life. The socially conscious form. Drama as highest of arts we Germans know. No mere entertainment, please. *Lebensstimmung* it is. But it is workers untouched by middle class that will make spontaneous. Of Moscow Art Theatre you speak. So there was founded at Revolution both Theatre and Art Soviet, millions, billions of roubles set aside by Moscow Soviet of Soldier Deputies. Hundreds, thousands of persons. Actors, singers, clowns, dancers, musicians, craftsmen, designers, mechanics, electricians, scene-shifters, all kinds of manual workers, all trained, yes, and supplying themselves to make. Two years to have one perfect single production—if needed so, three, four, five, ten years. At other time, fifty plays on fifty successive nights. It is not be getting money, no.'

His cold, hard voice, offering instruction, stopped abruptly.

'Any ventriloquists?' Umfraville asked.

The remark passed unnoticed, because Anne Stepney broke in again.

'I can't think why we don't have a revolution here,' she said, 'and start something of that sort.'

'You would have a revolution here?' said Guggenbühl, smiling rather grimly. 'So? Then I am in agreement with you.'

'Werner thinks the time has come to act,' said Mrs. Andriadis, returning to her more decisive manner. 'He says we have been talking for too long.'

'Oh, I do agree,' said Anne Stepney.

I asked Guggenbühl if he had come across St. John Clarke that afternoon. At this question his manner at once changed.

'You know him? The writer.'

'I know the man and the girl who were pushing him.'

'Ach, so.'

He seemed uncertain what line to take about St. John Clarke. Perhaps he was displeased with himself for having made disparaging remarks about the procession in front of someone who knew two of the participants and might report his words.

'He is a famous author, I think.'

'Quite well known.'

'He ask me to visit him.'

'Are you going?'

'Of course.'

'Did you meet Quiggin—his secretary—my friend?'

'I think he goes away soon to get married.'

'To the girl he was with?'

'I think so. Mr. Clarke ask me to visit him when your friend is gone for some weeks. He says he will be lonely and would like to talk.'

Probably feeling that he had wasted enough time already with the company assembled in the room, and at the same time being unwilling to give too much away to someone he did not know, Guggenbühl returned, after saying this, to the model theatre. Ostentatiously, he continued to play about with its accessories. We drank our beer. Even Umfraville seemed a little put out of countenance by Guggenbühl, who had certainly brought an atmosphere of peculiar unfriendliness and disquiet into the room. Mrs. Andriadis herself perhaps took some pleasure in the general discomfiture for which he was responsible. The imposition of one kind of a guest upon another is a form of exercising power that appeals to most persons who have devoted a good deal of their life to entertaining. Mrs. Andriadis, as a hostess of long standing and varied experience, was probably no exception. In addition to that, she, like St. John Clarke, had evidently succumbed recently to a political conversion, using Guggenbühl as her vehicle. His uncompromising behaviour no doubt expressed to perfection the role to which he was assigned in her mind: the scourge of frivolous persons of the sort she knew so well.

However, one of the essential gifts of an accomplished hostess is an ability to dismiss, quietly and speedily, guests who have overstayed their welcome. Mrs. Andriadis must have possessed this ingenuity to an unusual degree. I can remember no details of how our party was shifted. Perhaps Umfraville made a movement to go that was quickly accepted. Brief good-byes were said. One way or another, in an unbelievably short space of time, we found ourselves once more in Park Lane.

'You see,' said Umfraville. 'Even Milly . . .'

Some sort of a discussion followed as to whether or not the evening should be brought to a close at this point. Umfraville and Anne Stepney were unwilling to go home; Barnby was uncertain what he wanted to do; Jean and I agreed that we had had enough. The end of it was that the other two decided to accompany Umfraville to a place where a 'last drink' could be obtained. Other people's behaviour seemed unimportant to me; for in some way the day had righted itself, and once more the two of us seemed close together.

5.

WHEN, in describing Widmerpool's new employment, Templer had spoken of 'the Acceptance World', I had been struck by the phrase. Even as a technical definition, it seemed to suggest what we are all doing; not only in business, but in love, art, religion, philosophy, politics, in fact all human activities. The Acceptance World was the world in which the essential element—happiness, for example—is drawn, as it were, from an engagement to meet a bill. Sometimes the goods are delivered, even a small profit made; sometimes the goods are not delivered, and disaster follows; sometimes the goods are delivered, but the value of the currency is changed. Besides, in another sense, the whole world is the Acceptance World as one approaches thirty; at least some illusions discarded. The mere fact of still existing as a human being proved that.

I did not see Templer himself until later in the summer, when I attended the Old Boy Dinner for members of Le Bas's house. That year the dinner was held at the Ritz. We met in one of the subterranean passages leading to the private room where we were to eat. It was a warm, rather stuffy July evening. Templer, like a Frenchman, wore a white waistcoat with his dinner-jacket, a fashion of the moment: perhaps by then already a little outmoded.

'We always seem to meet in these gorgeous halls,' he said.

'We do.'

'I expect you've heard that Mona bolted,' he went on quickly. 'Joined up with that friend of yours of the remarkable suit and strong political views.'

His voice was casual, but it had a note of obsession as if his nerves were on edge. His appearance was unchanged; possibly a little thinner.

Mona's elopement had certainly been discussed widely. In the break-up of a marriage the world inclines to take the side of the partner with most vitality, rather than the one apparently least to blame. In the Templers' case public opinion had turned out unexpectedly favourable to Mona; probably because Templer himself was unknown to most of the people who talked to me of the matter. Normal inaccuracies of gossip were increased by this ignorance. In one version, Mona was represented as immensely rich, ill treated by an elderly, unsuccessful stockbroker; another described Templer as unable to fulfil a husband's role from physical dislike of women. A third account included a twenty-minute hand-to-hand struggle between the two men, at the end of which Quiggin had gained the victory: a narrative sometimes varied to a form in which Templer beat Quiggin unconscious with a shooting-stick. In a different vein was yet another story describing Templer, infatuated with his secretary, paying Quiggin a large sum to take Mona off his hands.

On the whole people are unwilling to understand even comparatively simple situations where husband and wife are concerned; indeed, a simple explanation is the last thing ever acceptable. Here, certainly, was something complicated enough; a striking reversal of what might be thought the ordinary course of events. Templer, a man undoubtedly attractive to women, loses his wife to Quiggin, a man usually ill at ease in women's company: Mona, as Anna Karenin, directing her romantic feelings towards Karenin as a lover, rather than Vronsky as a husband. For me, the irony was emphasised by Templer being my first schoolboy friend to seem perfectly at home with the opposite sex; indeed, the first to have practical experience in that quarter. But conflict between the sexes might be compared with the engagement of boxers in which the best style is not always victorious.

'What will they live on?' Templer said. 'Mona is quite an expensive luxury in her way.'

I had wondered that, too, especially in the light of an experience of a few weeks before, when in the Café Royal with Barnby. In those days there was a female orchestra raised on a dais at one side of the huge room where you had drinks. They were playing *In a Persian Market,* and in that noisy, crowded, glaring, for some reason rather ominous atmosphere, which seemed specially designed to hear such confidences, Barnby had been telling me that matters were at an end between Anne Stepney and himself. That had not specially surprised me after the evening at Foppa's. Barnby had reached the climax of his story when Quiggin and Mark Members passed our table, side by side, on their way to the diners' end of the room. That was, to say the least, unexpected. They appeared to be on perfectly friendly terms with each other. When they saw us, Members had given a distant, evasive smile, but Quiggin stopped to speak. He seemed in an excellent humour.

'How are you, Nick?'

'All right.'

'Mark and I are going to celebrate the completion of *Unburnt Boats,*' he said. 'It is a wonderful thing to finish a book.'

'When is it to appear?'

'Autumn.'

I felt sure Quiggin had stopped like this in order to make some statement that would define more clearly his own position. That would certainly be a reasonable aim on his part. I was curious to know why the two of them were friends again; also to learn what was happening about Quiggin and Mona. Such information as I had then had been through Jean, who knew from her brother only that they had gone abroad together. At the same time, as a friend of Templer's, I did not want to appear too obviously willing to condone the fact that Quiggin had eloped with his wife.

'Mona and I are in Sussex now,' said Quiggin, in a voice that could almost be described as unctuous, so much did it avoid his usual harsh note. 'We have been lent a cottage. I am just up for the night to see Mark and make final arrangements with my publisher.'

He talked as if he had been married to Mona, or at least lived with her, for years; just as, a few months earlier, he had spoken as if he had always been St. John Clarke's secretary. It seemed hard to do anything but accept the relationship as a *fait accompli*. Such things have to be.

'Can you deal with St. John Clarke from so far away?'

'How do you mean?'

Quiggin's face clouded, taking on an expression suggesting he had heard the name of St. John Clarke, but was quite unable to place its associations.

'Aren't you still his secretary?'

'Oh, good gracious, no,' said Quiggin, unable to repress a laugh at the idea.

'I hadn't heard you'd left him.'

'But he has become a Trotskyist.'

'What form does it take?'

Quiggin laughed again. He evidently wished to show his complete agreement that the situation regarding St. John Clarke was so preposterous that only a certain degree of jocularity could carry it off. Laughter, his manner indicated, was a more civilised reaction than the savage rage that

173

would have been the natural emotion of most right-minded persons on hearing the news for the first time.

'The chief form,' he said, 'is that he consequently now requires a secretary who is also a Trotskyist.'

'Who has he got?'

'You would not know him.'

'Someone beyond the pale?'

'He has found a young German to pander to him, as a matter of fact. One Guggenbühl.'

'I have met him as a matter of fact.'

'Have you?' said Quiggin, without interest. 'Then I should advise you to steer clear of Trotskyists in the future, if I were you.'

'Was this very sudden?'

'My own departure was not entirely involuntary,' said Quiggin. 'At first I thought the man would rise above the difficulties of my domestic situation. I—and Mona, too—did everything to assist and humour him. In the end it was no good.'

He had moved off then, at the same time gathering in Members, who had been chatting to a girl in dark glasses sitting at a neighbouring table.

'We shall stay in the country until the divorce comes through,' he had said over his shoulder.

The story going round was that Mona had been introduced by Quiggin to St. John Clarke as a political sympathiser. Only later had the novelist discovered the story of her close association with Quiggin. He had begun to make difficulties at once. Quiggin, seeing that circumstances prevented the continuance of his job, made a goodish bargain with St. John Clarke, and departed. Guggenbühl must have stepped into the vacuum. No one seemed to know the precise moment when he had taken Quiggin's place; nor how matters remained regarding Mrs. Andriadis.

174

Like Templer, I wondered how Quiggin and Mona would make two ends meet, but these details could hardly be gone into then and there in the Ritz.

'I suppose Quiggin keeps afloat,' I said. 'For one thing, he must have just had an advance for his book. Still, I don't expect that was anything colossal.'

'That aunt of Mona's died the other day,' said Templer. 'She left Mona her savings—a thousand or so, I think.'

'So they won't starve.'

'As a matter of fact I haven't cut her allowance yet,' he said, reddening slightly. 'I suppose one will have to in due course.'

He paused.

'I must say it was the hell of a surprise,' he said. 'We'd had plenty of rows, but I certainly never thought she would go off with a chap who looked quite so like something the cat had brought in.'

I could only laugh and agree. These things are capable of no real explanation. Mona's behaviour was perhaps to be examined in the light of her exalted feelings for Quiggin as a literary figure. Combined with this was, no doubt, a kind of envy of her husband's former successes with other women; for such successes with the opposite sex put him, as it were, in direct competition with herself. It is, after all, envy rather than jealousy that causes most of the trouble in married life.

'I've really come here tonight to see Widmerpool,' said Templer, as if he wished to change the subject. 'Bob Duport is in England again. I think I told you Widmerpool might help him land on his feet.'

I felt a sense of uneasiness that he found it natural to tell me this. Jean had always insisted that her brother knew nothing of the two of us. Probably she was right; though I could never be sure that someone with such highly developed instincts where relations between the sexes were concerned could remain entirely unaware that his sister was having a love affair. On the other hand he never saw us together. No doubt, so far as Jean was concerned, he would have regarded a lover as only natural in her situation. He was an exception to the general rule that made Barnby, for example, puritanically disapproving of an irregular life in others. In any case, he probably spoke of Duport in the way people so often do in such circumstances, ignorant of the facts, yet moved by some unconscious inner process to link significant names together. All the same, I was conscious of a feeling of foreboding. I was going to see Jean that night; after the dinner was at an end.

'I am rather hopeful things will be patched up with Jean, if Bob's business gets into running order again,' Templer said. 'The whole family can't be in a permanent state of being deserted by their husbands and wives. I gather Bob is no longer sleeping with Bijou Ardglass, which was the real cause of the trouble, I think.'

'Prince Theodoric's girl friend?'

'That's the one. Started life as a mannequin. Then married Ardglass as his second wife. When he died the title, and nearly all the money, went to a distant cousin, so she had to earn a living somehow. Still, it was inconvenient she should have picked on Bob.'

By this time we had reached the ante-room where Le Bas's Old Boys were assembling. Le Bas himself had not yet arrived, but Whitney, Maiden, Simson, Brandreth, Ghika, and Fettiplace-Jones were standing about, sipping drinks, and chatting uneasily. All of them, except Ghika, were already showing signs of the wear and tear of life. Whitney was all but unrecognisable with a moustache; Maiden had taken to spectacles; Simson was prematurely bald; Fettiplace-Jones, who was talking to Widmerpool

176

without much show of enjoyment, although he still looked like a distinguished undergraduate, had developed that ingratiating, almost cringing manner that some politicians assume to avoid an appearance of thrusting themselves forward. Fettiplace-Jones had been Captain of the House when I had arrived there as a new boy and had left at the end of that term. He was now Member of Parliament for some northern constituency.

Several others came in behind Templer and myself. Soon the room became fairly crowded. Most of the new arrivals were older or younger than my own period, so that I knew them only by sight from previous dinners. As it happened, I had not attended a Le Bas dinner for some little time. I hardly knew why I was there that year, for it was exceptional for an old friend like Templer to turn up. I think I had a subdued curiosity to see if Dicky Umfraville would put in an appearance, and fulfil his promise to 'tear the place in half'. A chance meeting with Maiden, one of the organisers had settled it, and I came. Maiden now buttonholed Templer, and, at the same moment, Fettiplace-Jones moved away from Widmerpool to speak with Simson, who was said to be doing well at the Bar. I found Widmerpool beside me.

'Why, hullo—hullo—Nicholas——' he said.

He glared through his thick glasses, the side pieces of which were becoming increasingly embedded in wedges of fat below his temples. At the same time he transmitted one of those skull-like smiles of conventional friendliness to be generally associated with conviviality of a political sort. He was getting steadily fatter. His dinner-jacket no longer fitted him: perhaps had never done so with much success. Yet he carried this unhappy garment with more of an air than he would have achieved in the old days; certainly with more of an air than he had ever worn the famous overcoat for which he had been notorious at school.

177

We had met once or twice, always by chance, during the previous few years. On each occasion he had been going abroad for the Donners-Brebner Company. 'Doing pretty well,' he had always remarked, when asked how things were with him. His small eyes had glistened behind his spectacles when he had said this. There was no reason to disbelieve in his success, though I suspected at the time that his job might be more splendid in his own eyes than when regarded by some City figure like Templer. However, after Templer's more recent treatment of him, I supposed that I must be wrong in presuming exaggeration on Widmerpool's part. Although two or three years older than myself, he could still be little more than thirty. No doubt he was 'doing well'. With the self-confidence he had developed, he moved now with a kind of strut, a curious adaptation of that uneasy, rubber-shod tread, squeaking rhythmically down the interminable linoleum of our school-days. I remembered how Barbara Goring (whom we had both been in love with, and now I had not thought of for years) had once poured sugar over his head at a dance. She would hardly do that today. Yet Widmerpool had never entirely overcome his innate oddness; one might almost say, his monstrosity. In that he resembled Quiggin. Perhaps it was the determination of each to live by the will alone. At any rate, you noticed Widmerpool immediately upon entering a room. That would have given him satisfaction.

'Do you know, I nearly forgot your Christian name,' he said, not without geniality. 'I have so many things to re-member these days. I was just telling Fettiplace-Jones about North Africa. In my opinion we should hand back Gibraltar to Spain, taking Ceuta in exchange. Fettiplace-Jones was in general agreement. He belongs to a group in Parliament particularly interested in foreign affairs. I have just come back from those parts.'

'For Donners-Brebner?'

He nodded, puffing out his lips and assuming the appearance of a huge fish.

'But not in the future,' he said, breathing inward hard. 'I'm changing my trade.'

'I heard rumours.'

'Of what?'

'That you were joining the Acceptance World.'

'That's one way of putting it.'

Widmerpool sniggered.

'And you?' he asked.

'Nothing much.'

'Still producing your art books? It was art books, wasn't it?'

'Yes—and I wrote a book myself.'

'Indeed, Nicholas. What sort of a book?'

'A novel, Kenneth.'

'Has it been published?'

'A few months ago.'

'Oh.'

His ignorance of novels and what happened about them was evidently profound. That was, after all, reasonable enough. Perhaps it was just lack of interest on his part. Whatever the reason, he looked not altogether approving, and did not enquire the name of the book. However, probably feeling a moment later that his reply may have sounded a shade flat, he added: 'Good . . . good,' rather in the manner of Le Bas himself, when faced with an activity of which he was uninformed and suspicious, though at the same time unjustified in categorically forbidding.

'As a matter of fact I am making some notes for a book myself,' said Widmerpool. 'Quite a different sort of book from yours, of course. So we may be authors together. Do you always come to these dinners? I have been abroad, or otherwise prevented, on a number of occasions, and thought I would see what had happened to everybody. One sometimes makes useful contacts in such ways.'

Le Bas himself arrived in the room at that moment, bursting through the door tumultuously, exactly as if he were about to surprise the party assembled there at some improper activity. It was in this explosive way that he had moved about the house at school. For a second he made me feel as if I were back again under his surveillance; and one young man, with very fair hair, whose name I did not know, went scarlet in the face at his former housemaster's threatening impetuosity, just as if he himself had a guilty conscience.

However, Le Bas, as it turned out, was in an excellent humour. He went round the room shaking hands with everyone, making some comment to each of us, more often than not hopelessly inappropriate, showing that he had mistaken the Old Boy's name or generation. In spite of that I was aware of a feeling of warmth towards him that I had never felt when at school; perhaps because he seemed to represent, like a landscape or building, memories of a vanished time. He had become, if not history, at least part of one's own autobiography. In his infinitely ancient dinner-jacket and frayed tie he looked, as usual, wholly unchanged. His clothes were as old as Sillery's, though far better cut. Tall, curiously Teutonic in appearance, still rubbing his red, seemingly chronically sore eyes, as from time to time he removed his rimless glasses, he came at last to the end of the diners, who had raggedly formed up in line round the room, as if some vestige of school discipline was reborn in them at the appearance of their housemaster. After the final handshake, he took up one of those painful, almost tortured positions habitually affected by him, this particular one seeming to indicate that he had just landed on his heels in the sand after making the long jump.

Maiden, who, as I have said, was one of the organisers of the dinner, and was in the margarine business, now began fussing, as if he thought that by his personal exertions alone would anyone get anything to eat that night. He came up to me, muttering agitatedly.

'Another of your contemporaries accepted—Stringham,' he said. 'I suppose you don't know if he is turning up? We really ought to go into dinner soon. Should we wait for him? It is really too bad of people to be late for this sort of occasion.'

He spoke as if I, or at least all my generation, were responsible for the delay. The news that Stringham might be coming to the dinner surprised me. I asked Maiden about his acceptance of the invitation.

'He doesn't turn up as a rule,' Maiden explained, 'but I ran into him the other night at the Silver Slipper and he promised to come. He said he would attend if he were sober enough by Friday. He wrote down the time and place on a menu and put it in his pocket. What do you think?'

'I should think we had better go in.'

Maiden nodded, and screwed up his yellowish, worried face, which seemed to have taken on sympathetic colouring from the commodity he marketed. I remembered him as a small boy, perpetually preoccupied with the fear that he would be late for school or games: this tyranny of Time evidently pursuing him no less in later life. Finally, his efforts caused us to troop into the room where we were to dine. From what I had heard of Stringham recently, I thought his appearance at such a dinner extremely unlikely.

At the dinner table I found myself between Templer and a figure who always turned up at these dinners whose name I did not know: a middle-aged—even elderly, he then seemed—grey-moustached man. I had, rather half-heartedly, tried to keep a place next to me for Stringham, but gave up the idea when this person diffidently asked if he might occupy the chair. There were, in any case, some spare places at the end of the table, where Stringham could sit, if he arrived, as a certain amount of latitude always existed regarding the size of the party. It was to be presumed that the man with the grey moustache had been at Corderey's, in the days before Le Bas took over the house; if so, he was the sole survivor from that period who ever put in an appearance. I remembered Maiden had once commented to me on the fact that one of Corderey's Old Boys always turned up, although no one knew him. He had seemed perfectly happy before dinner, drinking a glass of sherry by himself. Hitherto, he had made no effort whatever to talk to any of the rest of the party. Le Bas had greeted him, rather unenthusiastically, with the words 'Hullo, Tolland'; but Le Bas was so notoriously vague regarding nomenclature that this name could be accepted only after corroboration. Something about his demeanour reminded me of Uncle Giles, though this man was, of course, considerably younger. There had been a Tolland at school with me, but I had known him only by sight. I asked Templer whether he had any news of Mrs. Erdleigh and Jimmy Stripling.

'I think she is fairly skinning Jimmy,' he said, laughing. 'They are still hard at it. I saw Jimmy the other day in Pimm's.'

The time having come round for another tea at the Ufford, I myself had visited Uncle Giles fairly recently. While there I had enquired, perhaps unwisely, about Mrs. Erdleigh. The question had been prompted partly by curiosity as to what his side of the story might be, partly from an inescapable though rather morbid interest in what happened to Stripling. I should have known better than to have been surprised by the look of complete incomprehension that came over Uncle Giles's face. It was similar technique, though put into more absolute execution, that Quiggin had used when asked about St. John Clarke. No doubt it would have been better to have left the matter of Mrs. Erdleigh alone. I should have known from the start that interrogation would be unproductive.

'Mrs. Erdleigh?'

He had spoken not only as if he had never heard of Mrs. Erdleigh but as if even the name itself could not possibly belong to anyone he had ever encountered.

'The lady who told our fortunes.'

'What fortunes?'

'When I was last here.'

'Can't understand what you're driving at.'

'I met her at tea when I last came here—Mrs. Erdleigh.'

'Believe there was someone of that name staying here.'

'She came in and you introduced me.'

'Rather an actressy woman, wasn't she? Didn't stay very long. Always talking about her troubles, so far as I can remember. Hadn't she been married to a Yangtze pilot, or was that another lady? There was a bit of a fuss about the bill, I believe. Interested in fortune-telling, was she? How did you discover that?'

'She put the cards out for us.'

'Never felt very keen about all that fortune-telling stuff,' said Uncle Giles, not unkindly. 'Doesn't do the nerves any good, in my opinion. Rotten lot of people, most of them, who take it up.'

Obviously the subject was to be carried no further. Perhaps Mrs. Erdleigh, to use a favourite phrase of my uncle's, had 'let him down'. Evidently she herself had been removed from his life as neatly as if by a surgical operation, and, by this mysterious process of voluntary oblivion, was excluded even from his very consciousness; all done, no doubt, by an effort of will. Possibly everyone could live equally untrammelled lives with the same determination. However, this mention of Uncle Giles is by the way.

'Jimmy is an extraordinary fellow,' said Templer, as if pondering my question. 'I can't imagine why Babs married him. All the same, he is more successful with the girls than you might think.'

Before he could elaborate this theme, his train of thought, rather to my relief, was interrupted. The cause of this was the sudden arrival of Stringham. He looked horribly pale, and, although showing no obvious sign of intoxication, I suspected that he had already had a lot to drink. His eyes were glazed, and, holding himself very erect, he walked with the slow dignity of one who is not absolutely sure what is going on round him. He went straight up to the head of the table where Le Bas was sitting and apologised for his lateness—the first course was being cleared—returning down the room to occupy the spare chair beside Ghika at the other end.

'Charles looks as if he has been hitting the martinis pretty hard,' said Templer.

I agreed. After a consultation with the wine waiter, Stringham ordered a bottle of champagne. Since Ghika had already provided himself with a whisky and soda there was evidently no question of splitting it with his next-door neighbour. Templer commented on this to me, and laughed. He seemed to have obtained relief from having discussed the collapse of his marriage with a friend who knew something of the circumstances. He was more cheerful now and spoke of his plans for selling the house near Maidenhead. We began to talk of things that had happened at school.

'Do you remember when Charles arranged for Le Bas

to be arrested by the police?' said Templer. 'The Braddock alias Thorne affair.'

We were sitting too far away from Le Bas for this remark to be overheard by him. Templer looked across to where Stringham was sitting and caught his eye. He jerked his head in Le Bas's direction and held his own wrists together as if he wore handcuffs. Stringham seemed to understand his meaning at once. His face brightened, and he made as if to catch Ghika by the collar. This action had to be explained to Ghika, and, during the interlude, Parkinson, who was on Templer's far side, engaged him in conversation about the Test Match.

I turned to the man with the grey moustache. He seemed to be expecting an approach of some sort, because, before I had time to speak, he said:

'I'm Tolland.'

'You were at Corderey's, weren't you?'

'Yes, I was. Seems a long time ago now.'

'Did you stay on into Le Bas's time?'

'No. Just missed him.'

He was infinitely melancholy; gentle in manner, but with a suggestion of force behind this sad kindliness.

'Was Umfraville there in your time?'

'R. H. J. Umfraville?'

'I think so. He's called "Dicky".'

Tolland gave a slow smile.

'We overlapped,' he admitted.

There was a pause.

'Umfraville was my fag,' said Tolland, as if drawing the fact from somewhere very deep down within him. 'At least I believe he was. I was quite a bit higher up in the school, of course, so I don't remember him very well.'

A terrible depression seemed to seize him at the thought of this great seniority of his to Umfraville. There was a

lack of serenity about Tolland at close quarters, quite different from the manner in which he had carried off his own
loneliness in a crowd. I felt rather uneasy at the thought
of having to deal with him, perhaps for the rest of dinner.
Whitney was on the other side and there was absolutely
no hope of his lending a hand in a case of that sort.

'Umfraville a friend of your?' asked Tolland.

He spoke almost as if he were condoling with me.

'I've just met him. He said he might be coming tonight.'

Tolland looked at me absently. I thought it might be
better to abandon the subject of Umfraville. However, a
moment or two later he himself returned to it.

'I don't think Umfraville will come tonight,' he said. 'I
heard he'd just got married.'

It certainly seemed unlikely that even Umfraville would
turn up for dinner at this late stage in the meal, though
the reason given was unexpected, even scriptural. Tolland
now seemed to regret having volunteered the information.

'Who did he marry?'

This question discomposed him even further. He cleared
his throat several times and took a gulp of claret, nearly
choking himself.

'As a matter of fact I believe she is a distant cousin of
mine—perhaps not,' he said. 'I can never remember that sort
of thing—yes, she is, though. Of course she is.'

'Yes?'

'One of the Bridgnorth girls—Anne, I think.'

'Anne Stepney?'

'Yes, yes. That's the one. You probably know her.'

'I do.'

'Thought you would.'

'But she is years younger.'

'She is a bit younger. Yes, she is a bit younger. Quite
a bit younger. And he has been married before, of course.'

186

'It makes his fourth wife, doesn't it?'

'Yes, I believe it does. His fourth wife. Pretty sure it does make his fourth.'

Tolland looked at me in absolute despair, I think not so much at the predicament in which Anne Stepney had involved herself, as at the necessity for such enormities to emerge in conversation. The news was certainly unforeseen.

'What do the Bridgnorths think about it?'

It was perhaps heartless to press him on such a point, but, having been told something so extraordinary as this, I wanted to hear as much as possible about the circumstances. Rather unexpectedly, he seemed almost relieved to report on that aspect of the marriage.

'The fellow who told me in the Guards' Club said they were making the best of it.'

'There was no announcement?'

'They were married in Paris,' said Tolland. 'So this fellow in the Guards' Club—or was it Arthur's?—told me. My brother, Warminster, when he was alive, used to talk about Umfraville. I think he liked him. Perhaps he didn't. But I think he did.'

'I was at school with a Tolland.'

'My nephew. Did you know his brother, Erridge? Erridge has succeeded now. Funny boy.'

Sir Gavin Walpole-Wilson had mentioned a 'Norah Tolland' as friend of his daughter, Eleanor. She turned out to be a niece.

'Warminster had ten children. Big family for these days.'

We rose at that moment to drink the King's health; and Le Bas's. Then Le Bas stood up, gripping the table with both hands as if he proposed to overturn it. This was in preparation for the delivery of his accustomed speech, which varied hardly at all year by year. His guttural, carefully enunciated consonants echoed through the room.

187

'. . . cannot fail to be gratifying to see so many of my
former pupils here tonight . . . do not really know what to
say to you all . . . certainly shall not make a long speech
. . . these annual meetings have their importance . . . encourage a sense of continuity . . . give perhaps an opportunity
of taking stock . . . friendship . . . I've said to some of you
before . . . needs keeping up . . . probably remember, most
of you, lines quoted by me on earlier occasions . . .

> And I sat by the shelf till I lost myself,
> And roamed in a crowded mist,
> And heard lost voices and saw lost looks,
> As I pored on an old School List.

. . . verses not, of course, in the modern manner . . . some
of us do not find such appeals to sentiment very sympathetic
. . . typically Victorian in their emphasis . . . all the . . .
rather well describe what most of us—well—at least some
of us—may—feel—experience—when we meet and talk over
our . . .'
Here Le Bas, as usual, paused; probably from the conviction that the word 'schooldays' had accumulated various
associations in the minds of his listeners to which he was
unwilling to seem to appeal. The use of hackneyed words
had always been one of his preoccupations. He was, I think,
dimly aware that his own bearing was somewhat clerical,
and was accordingly particularly anxious to avoid the
appearance of preaching a sermon. He compromised at last
with '. . . other times . . .' returning, almost immediately, to
the poem; as if the increased asperity that the lines now
assumed would purge him from the imputation of senti-
mentality to which he had referred. He cleared his throat
harshly.
'. . . You will remember how it goes later . . .

There were several duffers and several bores,
   Whose faces I've half forgot,
Whom I lived among, when the world was young
   And who talked no end of rot;

. . . of course I do not mean to suggest that there was anyone like that at my house . . .'

This comment always caused a certain amount of mild
laughter and applause. That evening Whitney uttered some
sort of a cry reminiscent of the hunting field, and Widmerpool grinned and drummed on the tablecloth with his fork,
slightly shaking his head at the same time to indicate that
he did not concur with Le Bas in supposing his former
pupils entirely free from such failings.

'. . . certainly nobody of that sort here tonight . . . but at
the same time . . . no good pretending that all time spent
at school was—entirely blissful . . . certainly not for a housemaster . . .'

There was more restrained laughter. Le Bas's voice tailed
away. In his accustomed manner he had evidently tried to
steer clear of any suggestion that schooldays were the
happiest period of a man's life, but at the same time feared
that by tacking too much he might become enmeshed in
dangerous admissions from which escape could be difficult.
This had always been one of his main anxieties as a school-
master. He would go some distance along a path indicated
by common sense, but, overcome by caution, would stop
half-way and behave in an unexpected, illogical manner.
Most of the conflicts between himself and individual boys
could be traced to these hesitations at the last moment.
Now he paused, beginning again in more rapid sentences:

'. . . as I have already said . . . do not intend to make a
long, prosy after-dinner speech . . . nothing more boring
. . . in fact my intention is—as at previous dinners—to ask

some of you to say a word or two about your own activities since we last met together . . . For example, perhaps Fetti-place-Jones might tell us something of what is going forward in the House of Commons . . .'

Fettiplace-Jones did not need much pressing to oblige in this request. He was on his feet almost before Le Bas had finished speaking. He was a tall, dark, rather good-looking fellow, with a lock of hair that fell from time to time over a high forehead, giving him the appearance of a Victorian statesman in early life. His maiden speech (tearing Ramsay MacDonald into shreds) had made some impression on the House, but since then there had been little if any brilliance about his subsequent parliamentary performances, though he was said to work hard in committee. India's eventual independence was the subject he chose to tell us about, and he continued for some little time. He was followed by Simson, a keen Territorial, who asked for recruits. Widmer-pool broke into Simson's speech with more than one 'hear, hear'. I remembered that he had told me he too was a Terri-torial officer. Whitney had something to say of Tanganyika. Others followed with their appointed piece. At last they came to an end. It seemed that Le Bas had exhausted the number of his former pupils from whom he might hope to extract interesting or improving comment. Stringham was sitting well back in his chair. He had, I think, actually gone to sleep.

There was a low buzz of talking. I had begun to wonder how soon the party would break up, when there came the sound of someone rising to their feet. It was Widmerpool. He was standing up in his place, looking down towards the table, as he fiddled with his glass. He gave a kind of intro-ductory grunt.

'You have heard something of politics and India,' he said, speaking quickly, and not very intelligibly, in that thick,

190

irritable voice which I remembered so well. 'You have been asked to join the Territorial Army, an invitation I most heartily endorse. Something has been said of county cricket. We have been taken as far afield as the Congo Basin, and as near home as this very hotel, where one of us here tonight worked as a waiter while acquiring his managerial training. Now I—I myself—would like to say a word or two about my experiences in the City.'

Widmerpool stopped speaking for a moment, and took a sip of water. During dinner he had shared a bottle of Graves with Maiden. There could be no question that he was absolutely sober. Le Bas—indeed everyone present—was obviously taken aback by this sudden, uncomfortable diversion. Le Bas had never liked Widmerpool, and, since the party was given for Le Bas, and Le Bas had not asked Widmerpool to speak, this behaviour was certainly uncalled for. In fact it was unprecedented. There was, of course, no cogent reason, apart from that, why Widmerpool should not get up and talk about the life he was leading. Just as other speakers had done. Indeed, it could be argued that the general invitation to speak put forward by Le Bas required acceptance as a matter of good manners. Perhaps that was how Widmerpool looked at it, assuming that Le Bas had only led off with several individual names as an encouragement for others to take the initiative in describing their lives. All that was true. Yet, in some mysterious manner, school rules, rather than those of the outer world, governed that particular assembly. However successful Widmerpool might have become in his own eyes, he was not yet important in the eyes of those present. He remained a nonentity, perhaps even an oddity, remembered only because he had once worn the wrong sort of overcoat. His behaviour seemed all the more outrageous on account of the ease with which, at that moment on account of the special circumstances, he could force us to listen to him without protest.

'This is terrific,' Templer muttered.

I looked across at Stringham, who had now woken up, and, having finished his bottle, was drinking brandy. He did not smile back at me, instead twisting his face into one of those extraordinary resemblances to Widmerpool at which he had always excelled. Almost immediately he resumed his natural expression, still without smiling. The effect of the grimace was so startling that I nearly laughed aloud. At the same time, something set, rather horrifying, about Stringham's own features, put an abrupt end to this sudden spasm of amusement. This look of his even made me feel apprehension as to what Stringham himself might do next. Obviously he was intensely, if quietly, drunk.

Meanwhile, Widmerpool was getting into his stride:

'. . . tell you something of the inner workings of the Donners-Brebner Company,' he was saying in a somewhat steadier voice than that in which he had begun his address. 'There is not a man of you, I can safely say, who would not be in a stronger position to face the world if he had some past experience of employment in a big concern of that sort. However, several of you already know that I am turning my attention to rather different spheres. Indeed, I have spoken to some of you of these changes in my life when we have met in the City . . .'

He looked round the room and allowed his eyes to rest for a moment on Templer, smiling again that skull-like grin with which he had greeted us.

'This is getting embarrassing,' said Templer.

I think Templer had begun to feel he had too easily allowed himself to accept Widmerpool as a serious person. It was impossible to guess what Widmerpool was going to say next. He was drunk with his own self-importance.

'. . . at one time these financial activities were devoted to the satisfaction of man's greed. Now we have a rather different end in view. We have been suffering—it is true to say that we are still suffering and shall suffer for no little time —from the most devastating trade depression in our recorded history. We have been forced from the Gold Standard, so it seems to me, and others not unworthy of a public hearing, because of the insufficiency of money in the hands of consumers. Very well. I suggest to you that our contemporary anxieties are not entirely vested in the question of balance of payment, that is at least so far as current account may be concerned, and I put it to you that certain persons, who should perhaps have known better, have been responsible for unhappy, indeed catastrophic capital movements through a reckless and inadmissible lending policy.'

I had a sudden memory of Monsieur Dubuisson talking like this when Widmerpool and I had been at La Grenadière together.

'. . . where our troubles began,' said Widmerpool. 'Now if we have a curve drawn on a piece of paper representing an average ratio of persistence, you will agree that authentic development must be demonstrated by a register alternately ascending and descending the level of our original curve of homogeneous development. Such an image, or, if you prefer it, such a geometrical figure, is dialectically implied precisely by the notion, in itself, of an average ratio of progress. No one would deny that. Now if a governmental policy of regulating domestic prices is to be arrived at in this or any other country, the moment assigned to the compilation of the index number which will establish the par of interest and prices must obviously be that at which internal economic conditions are in a condition of relative equilibrium. So far so good. I need not remind you that the universally accepted process in connexion with everyday commodities is for their production to be systematised by

193

the relation between their market value and the practicability of producing them, a steep ascent in value in contrast with the decreased practicability of production proportionately stimulating, and a parallel descent correspondingly depressing production. All that is clear enough. The fact that the index number remains at par regardless of alterations in the comparative prices of marketable commodities included in it, necessarily expresses the unavoidable truth that ascent or descent of a specific commodity is compensated by analogous adjustments in the opposite direction in prices of residual commodities . . .'

How long Widmerpool would have continued to speak on these subjects, it is impossible to say. I think he had settled down in his own mind to make a lengthy speech, whether anyone else present liked it or not. Why he had decided to address the table in this manner was not clear to me. Possibly, he merely desired to rehearse aloud certain economic views of his own, expressing them before an indifferent, even comparatively hostile audience, so that he might judge what minor adjustments ought to be made when the speech was delivered on some far more important occasion. Such an action would not be out of keeping with the eccentric, dogged manner in which he ran his life. At the same time, it was also likely enough that he wanted to impress Le Bas's Old Boys—those former schoolfellows who had so greatly disregarded him—with the fact that he was getting on in the world in spite of them; that he had already become a person to be reckoned with.

Widmerpool may not even have been conscious of this motive, feeling it only instinctively; for there could be no doubt that he now thought of his schooldays in very different terms from any that his contemporaries would have used. Indeed, such references as he had ever made to his time at school, for example when we had been in France

together, always suggested that he saw himself as a boy
rather above the average at work and games. That justice
had never been done to his energies in either direction was
on account of the unsatisfactory manner in which both these
sides of life were administered by those in authority; the
same view, in fact, as that held by Uncle Giles. Widmerpool
had once said this to me in so many words.

The effect of his discourse on those sitting round the
table had been mixed. Fettiplace-Jones's long, handsome,
pasty face assumed a serious, even worried expression, implying neither agreement nor disagreement with what was
being said: merely a public indication that, as a Member of
Parliament, he was missing nothing. It was as if he were
waiting for the Whip's notification of which way he should
vote. Parkinson gave a kind of groan of boredom, which I
heard distinctly, although he was separated from me by
Templer. Tolland, on the other hand, leant forward as if he
feared to miss a syllable. Simson looked very stern. Whitney
and Brandreth had begun a whispered conversation together. Maiden, who was next to Widmerpool, was throwing anxious, almost distracted glances about him. Ghika,
like Tolland, leant forward. He fixed his huge black eyes
on Widmerpool, concentrating absolutely on his words, but
whether with interest, or boredom of an intensity that
might lead even to physical assault, it was impossible to say.
Templer had sat back in his chair, clearly enjoying every
phrase to the full. Stringham also expressed his appreciation, though only by the faintest smile, as if he saw all
through a cloud. Then, suddenly, the scene was brought
abruptly to a close.

'Look at Le Bas,' said Templer.

'It's a stroke,' said Tolland.

Afterwards—I mean weeks or months afterwards, when
I happened upon any of the party then present, or heard

the incident discussed—there was facetious comment suggesting that Le Bas's disabling attack had been directly brought about by Widmerpool's speech. Certainly no one was in a position categorically to deny that there was no connection whatever between Widmerpool's conduct and Le Bas's case. Knowing Le Bas, I have no doubt that he was sitting in his chair, bitterly regretting that he was no longer in a position to order Widmerpool to sit down at once. That would have been natural enough. A sudden pang of impotent rage may even have contributed to other elements in bringing on his seizure. But that was to take rather a melodramatic view. More probably, the atmosphere of the room, full of cigar smoke and fumes of food and wine, had been too much for him. Besides, the weather had grown distinctly hotter as the night wore on. Le Bas himself had always been a great opener of windows. He would insist on plenty of fresh air on the coldest winter day at early school in any room in which he was teaching. His ordinary life had not accustomed him to gatherings of this sort, which he only had to face once a year. No doubt he had always been an abstemious man, in spite of Templer's theory, held at school, that our housemaster was a secret drinker. That night he had possibly taken more wine than he was accustomed. He was by then getting on in years, though no more than in his sixties. The precise cause of his collapse was never known to me. These various elements probably all played a part.

Lying back in his chair, his cheeks flushed and eyes closed, one side of Le Bas's face was slightly contorted. Fettiplace-Jones and Maiden must have taken in the situation at once, because I had scarcely turned in Le Bas's direction before these two had picked him up and carried him into the next room. Widmerpool followed close behind them. There was some confusion when people rose from the table. I followed the rest through the door to the ante-room, where Le Bas was placed full-length on the settee. Somebody had removed his collar.

This had probably been done by Brandreth, who now took charge. Brandreth, whose father had acquired a baronetcy as an ear-specialist, was himself a doctor. He began immediately to assure everyone that Le Bas's condition was not serious.

'The best thing you fellows can do is to clear off home and leave the room as empty as possible,' Brandreth said. 'I don't want all of you crowding round.'

Like most successful medical men in such circumstances, he spoke as if the matter had now automatically passed from the sphere of Le Bas's indisposition to the far more important one of Brandreth's own professional convenience. Clearly there was something to be said for following his recommendation. Brandreth seemed to be handling the matter competently, and, after a while, all but the more determined began to disappear from the room. Tolland made a final offer to help before leaving, but Brandreth snapped at him savagely and he made off; no doubt to appear again the following year. I wondered how he filled in the time between Old Boy dinners.

'I shall have to be going, Nick,' said Templer. 'I have to get back to the country tonight.'

'This dinner seems to have been rather a fiasco.'

'Probably my fault,' said Templer. 'Le Bas never liked me. However, I think it was really Widmerpool this time. What's happened to him, by the way? I never had my chat about Bob.'

Widmerpool was no longer in the room. Maiden said he had gone off to ring up the place where Le Bas was staying, and warn them what had happened. By then Le Bas was sitting up and drinking a glass of water.

'Well, fixing old Bob up will have to wait,' said Templer. 'I want to do it for Jean's sake. I'm afraid you had to listen to a lot of stuff about my matrimonial affairs tonight.'

'What are your plans?'

'Haven't got any. I'll ring up some time.'

Templer went off. I looked round for Stringham, thinking I would like a word with him before leaving. It was a long time since we had met, and I was not due to arrive at Jean's until late. Stringham was not in the small group that remained. I supposed he had left; probably making his way to some other entertainment. There was nothing surprising in that. In any case, it was unlikely that we should have done more than exchange a few conventional sentences, even had he remained to talk for a minute or two. I knew little or nothing of how he lived since his divorce. His mother's picture still appeared from time to time in the illustrated papers. No doubt her house in the country provided some sort of permanent background into which he could retire when desirable.

On the way out, I glanced by chance through the door leading to the room where we had dined. Stringham was still sitting in his place at the table, smoking a cigarette and drinking coffee. The dining-room was otherwise deserted. I went through the door and took the chair beside him.

'Hullo, Nick.'

'Are you going to sit here all night?'

'Precisely the idea that occurred to me.'

'Won't it be rather gloomy?'

'Not as bad as when they were all here. Shall we order another bottle?'

'Let's have a drink at my club.'

'Or my flat. I don't want to look at any more people.'

'Where is your flat?'

'West Halkin Street.'

'All right. I shan't be able to stay long.'

'Up to no good?'

'That's it.'

'I haven't seen you for ages, Nick.'

'Not for ages.'

'You know my wife, Peggy, couldn't take it. I expect you heard. Not surprising, perhaps. She has married an awfully nice chap now. Peggy is a really lucky girl now. A really charming chap. Not the most amusing man you ever met, but a really *nice chap*.'

'A relation of hers, isn't he?'

'Quite so. A relation of hers, too. He will be already familiar with all those lovely family jokes of the Stepney family, those very amusing jokes. He will not have to have the points explained to him. When he stays at Mountfichet, he will know where all the lavatories are—if there is, indeed, more than one, a matter upon which I cannot speak with certainty. Anyway, he will not always have to be bothering the butler to direct him to where that one is—and losing his way in that awful no-man's-land between the servants' hall and the gun-room. What a house! Coronets on the table napkins, but no kind hearts between the sheets. He will be able to discuss important historical events with my ex-father-in-law, such as the fact that Red Eyes and Cypria dead-heated for the Cesarewitch in 1893—or was it 1894? I shall forget my own name next. He will be able to talk to my ex-mother-in-law about the time Queen Alexandra made that *double entendre* to her uncle. The only thing he won't be able to do is to talk about Braque and Dufy with my ex-sister-in-law, Anne. Still, that's a small matter. Plenty of people about to talk to girls of Braque and Dufy these days. I heard, by the way, that Anne had got a painter of her own by now, so perhaps even Braque and Dufy are things of the past. Anyway, he's a jolly nice chap and Peggy is a very lucky girl.'

'Anne has married Dicky Umfraville.'

'Not *the* Dicky Umfraville?'

'Yes.'

'Well I never.'

Even that did not make much impression on him. The fact that he had not already heard of Anne Stepney's marriage suggested that Stringham must pass weeks at a time in a state in which he took in little or nothing of what was going on round him. That could be the only explanation of ignorance of an event with which he had such close connexions.

'Shall we make a move?'

'Where is Peter Templer? I saw his face—sometimes two or three of them—during that awful dinner. We might bring him along as well. Always feel a bit guilty about Peter.'

'He has gone home.'

'I bet he hasn't. He's gone after some girl. Always chasing the girls. Let's follow him.'

'He lives near Maidenhead.'

'Too far. He must be mad. Is he married?'

'His wife has just left him.'

'There you are. Women are all the same. My wife left me. Has your wife left you, Nick?'

'I'm not married.'

'Lucky man. Who *was* Peter's wife, as they say?'

'A model called Mona.'

'Sounds like the beginning of a poem. Well, I should have thought better of her. One of those long-haired painter fellows must have got her into bad habits. Leaving her husband, indeed. She oughtn't to have left Peter. I was always very fond of Peter. It was his friends I couldn't stand.'

'Let's go.'

'Look here, do let's have another drink. What happened to Le Bas?'

'He is going to be taken home in an ambulance.'

'Is he too tight to walk?'

'He had a stroke.'

'Is he dead?'

'No—Brandreth is looking after him.'

'What an awful fate. Why Brandreth?'

'Brandreth is a doctor.'

'Hope I'm never ill when Brandreth is about, or he might look after me. I'm not feeling too good at the moment as a matter of fact. Perhaps we'd better go, or Brandreth will start treating me too. It was Widmerpool's speech, of course. Knocked Le Bas out. Knocked him out cold. Nearly knocked me out too. Do you remember when we got Le Bas arrested?'

'Let's go to your flat.'

'West Halkin Street. Where I used to live before I was married. Surely you've been there.'

'No.'

'Ought to have asked you, Nick. Ought to have asked you. Been very remiss about things like that.'

He was extremely drunk, but his legs seemed fairly steady beneath him. We went upstairs and out into the street.

'Taxi?'

'No,' said Stringham. 'Let's walk for a bit. I want to cool off. It was bloody hot in there. I don't wonder Le Bas had a stroke.'

There was a rich blue sky over Piccadilly. The night was stiflingly hot. Stringham walked with almost exaggerated sobriety. It was remarkable considering the amount he had drunk.

'Why did you have so many drinks tonight?'

'Oh, I don't know,' he said. 'I do sometimes. Rather often nowadays, as a matter of fact. I felt I couldn't face Le Bas and his Old Boys without an alcoholic basis of some sort. Yet for some inexplicable reason I wanted to go. That was why I had a few before I arrived.'

He put out his hand and touched the railings of the Green Park as we passed them.

'You said you were not married, didn't you, Nick?'

'Yes.'

'Got a nice girl?'

'Yes.'

'Take my advice and don't get married.'

'All right.'

'What about Widmerpool. Is he married?'

'Not that I know of.'

'I'm surprised at that. Widmerpool is the kind of man to attract a woman. A good, sensible man with no nonsense about him. In that overcoat he used to wear he would be irresistible. Quite irresistible. Do you remember that overcoat?'

'It was before my time.'

'It's a frightful shame,' said Stringham. 'A frightful shame, the way these women go on. They are all the same. They leave me. They leave Peter. They will probably leave you. . . . I say, Nick, I am feeling extraordinarily odd. I think I will just sit down here for a minute or two.'

I thought he was going to collapse and took his arm. However, he settled down in a sitting position on the edge of the stone coping from which the railings rose.

'Long, deep breaths,' he said. 'Those are the things.'

'Come on, let's try and get a cab.'

'Can't, old boy. I just feel too, too sleepy to get a cab.'

As it happened, there seemed to be no taxis about at that moment. In spite of what must have been the intense discomfort of where he sat, Stringham showed signs of dropping off to sleep, closing his eyes and leaning his head back against the railings. It was difficult to know what to do. In this state he could hardly reach his flat on foot. If a taxi appeared, he might easily refuse to enter it. I remembered how once at school he had sat down on a staircase and refused to move, on the grounds that so many annoying things had happened that afternoon that further struggle against life was useless. This was just such another occasion. Even when sober, he possessed that complete recklessness of behaviour that belongs to certain highly strung persons. I was still looking down at him, trying to decide on the next step, when someone spoke just behind me.

'Why is Stringham sitting there like that?'

It was Widmerpool's thick, accusing voice. He asked the question with a note of authority that suggested his personal responsibility to see that people did not sit about in Piccadilly at night.

'I stayed to make sure everything was done about Le Bas that should be done,' he said. 'I think Brandreth knows his job. I gave him my address in case of difficulties. It was a disagreeable thing to happen. The heat, I suppose. It ruined the few words I was about to say. A pity. I thought I would have a breath of fresh air after what we had been through, but the night is very warm even here in the open.'

He said all this with his usual air of immense importance.

'The present problem is how to get Stringham to his flat.'

'What is wrong with him? I wonder if it is the same as Le Bas. Perhaps something in the food——'

Widmerpool was always ready to feel disturbed regarding any question of health. In France he had been a great consumer of patent medicines. He looked nervously at Stringham. I saw that he feared the attack of some mysterious sickness that might soon infect himself.

'Stringham has had about a gallon to drink.'

'How foolish of him.'

I was about to make some reply to the effect that the speeches had needed something to wash them down with, but checked any such comment since Widmerpool's help was obviously needed to get Stringham home, and I thought it better not to risk offending him. I therefore muttered something that implied agreement.

'Where does he live?'

'West Halkin Street.'

Widmerpool acted quickly. He strolled to the kerb. A cab seemed to rise out of the earth at that moment. Perhaps all action, even summoning a taxi when none is there, is basically a matter of the will. Certainly there had been no sign of a conveyance a second before. Widmerpool made a curious, pumping movement, using the whole of his arm, as if dragging down the taxi by a rope. It drew up in front of us. Widmerpool turned towards Stringham, whose eyes were still closed.

'Take the other arm,' he said, peremptorily.

Although he made no resistance, this intervention aroused Stringham. He began to speak very quietly:

'Ah, with the Grape my fading Life provide,
And wash my Body whence the Life has died . . .'

We shoved him on to the back seat, where he sat between us, still murmuring to himself:

'. . . And lay me shrouded in the living leaf
By some not unfrequented garden-side . . .

I think that's quite a good description of the Green Park, Nick, don't you. . . . "Some not unfrequented garden-side" . . . Wish I sat here more often . . . Jolly nice. . . .'

204

'Does he habitually get in this state?' Widmerpool asked.

'I don't know. I haven't seen him for years.'

'I thought you were a close friend of his. You used to be—at school.'

'That's a long time ago.'

Widmerpool seemed aggrieved at the news that Stringham and I no longer saw each other regularly. Once decided in his mind on a given picture of what some aspect of life was like, he objected to any modification of the design. He possessed an absolutely rigid view of human relationships. Into this, imagination scarcely entered, and whatever was lost in grasping the niceties of character was amply offset by a simplification of practical affairs. Occasionally, it was true. I had known Widmerpool involved in situations which were extraordinary chiefly because they were entirely misunderstood, but on the whole he probably gained more than he lost by these limitations; at least in the spheres that attracted him. Stringham now lay between us, as if fast asleep.

'Where is he working at present?'

'I don't know.'

'It was a good thing he left Donners-Brebner,' said Widmerpool. 'He was doing neither himself nor the company any good.'

'Bill Truscott has gone, too, hasn't he?'

'Yes,' said Widmerpool, looking straight ahead of him. 'Truscott had become very interested in the by-products of coal and found it advantageous to make a change.'

We got Stringham out of the taxi on arrival without much difficulty and found his latchkey in a waistcoat pocket. Inside the flat, I was immediately reminded of his room at school. There were the eighteenth-century prints of the racehorses, Trimalchio and The Pharisee; the same large, rather florid photograph of his mother: a snapshot of his father still stuck in the corner of its frame. However, the picture of 'Boffles' Stringham—as I now thought of him after meeting Dicky Umfraville—showed a decidedly older man than the pipe-smoking, open-shirted figure I remembered from the earlier snapshot. The elder Stringham, looking a bit haggard and wearing a tie, sat on a seat beside a small, energetic, rather brassy lady, presumably his French wife. He had evidently aged considerably. I wondered if friendship with Dicky Umfraville had had anything to do with this. Opposite these photographs was a drawing by Modigliani, and an engraving of a seventeenth-century mansion done in the style of Wenceslaus Hollar. This was Glimber, the Warringtons' house, left to Stringham's mother during her lifetime by her first husband. On another wall was a set of coloured prints illustrating a steeplechase ridden by monkeys mounted on dogs.

'What are we going to do with him?'

'Put him to bed,' said Widmerpool, speaking as if any other action were inconceivable.

Widmerpool and I, therefore, set out to remove Stringham's clothes, get him into some pyjamas, and place him between the sheets. This was a more difficult job than might be supposed. His stiff shirt seemed riveted to him. However, we managed to get it off at last, though not without tearing it. In these final stages, Stringham himself returned to consciousness.

'Look here,' he said, suddenly sitting up on the bed, 'what is happening? People seem to be treating me roughly. Am I being thrown out of somewhere? If so, where? And what have I done to deserve such treatment? I am perfectly prepared to listen to reason and admit that I was in the wrong, and pay for anything I have broken. That is

206

provided, of course, that I was in the wrong. Nick, why are you letting this man hustle me? I seem for some reason to be in bed in the middle of the afternoon. Really, my habits get worse and worse. I am even now full of good resolutions for getting up at half-past seven every morning. But who is this man? I know his face.'

'It's Widmerpool. You remember Widmerpool?'

'Remember Widmerpool . . .' said Stringham. 'Remember Widmerpool. . . . Do I remember Widmerpool? . . . How could I ever forget Widmerpool? . . . How could anybody forget Widmerpool? . . .'

'We thought you needed help, Stringham,' said Widmerpool, in a very matter-of-fact voice. 'So we put you to bed.'

'You did, did you?'

Stringham lay back in the bed, looking fixedly before him. His manner was certainly odd, but his utterance was no longer confused.

'You needed a bit of looking after,' said Widmerpool.

'That time is past,' said Stringham.

He began to get out of bed.

'No. . . .'

Widmerpool took a step forward. He made as if to restrain Stringham from leaving the bed, holding both his stubby hands in front of him, as if warming them before a fire.

'Look here,' said Stringham, 'I must be allowed to get in and out of my own bed. That is a fundamental human right. Other people's beds may be another matter. In them, another party is concerned. But ingress and egress of one's own bed is unassailable.'

'Much better stay where you are,' said Widmerpool, in a voice intended to be soothing.

'Nick, are you a party to this?'

'Why not call it a day?'

'Take my advice,' said Widmerpool. 'We know what is best for you.'

'Rubbish.'

'For your own good.'

'I haven't got my own good at heart.'

'We will get you anything you want.'

'Curse your charity.'

Once more Stringham attempted to get out of the bed. He had pushed the clothes back, when Widmerpool threw himself on top of him, holding Stringham bodily there. While they struggled together, Stringham began to yell at the top of his voice.

'So these are the famous Widmerpool good manners, are they?' he shouted. 'This is the celebrated Widmerpool courtesy, of which we have always heard so much. Here is the man who posed as another Lord Chesterfield. Let me go, you whited sepulchre, you serpent, you small-time Judas, coming to another man's house in the guise of paying a social call, and then holding him down in his own bed.'

The scene was so grotesque that I began to laugh; not altogether happily, it was true, but at least as some form of nervous relief. The two of them wrestling together were pouring with sweat, especially Widmerpool, who was the stronger. He must have been quite powerful, for Stringham was fighting like a maniac. The bed creaked and rocked as if it would break beneath them. And then, quite suddenly, Stringham began laughing too. He laughed and laughed, until he could struggle no more. The combat ceased. Widmerpool stepped back. Stringham lay gasping on the pillows.

'All right,' he said, still shaking with laughter, 'I'll stay. To tell the truth, I am beginning to feel the need for a little rest myself.'

Widmerpool, whose tie had become twisted in the

struggle, straightened his clothes. His dinner-jacket looked more extraordinary than ever. He was panting hard.

'Is there anything you would like?' he asked in a formal voice.

'Yes,' said Stringham, whose mood was now completely changed. 'A couple of those little pills in the box on the left of the dressing-table. They will knock me out finally. I do dislike waking at four and thinking things over. Perhaps three of the pills would be wiser, on second thoughts. Half measures are never any good.'

He was getting sleepy again, and spoke in a flat, mechanical tone. All his excitement was over. We gave him the sleeping tablets. He took them, turned away from us, and rolled over on his side.

'Good-night, all,' he said.

'Good-night, Charles.'

'Good-night, Stringham,' said Widmerpool, rather severely.

We perfunctorily tidied some of the mess in the immediate neighbourhood of the bed. Stringham's clothes were piled on a chair. Then we made our way down into the street.

'Great pity for a man to drink like that,' said Widmerpool.

I did not answer, largely because I was thinking of other matters: chiefly of how strange a thing it was that I myself should have been engaged in a physical conflict designed to restrict Stringham's movements: a conflict in which the moving spirit had been Widmerpool. That suggested a whole social upheaval: a positively cosmic change in life's system. Widmerpool, once so derided by all of us, had become in some mysterious manner a person of authority. Now, in a sense, it was he who derided us; or at least his disapproval had become something far more powerful than the merely defensive weapon it had once seemed.

I remembered that we were not far from the place where formerly Widmerpool had run into Mr. Deacon and Gypsy Jones on the night of the Huntercombes' dance. Then he had been on his way to a flat in Victoria. I asked if he still lived there with his mother.

'Still there,' he said. 'Though we are always talking of moving. It has great advantages, you know. You must come and see us. You have been there in the past, haven't you?'

'I dined with you and your mother once.'

'Of course. Miss Walpole-Wilson was at dinner, wasn't she? I remember her saying afterwards that you did not seem a very serious young man.'

'I saw her brother the other day at the Isbister Retrospective Exhibition.'

'I do not greatly care for the company of Sir Gavin,' said Widmerpool. 'I dislike failure, especially failure in one holding an official position. It is letting all of us down. But—as I was saying—we shall be rather occupied with my new job for a time, so that I expect we shall not be doing much entertaining. When we have settled down, you must come and see us again.'

I was not sure if his 'we' was the first person plural of royalty and editors, or whether he spoke to include his mother; as if Mrs. Widmerpool were already a partner with him in his bill-broking. We said good-night, and I wished him luck in the Acceptance World. It was time to make for Jean's. She was arriving in London by a late train that evening, again lodged in the flat at the back of Rutland Gate.

On the way there I took from my pocket the post-card she had sent telling me when to arrive. I read it over, as I had already done so many times that day. There was no mistake. I should be there at the time she asked. The events of the evening seemed already fading into unreality at the prospect of seeing her once more.

The card she had sent was of French origin, in colour, showing a man and woman seated literally one on top of the other in an armchair upholstered with crimson plush. These two exchanged ardent glances. They were evidently on the best of terms, because the young man, fair, though at the same time rather semitic of feature, was squeezing the girl's arm just above the elbow. Wearing a suit of rich brown material, a tartan tie and a diamond ring on the third finger of his right hand, his face, as he displayed a row of dazzling teeth, reminded me of Prince Theodoric's profile—as the Prince might have been painted by Isbister. The girl smiled back approvingly as she balanced on his knee.

'Doesn't she look like Mona?' Jean had written on the back. Dark, with corkscrew curls, the girl was undeniably pretty, dressed in a pink frock, its short sleeves frilled with white, the whole garment, including the frills, covered with a pattern of small black spots. The limits of the photograph caused her legs to fade suddenly from the picture, an unexpected subordination of design created either to conceal an impression of squatness, or possibly a purely visual effect —the result of foreshortening—rather than because these lower limbs failed in the eyes of the photographer to attain a required standard of elegance. For whichever reason, the remaining free space at the foot of the postcard was sufficient to allow the title of the caption below to be printed in long, flourishing capitals:

Sex Appeal
Ton regard et ta voix ont un je ne sais quoi . . .
D'étrange et de troublant qui me met en émoi.

Although in other respects a certain emptiness of background suggested a passage or hall, dim reflections of looking-glass set above a shelf painted white seemed to belong to a dressing-table: a piece of furniture hinting, consequently, of bedrooms. To the left, sprays of artificial flowers, red and yellow, drooped from the mouth of a large vase of which the base was invisible. This gigantic vessel assumed at first sight the proportions of a wine vat or sepulchral urn, even one of those legendary jars into which Morgiana, in the Arabian Nights, poured boiling oil severally on the Forty Thieves: a public rather than private ornament, it might be thought, decorating presumably the bedroom, if bedroom it was, of a hotel. Indeed, the style of furnishing was reminiscent of the Ufford.

Contemplating the blended tones of pink and brown framed within the postcard's scalloped edge of gold, one could not help thinking how extraordinarily unlike 'the real thing' was this particular representation of a pair of lovers; indeed, how indifferently, at almost every level except the highest, the ecstasies and bitterness of love are at once conveyed in art. So much of the truth remains finally unnegotiable; in spite of the fact that most persons in love go through remarkably similar experiences. Here, in the picture, for example, implications were misleading, if not positively inaccurate. The matter was presented as all too easy, the twin flames of dual egotism reduced almost to nothing, so that there was no pain; and, for that matter, almost no pleasure. A sense of anxiety, without which the condition could scarcely be held to exist, was altogether absent.

Yet, after all, even the crude image of the postcard depicted with at least a degree of truth one side of love's outward appearance. That had to be admitted. Some of love was like the picture. I had enacted such scenes with

Jean: Templer with Mona: now Mona was enacting them with Quiggin: Barnby and Umfraville with Anne Stepney: Stringham with her sister Peggy: Peggy now in the arms of her cousin: Uncle Giles, very probably, with Mrs. Erdleigh: Mrs. Erdleigh with Jimmy Stripling: Jimmy Stripling, if it came to that, with Jean: and Duport, too.

The behaviour of the lovers in the plush armchair beside the sparse heads of those sad flowers was perfectly normal; nor could the wording of the couplet be blamed as specially far-fetched, or in some other manner indefensible. 'D'étrange et de troublant' were epithets, so far as they went, perfectly appropriate in their indication of those indefinable, mysterious emotions that love arouses. In themselves there was nothing incongruous in such descriptive labels. They might, indeed, be regarded as rather apt. I could hardly deny that I was at that moment experiencing something of the sort.

The mere act of a woman sitting on a man's knee, rather than a chair, certainly suggested the Templer *milieu*. A memorial to Templer himself, in marble or bronze, were public demand ever to arise for so unlikely a cenotaph, might suitably take the form of a couple so grouped. For some reason—perhaps a confused memory of *Le Baiser*—the style of Rodin came to mind. Templer's own point of view seemed to approximate to that earlier period of the plastic arts. Unrestrained emotion was the vogue then, treatment more in his line than some of the bleakly in-tellectual statuary of our own generation.

Even allowing a fairly limited concession to its character as a kind of folk perception—an eternal girl sitting on an eternal young man's knee—the fact remained that an infinity of relevant material had been deliberately omitted from this vignette of love in action. These two supposedly good-looking persons were, in effect, going through the

213

motions of love in such a manner as to convince others, perhaps less well equipped for the struggle than themselves, that they, too, the spectators, could be easily identified with some comparable tableau. They, too, could sit embracing on crimson chairs. Although hard to define with precision the exact point at which a breach of honesty had occurred, there could be no doubt that this performance included an element of the confidence-trick.

The night was a shade cooler now. Jean was wearing a white blouse, or sports shirt, open at the neck. Beneath it, her body trembled a little.

'What was your dinner like?' she asked.

'Peter turned up.'

'He said he would probably go there.'

I told her about Le Bas; and also about Stringham.

'That is why I am a bit late.'

'Did Peter mention that Bob is back in England?'

'Yes.'

'And that his prospects are not too bad?'

'Yes.'

'That may make difficulties.'

'I know.'

'Don't let's talk of them.'

'No.'

'Darling Nick.'

Outside, a clock struck the hour. Though ominous, things still had their enchantment. After all, as St. John Clarke was reported to have said at the Huntercombes', 'All blessings are mixed blessings.' Perhaps, in spite of everything, the couple of the postcard could not be dismissed so easily. It was in their world that I seemed now to find myself.